ELEMENTS OF MATHEMATICS

ELEMENTS OF
MATHEMATICS

SECOND EDITION

J. HOUSTON BANKS

GEORGE PEABODY COLLEGE FOR TEACHERS

ALLYN AND BACON, INC.

Boston

COLLEGE MATHEMATICS SERIES

PREFACE

The point of view and basic objectives of the first edition of *Elements of Mathematics* have been preserved in this edition. The central purpose is the development of the fundamental concepts and techniques of mathematics at a level of abstraction appropriate for the college student who has studied no mathematics beyond the secondary school.

The text is an outgrowth of the author's experience with a class designed to serve all students. For those who plan no further formal work in mathematics it serves to give perspective to the mathematics of the elementary and secondary school. It is not "remedial" or "refresher" in the sense that the student repeats the same material, in the same way, with the same emphasis. It is rather an opportunity to approach the material from a different point of view, to give it a new, mathematically sound, treatment. Emphasis is placed on the development of mature understanding. For those who plan to continue their study of mathematics it serves as an orientation to advanced work. It gives the student an opportunity to discover, in the context of familiar material, the true nature of mathematics as an abstract structure. In this connection $+$ and $\times$, rather than $\cup$ and $\cap$, have been used in Boolean algebra in order to highlight the contrast with a field. Many concepts are developed which in the past have been postponed until a more advanced level is reached. The book not only offers material that is new for the reader but also gives the traditional subject matter a novel treatment.

The book is written for the student. The informal, conversational style and full expository discussions are used to smooth the way for the reader.

Major revisions consist of the addition of a chapter on the nature of geometry, Chapter XI, an expanded and revised treatment of the nature of proof, Chapter II, a revised and more comprehensive treatment of algebraic structures, Chapter V, and a greatly increased number of exercises which are more strategically placed throughout the text.

The book is centered around four broad aspects of elementary mathematics: number, proof, measurement, and function.   The flexibility of the text has been preserved.   Some knowledge of secondary school algebra will be an aid in mastery of Chapters V, VII, and XII. A knowledge of secondary school geometry is presupposed in Chapter XI.   The chapters are almost wholly self-contained.   Chapter V is prerequisite to Chapter VII.   Chapters V, VI, and VII are prerequisite to Chapter XII.   Within the above limitations, any combination of chapters may be used in any desired order.   This makes possible a variety of courses as to length, emphasis, and background of students. For example, a short course emphasizing number and measurement could cover Chapters III, IV, VIII, IX, and X.   A course for those with better-than-average preparation could include Chapters II, V, VI, VII, XI, and XII.   The author has found the material of the text ideally suited for instruction by television.

In a very real sense this revision is a cooperative undertaking. Suggestions from many users of the earlier edition have been invaluable in planning this revision.

J. H. B.

TABLE OF CONTENTS

Study chapter 2

ELEMENTS OF MATHEMATICS

CHAPTER I   1-7

INTRODUCTION

Attempts to "make mathematics easy" have not met with success. It was an astute student who observed, "The only easy mathematics is the mathematics you have already learned." This book is dedicated to the proposition that, though you can't make it easy, you can make it understandable and interesting.

As we begin the study of this book the question, "What is it all about?" is quite appropriate. The most immediate answer is, "It is about mathematics." But what is mathematics? The answer to this question takes some doing. The term *mathematics* means many different things to different people. To a great many persons mathematics is merely the art of calculation and measurement. To far too many it is an incomprehensible mystery somewhat akin to black magic. One of the major objectives of this book is to supply you with a clearer, more nearly complete conception of what mathematics is.

If you are one of those persons who for one reason or another has developed an emotional block toward mathematics, you should attempt to keep an open-minded attitude. Most people who think they can't "get" mathematics either are the victims of adverse conditioning or are mentally lazy. Mathematics is not easy but neither is it reserved exclusively for genius. Intellectual curiosity and the willingness to exert mental effort are the most important prerequisites to success. A little stubbornness, refusal to give up on a problem or idea, helps too.

The following sections are not definitions of mathematics. They are descriptive statements about some of the facets of mathematics. They should become more meaningful as you progress in your study and should be reread when the book is completed. One group of students concluded from the next four sections that mathematics is the salt of the earth: S — science; A — art; L — language; T — tool.

MATHEMATICS IS A SCIENCE

1.1   Mathematics is a science, yet it is singularly different from the physical and biological sciences.   Man's endless search for truth has taken many forms.   This search is the concern of philosophy, theology, and science.   Ultimate, absolute truth is a will-o'-the-wisp in so far as the methods of science are concerned.   The truths of science are conditional truths.   The natural scientist reaches his conclusions as a result of experimentation.   He arrives at the general principles which best explain observable phenomena.   The physical scientist says, "In the light of all the evidence at my command, this conclusion is the most plausible, the most likely one I can make."   There is always the possibility that more evidence will alter the conclusions.   The truths of natural science are *probable truths*.

Nor does the mathematician establish absolute truth.   The conclusions of mathematics are necessary consequences of the assumptions, definitions, and primitive elements we accept.   They are unalterably and inescapably true *if* our assumptions are true.   The mathematician says, "If you accept my premises you must accept my conclusions."   Mathematical truth is *relative truth*.   The conclusions are true, relative to the truth of the original assumptions.

From the logical standpoint, the mathematician is not concerned with whether or not his assumptions are true.   Mind you, he may be very much concerned with whether or not they are true where applied to a physical situation.   But, as we shall see later, it would be a little silly to make any assertion concerning the truth of a statement about the behavior of certain "things" when we do not know what those things are.   As we shall see, some things must remain undefined.

We should not infer that the scientist is never interested in relative truth, or that the mathematician is never interested in probable truth.   The scientist is a mathematician in that he uses mathematics and sometimes creates it because he needs it.   It is equally true that the mathematician uses the methods of the scientist in discovering possible mathematical properties.

Mathematics differs from the other sciences in another striking way.   The natural scientist is concerned with matter and energy and living things, but the whole of mathematics is constructed from ideas.   It exists in men's minds.

MATHEMATICS IS AN ART

1.2   It is true that mathematics has a tremendous impact on the graphic arts and musical theory.   A knowledge of mathematics may well aid one in an appreciation of these arts.   And though many artists are doubtless not too literate mathematically, a knowledge of mathematics might also help them.   Mathematics undoubtedly can be an invaluable tool for the arts.   But that is only half the story. Mathematics is an art in its own right.   Esthetic satisfaction can be derived therefrom.   However, as was the case with science, it is peculiarly different from the other arts.   There are three levels of participation in music — the composer or producer, the performer, and the listener.   There are no mathematical listeners.   The only ways in which one may participate in mathematics are to produce or to "perform."   Mathematics is not a spectator sport.   The only way we can derive any satisfaction from mathematics is to "get our feet wet" and *do* some mathematics.   Though no one will expect you to produce any new mathematics in this course you will be able to experience the satisfaction of producing as well as of "performing."

MATHEMATICS IS A LANGUAGE

1.3   Written and spoken language enables man to record his ideas and to communicate them to others.   In fact, it makes the ideas themselves possible.   A surprisingly large part of our thinking is mental "talking."   We think the word symbols rather than the things for which the symbols stand.   And so it is with mathematics.   As a language, mathematics has characteristics peculiarly its own.   In the first place, mathematics is an extremely exact language.   If I say, "I went to the fair and saw a fast horse," what do I mean?   Did I see a horse that is a swift runner or did I see a horse that was securely tied?   Those persons given to anthropomorphism might insist that I saw a naughty horse!   Such multiple interpretations are not permissible in mathematics.   In mathematics we must say what we mean and mean what we say.   Now, it is true that certain terms used in mathematics also have nonmathematical meanings. For example, when we talk of irrational numbers we do not mean numbers that are "off their rockers." The word *irrational* as a mathematical term has an exact, precise, unambiguous meaning. Bertrand Russell has said that mathematics is the subject in which we don't know what we are talking about or whether what we say about it is so. How then can it be such an exact language? Russell was merely pointing out certain characteristics of a mathematical system, one of which is the fact that we use certain undefined terms. This is inevitable because every time we define something we must do so in terms of something else, and this something else in turn must be defined. We are faced with three alternatives: (1) we continue defining from now on, or (2) we finally define something in terms of the thing we set out to define originally, or (3) we agree that there shall be certain terms which will go undefined. Mathematics chooses the third course. We do not contend that the undefined terms do not need defining; we hope that they will have the same meaning for everyone concerned but we can never be sure. That is what Russell meant when he said that we don't know what we are talking about. There are undefined terms because it is impossible to define everything. Our second alternative accomplishes exactly nothing. The fact that the undefined terms are made as simple as possible and all other terms are defined in terms of them contributes to the exactness of the language of mathematics. Which of the three above alternatives does the dictionary adopt?

Mathematics is a concise language; it says a lot in a little space.

$$y = \frac{d}{dx} e \int \text{arc sin } x^2 dx$$

This equation is not meant to scare anyone; in fact, one would not come in contact with all the ideas involved until he had studied a considerable amount of college mathematics. But it would take at least a page to write out only what the equation says, let alone explain what it means. Mathematics is a universal language: it is the same in the Orient, America, and Central Europe. Before it can be of any value to an individual, he must be able to translate both from ordinary language to mathematics and from mathematics to ordinary language. Of course, the language of mathematics is limited to certain kinds of ideas. It is the language of form, size, and quantitative relationships. Its function as a language is not *merely* to enable the individual to convey his ideas to others: it is of inestimable value in aiding one to organize those ideas.

MATHEMATICS IS A TOOL

1.4   An ever growing number of fields of endeavor employs advanced mathematics as a tool.   The arithmetic of the elementary school is so used almost exclusively.   But as we have already indicated, mathematics is not *just* a tool.

What is the distinction between mathematics, the tool of science, and mathematics, the science?   Mathematics is sometimes divided into two categories, *applied mathematics* and *pure mathematics*.   When we use mathematics as a tool we are dealing with applied mathematics. But we cannot apply something which does not exist.   The creation of a mathematical system is in the realm of pure mathematics.

MATHEMATICAL SYSTEMS

1.5   A mathematical system consists of (1) *undefined terms*, (2) *axioms*, (3) *defined terms*, and (4) *theorems*.   A *proposition* is a statement about two or more terms, defined or undefined.   If the proposition is *assumed* to be true it is an axiom.   As we noted in Section 1.3, we cannot define everything.   Neither can we prove everything.   An axiom is not a "self-evident truth," that is, a statement that needs no proof.   It is not necessarily a statement that cannot be proved. It is merely a statement that we agree to accept without proof.   The first step in constructing a mathematical system consists of enumerating undefined terms and unproved statements (axioms).   We may then define other terms by using only undefined terms, previously defined terms, axioms, and other words which have no special mathematical meaning.   Finally, we establish other propositions (theorems) by making logical inferences from the terms, axioms, and previously established theorems.

Point and *line* are usually taken as undefined terms in geometry. *Two points determine one and only one line* is an example of an axiom. We may take as a definition: *A triangle is determined by three points not on a line*.   A simple theorem which can be derived from the above is: *A triangle determines three lines*.

When we draw a triangle on the chalkboard, we have not drawn the thing we defined as a *triangle* in the above paragraph.   We cannot say that the smears of chalk which are the sides of our triangle are the mathematical lines which we took as undefined.   Our mathematical structure has no physical existence: it is a pure abstraction. When we identify the undefined *line* with such things as smears of chalk, strings, and edges of solids, and the undefined *point* with little daubs of print-er's ink, corners of a building, and pairs of numbers, we are in the realm of applied mathematics.

The abstract mathematical system is called a "mathematical model" for its concrete physical counterpart. A given mathematical system can serve as a model for more than one practical situation. It is also true that more than one model can be used in studying a given physical situation.

From the historical standpoint, the model is abstracted from the concrete situation. Theorems derived within the mathematical sys-tem can then be applied to the concrete situation. The derived theorems are "true" within the mathematical model. They are as true as the axioms from which they are derived. But they may and may not agree with the facts of the concrete situation.

There is no logical necessity for the mathematical system to be abstracted from a given physical situation. The creator of the system is not required to have any practical application in mind. However, the history of the subject contains many examples of mathematics which was developed without any thought of application but which someone put to practical use.

USING THE BOOK

1.6   What should you gain from a study of this book? First, you should have a better understanding of what mathematics really is, its structure, what it deals with, and its techniques. You should gain a fuller appreciation of man's struggle to develop it to its present state and of the role it plays in our evolving civilization. The basic concepts of mathematics should become more meaningful. The processes of mathematics should cease to be meaningless rule-of-thumb procedures and should become reasonable and logical systematized common sense. Most important of all, you should become more proficient in the use of that elementary mathematics which educated men and women find most occasion to use.

If you have mastered high school algebra you will find here some needless repetition and detail in spots. A word of caution in this respect: read the familiar material rapidly but carefully, for shortly you will come to a new idea.   Most of the material contains ideas entirely new to you or familiar ones presented in a new light.

Many students think of a mathematics course solely as a series of exercises in finding correct answers to assigned problems.   Accordingly, the developmental explanatory material is considered merely an aid when the student is stuck in a problem.   That procedure is putting the cart before the horse as far as this book is concerned.   The exercises help you make the ideas developed become your own.   The solution of the exercises is a means to an end, not an end in itself.

However, the importance of solving the exercises should not be minimized.   As you study, keep a supply of sharp pencils handy. They are useful not only for working through the examples but also for arguing with yourself and the author.   That is one reason the printer leaves margins on the page.

One final word of advice.   Mathematics is a sequential subject; we cannot hope to get the roof on if we have not constructed the foundation.   In this book the sequential aspect is confined as much as possible to chapters, and each chapter is as nearly independent as possible. Do not feel that all is lost if you fail to understand something in Chapter III.   The thing you missed may not be essential to the mastery of Chapter IV.

───────────   E   X   E   R   C   I   S   E   S   ───────────

1.   Explain Bertrand Russell's definition of mathematics.

2.   According to the dictionary, *freedom* is defined as *independence* and *independence* is defined as *freedom*.   Select some ordinary word and, using a dictionary, construct a chain of definitions that leads back to the original word.   Try to have at least five links in the chain.

3.   Rewrite the second paragraph of Section 1.5, interchanging *point* and *line*.   Are you still willing to accept the axiom?   The definition?   The theorem?

4.   Rewrite the second paragraph of Section 1.5, replacing *point* with *snok*, *line* with *blure*, and *triangle* with *glud*.   Since *point* and *line* are undefined, do the *snok*, *blure*, and *glud* statements mean anything different from the original?

5.   Suggest a way of eliminating the following circular defining:
(a)   An angle of one degree is $1/90$ of a right angle.
(b)   A right angle is the angle formed by perpendicular lines.
(c)   Perpendicular lines are lines which form a 90° angle.

The difference between the conclusions of the scientist and those of the mathematician?

You can prove anything you want to if you have complete freedom in picking your assumptions?

A valid conclusion is not necessarily a true one?

It is possible to reason incorrectly and still reach a true conclusion?

The converse of a true proposition is not necessarily true?

Every time you solve an algebraic equation you actually establish a deductive proof?

The difference between necessary and sufficient conditions? Is having a dollar a necessary or a sufficient condition for being able to buy a loaf of bread? Is it both necessary and sufficient?

The difference between inductive reasoning and mathematical induction?

What indirect proof is and on what principles of logic it rests?

syl. - series of 3 statements
2 ass. gen., par.
then conclusion

9-12

LOGIC AND PROOF

In this chapter we shall attempt to find just what constitutes mathematical proof from the standpoint of logic, and to study in some detail certain methods of establishing deductive proof.

RULES OF LOGIC

2.1   The American mathematician Benjamin Peirce described mathematics as "the science which draws necessary conclusions." This is an apt description of mathematical proof. The "necessary conclusions" are drawn from the assumptions (hypotheses) by the application of logic. The logic employed is that of the Greek philosopher Aristotle, who laid down three fundamental laws of reasoning, or *canons of logic:* (1) the principle of *identity*, (2) the principle of *excluded middle*, and (3) the principle of *contradiction*. The first of these asserts that a thing is itself: a dog is a dog, a positive integer is a positive integer. The second principle asserts that a statement is either true or false: a dog is or is not a four-legged animal, minus *a* either is or is not a negative number. The third principle asserts that no statement can be both true and false: a dog cannot both be and not be a four-legged animal, zero cannot both be and not be a negative number.

There is a fourth principle of logic known as the law of *implication*. Statement *a* implies statement *b* if *b* is true whenever *a* is true. This is the cornerstone of deductive reasoning. It will be discussed at length in the following sections.

These principles of logic are themselves axioms. Even though it might never occur to us to question them, that does not alter the fact that they cannot be *proved*. Even the logicians have their troubles. Consider this paraphrase of an old favorite: A prisoner of war, as one final bit of torture, was told he could choose the method of his execution. He was to make a statement: if he made a true statement he was to be shot; if false, he was to be hanged. The prisoner replied, "Well, I'll be hanged."

COMPOUND STATEMENTS

2.2   Simple statements are frequently quite difficult to analyze. Such statements as "The Democratic party is the War party" and "The Republican party is the Big Business party" are apt to cause considerable controversy. "Mr. James was a notorious criminal" would elicit quite different responses from those who were thinking of Jesse and those who were thinking of William. The reaction to "Mary has beautiful blue eyes" will depend not only upon which Mary but also upon one's preference for blue.

A *compound statement* is formed by combining two or more simple statements. The truth or falsity of compound statements may be determined rather easily when the truth or falsity of its component simple statements is granted.

There are a number of ways in which simple statements may be combined. The *conjunction* of two statements p and q is obtained by connecting them with "and." The symbol for conjunction is $\wedge$. Thus, the conjunction of p and q is written $p \wedge q$. If p is the statement "It is raining" and q is "It is cold outside," then $p \wedge q$ is "It is raining and it is cold outside." The conjunction asserts that both p and q are true. The truth of a compound statement depends on the truth of its components. We can show the relationship conveniently by means of a *truth table*. Table 2.1 gives the truth table for conjunction.

Table 2.1

p	q	$p \wedge q$
T	T	T
T	F	F
F	T	F
F	F	F

In the p and q columns we find every possible true-false combination. In the conjunction column we find a true statement *only* when both p and q are true.

Another frequently used connective is called *disjunction*. This is the *or* connective; its symbol is $\vee$. We may translate $p \vee q$ as "It is cold outside *or* it is raining." In ordinary English there is a slight ambiguity here. We sometimes use *or* to mean at least one. "Betty wants a kitten or a parakeet for her birthday." She would not object in the least if she got both, but she would be very much disappointed if she got neither. On the other hand, Carol can hardly do both if she plans to take French or chemistry at three o'clock Monday, Wednesday, and Friday. In this instance *or* means one but not both. We eliminate the possibility of ambiguity by recognizing both kinds of disjunction. *Inclusive disjunction* (∨) means "*p* or *q* or both," (*p* ∨ *q*). *Exclusive disjunction* (∨̲) means "*p* or *q* but not both," (*p* ∨̲ *q*). Table 2.2 gives the truth table for disjunction.

Table 2.2 Inclusive and exclusive disjunction.

p	q	$p \vee q$	$p \veebar q$
T	T	T	F
T	F	T	T
F	T	T	T
F	F	F	F

It is convenient to have a symbol to indicate that a statement is false. This is called *negation*. If *p* is the statement "It is raining," its negation, ∼*p*, asserts that "It is raining" is false. It does not assert, "The sun is shining." It may be midnight, or cloudy, or snowing. "It is not raining" is all that we can conclude from ∼*p*. By the principle of excluded middle either *p* or ∼*p* must be true, and by the principle of contradiction only one of them can be true. The truth table for negation is given in Table 2.3.

Table 2.3 A statement and its negative cannot both be true.

p	$\sim p$
T	F
F	T

The three symbols ∧, ∨, and ∼ can be used together to form more complicated compound statements. Truth tables can be constructed to exhibit their truth values. We illustrate the method with the following.

Example Find the truth values for $(p \vee q) \wedge \sim (p \wedge q)$.

Table 2.4

1	2	3	6	5	4
p	q	$(p \vee q)$	$\wedge$	$\sim$	$p \wedge q$
T	T	T	F	F	T
T	F	T	T	T	F
F	T	T	T	T	F
F	F	F	F	T	F

In Columns 1 and 2 we place every possible T-F pairing. Columns 3 and 4 are completed in accordance with the basic rules of disjunction (Table 2.2) and conjunction (Table 2.1). Column 5 is obtained by negating Column 4. Column 6 is obtained by applying the rule of conjunction to Columns 3 and 5.

If we compare the result in Column 6 with that of exclusive disjunction (Table 2.2), we see they are identical. In other words, the compound under investigation is true or false under exactly the same circumstances that $p \vee q$ is true or false. The translation of $(p \vee q) \wedge \sim (p \wedge q)$ into ordinary language is: "p or q is true and p and q is not true." This is the meaning of $p \veebar q$.

—————— E   X   E   R   C   I   S   E   S ——————

1. Find the simple statements from which the following compound statements are obtained. Identify the connectives used in each.
   (a) The Dodgers and the White Sox won the pennants.
   (b) It is raining and turning cold.
   (c) Either the Dodgers or the White Sox won the series.
   (d) Jim's friends will vacation in the mountains or on the coast.
   (e) It is raining cats but not dogs.
   (f) Sue likes cats but does not dislike dogs.
   (g) That is neither here nor there.

2. Write the following in symbolic form. Let p be "The moon is made of green cheese" and q be "Cheese is made from milk."
   (a) The moon is not made of green cheese but cheese is made from milk.
   (b) Either cheese is not made from milk or the moon is not made of green cheese.
   (c) It is not true that the moon is not made of green cheese and cheese is not made from milk.
   (d) Neither is the moon made of green cheese nor is cheese made from milk.
   (e) Either the moon is made of green cheese or cheese is not made from milk.
   (f) It is not true that the moon is made of green cheese or cheese is made from milk.

3. Construct truth tables for each symbolic statement in Exercise 2. Which, if any, of the statements are equivalent?

4. Translate each of the following into words if p means "Sam is rich," q means "Tom is handsome," and r means "Jim is lucky."

(a) $(p \wedge \sim q) \vee r$ (e) $(p \wedge q) \vee \sim r$
(b) $\sim p \vee (q \wedge \sim r)$ (f) $p \vee \sim (q \wedge r)$
(c) $(\sim p \vee q) \wedge (\sim p \vee \sim r)$ (g) $p \vee (\sim q \wedge r)$
(d) $\sim[(p \vee q) \wedge \sim r]$ (h) $(p \vee \sim q) \wedge r$

5. Which statements in Exercise 4 are true if Sam is rich, Tom is ugly, and Jim is lucky?

6. Take the definitions of p, q, and r given in Exercise 4, translate the following, then write each in simple symbolic form.
(a) $\sim(\sim p \vee \sim q)$
(b) $(\sim p \vee q) \wedge (\sim p \vee r)$
(c) $(p \wedge \sim q) \vee (p \wedge \sim r)$

7. Write the following in symbolic form, then construct a truth table for each result.
(a) This polygon is not a square or it is a rectangle.
(b) This polygon is both a square and a rectangle or it is not a square.
(c) It is untrue that this polygon is not a rectangle and is a square.

8. Which, if any, of the statements in Exercise 7 have the same truth functions?

IMPLICATION

2.3 Another common compound statement is the *conditional*. It customarily takes the form "If p, then q." The conditional connective symbol is $\rightarrow$. "If p, then q" is written $p \rightarrow q$. The truth function for the conditional is not as readily apparent as it is for conjunction, disjunction, and negation. This is owing partly to the fact that we usually expect some kind of causal relationship between the two simple statements when we join them by "if-then." This is not the case of the other compounds we have studied. "I like tomatoes and Joe Louis was a great fighter" may seem a bit incongruous. But "If I like tomatoes, then Joe Louis was a great fighter" is ridiculous.

However, we wish to consider the new statement formed in combining two simple statements by "if-then," whether the simple statements appear to be related or not.

If both p and q are true it seems reasonable to accept $p \rightarrow q$ as a true statement. "If this triangle is equilateral, then it is isosceles" we accept as a true statement if a given triangle is both equilateral and isosceles. On the other hand, "If this triangle is isosceles, then it is equilateral" is not so readily accepted as true. We agree that it is true only when "This triangle is isosceles" is true and when "This triangle is equilateral" is also true.

If p is true and q false it seems reasonable to reject the conditional $p \rightarrow q$ as false. "If this triangle is isosceles, then it is equilateral" is certainly a false statement when the triangle in question is isosceles but not equilateral.

If p is false, we accept the conditional $p \rightarrow q$ as true, regardless of the truth or falsity of q. At first glance this seems a bit strange. But we must remember that we are considering the truth of the compound statement, not of its components. "If $2 + 2 = 5$, then Alaska is the largest state in the Union" is a true statement. The statement does not require that $2 + 2$ equal 5. Since p ($2 + 2 = 5$) is false, the statement is true regardless of the size of Alaska.

Table 2.5 If the conditional $p \rightarrow q$ cannot be false, then p implies q.

p	q	$p \rightarrow q$
T	T	T
T	F	F
F	T	T
F	F	T

We have asserted that q is true provided p is true, and have been completely noncommittal about q if p is false. Table 2.5 gives the truth function of the conditional.

Closely associated with the conditional is the idea of *implication*. The conditional, $p \rightarrow q$, is a single compound statement. Implication is a relation *between* two statements. If the conditional $p \rightarrow q$ cannot be false, then p *implies* q.

The symbol $p \rightarrow q$ is often used to indicate the implication between p and q as well as to indicate the conditional compound. Table 2.5 serves as a truth table for implication in the sense that the implication relation does not exist ($p \rightarrow q$ is false) if it is possible for p to be true and q false. Let p be "The integer n is a multiple of 3" and let q be "The integer n has 4 as its units digit." If $n = 24$, both p and q are true. But this does not justify the implication $p \rightarrow q$. If $n = 25$, both p and q are false. If $n = 14$ then p is false and q is true. But if $n = 30$ then p is true and q is false. Therefore p does not imply q. When all four of the true-false possibilities for p and q can exist, we say p and q are *unrelated*.

Let p be "The integer n has units digit 5" and let q be "The integer n is a multiple of 5." In this case p does imply q. Note that the only impossible case is p true and q false. If $n = 15$, p and q are both true. If $n = 12$, p and q are both false. If $n = 20$, p is false and q is true.

The possibility of a false p and a true q is not essential to implication. If p is "The sum of the digits of the integer n is a multiple of 3," and

q is "The integer n is a multiple of 3," then neither false p and true q nor true p and false q is possible. Both statements are true, or both are false. In this instance p implies q, and q implies p; we call this relationship *equivalence*. The symbol for equivalence is $\leftrightarrow$. The truth table for equivalence is given in Table 2.6.

Table 2.6 Equivalence is a two-way implication.

p	q	$p \leftrightarrow q$
T	T	T
T	F	F
F	T	F
F	F	T

We demonstrate that $(p \rightarrow q$ and $q \rightarrow p)$ is equivalent to $p \leftrightarrow q$ by means of a truth table (Table 2.7) for the statement $[(p \rightarrow q) \wedge (q \rightarrow p)] \leftrightarrow (p \leftrightarrow q)$.

Table 2.7

1	2	3	5	4	7	6
p	q	$[(p \rightarrow q)$	$\wedge$	$(q \rightarrow p)]$	$\leftrightarrow$	$(p \leftrightarrow q)$
T	T	T	T	T	T	T
T	F	F	F	T	T	F
F	T	T	F	F	T	F
F	F	T	T	T	T	T

The columns are filled in the order indicated by the numbering. Column 5 is the conjunction of the two implications. It is identical with Column 6, the equivalence of p and q. In Column 7 we find only T, since 5 and 6 agree in each instance. The complete statement $[(p \rightarrow q) \wedge (q \rightarrow p)] \leftrightarrow (p \leftrightarrow q)$ is *logically true*. It is a true statement, regardless of the truth or falsity of p or q. Such statements are also referred to as *tautologies*.

Definition   A tautology is a compound statement which is true regardless of the truth or falsity of its components.

We should not confuse the truth function for equivalence, which is found in Column 6, with the results in Column 7. In Column 6 we are saying that p and q are equivalent *if* they are both true or both false. In Column 7 we are saying that the conjunction of the implications is *always* equivalent to the equivalence of p and q. In Column 6 we find a T where p and q agree as to true or false. In Column 7 we find a T where $(p \leftrightarrow q)$ and $[(p \rightarrow q) \wedge (q \rightarrow p)]$ agree as to true or false. Thus, we have used the definition of equivalence to fill both Columns 6 and 7.

———————— E   X   E   R   C   I   S   E   S ————————

1. In which of the following cases does p imply q? In which does q imply p?

   (a) p: Rhode Island is the largest state in the Union.
          q: Hawaii is the newest state in the Union.

   (b) p: The integer n is an odd number.
          q: The integer n is a prime number. (See definition of prime numbers, page 26.)

   (c) p: Triangle ABC is similar to triangle DEF.
          q: Triangle ABC is congruent to triangle DEF.

   (d) p: Canada is a member of the British Commonwealth.
          q: Mexico is an absolute monarchy.

   (e) p: $2 \times 3 = 11$.
          q: $3 + 4 = 12$.

   (f) p: Statement q is false.
          q: Statement p is false.

   (g) p: Statement q is true.
          q: Statement p is false.

2. In which of the parts of Exercise 1 are p and q equivalent? Unrelated?

3. Construct a truth table and show that $(\sim p \vee q) \leftrightarrow (p \rightarrow q)$ is a tautology.

4. Translate into English the symbolic statement in Exercise 3.

5. Construct a truth table and show that $\sim(p \wedge \sim q) \leftrightarrow (\sim p \vee q)$ is a tautology.

6. Translate into English the symbolic statement in Exercise 5.

7. The results of Exercises 3 and 5 suggest a third tautology. Write it in symbolic form and construct its truth table.

8. Construct a truth table for $p \wedge \sim p$ and show that it is logically false, that is, that it can never be true. This is merely a restatement of which of the canons of logic on page 9?

9. Construct a truth table for $(p \rightarrow q) \wedge p$. If we accept the truth of this conjunction, what are we forced to conclude in regard to q?

10. Construct a truth table for $(p \rightarrow q) \wedge \sim q$. If we accept the truth of this conjunction, what are we forced to conclude in regard to p?

11. Construct a truth table for $(p \rightarrow q) \wedge q$. What does the acceptance of the truth of this conjunction force us to conclude in regard to p?

12. Construct a truth table for $(p \rightarrow q) \wedge \sim p$. What does the acceptance of the truth of this conjunction force us to conclude in regard to q?

13. Illustrate with an example the distinction between a conditional statement and an implication.

PROOF

2.4   There are many kinds of proof. There is proof by performance. The Russian scientists proved a rocket could be shot to the
moon by doing it. Every time he flies, the bumblebee proves the
engineer who said it could not be done was wrong.

There is proof by induction. The sun will rise in the east next
Tuesday because it always has risen in the east on Tuesdays. There
is proof by authority. This is an it-is-so-because-the-experts-say-it-
is-so proof. There is legal proof, printer's proof, hundred proof. The
word "proof" has many meanings and shades of meaning.

Mathematical proof is none of these. Mathematical proof is proof
by *deduction*. It consists of showing that the statement to be proved
is a logical consequence of statements that have been assumed or
previously proved or both.

The implication relation is the all-
important key to deductive proof.
Exercise 9, Section 2.3, establishes its
significance. If we assume that the
conditional $p \to q$ is a tautology, in
other words, that p implies q, and we
also assume that p is true, we are
forced to admit that q is true also.

Table 2.8

p	$\to$	q	$\wedge$	p
T	T	T	T	T
T	F	F	F	T
F	T	T	F	F
F	T	F	F	F

The truth values for this conjunction show the conjunction is true
only in the first line. But q is true in that line. *If p implies q and
p is true, then q must be true.*

If q is the statement we seek to prove, it is necessary merely to
gain the acceptance of the implication $p \to q$ and the acceptance of p.
We do not establish the truth of q. We establish the necessity of a
true q, if p and $p \to q$ are true.

When we reach the conclusion q in the above manner we have a
valid argument. The truth or falsity of the conclusion has no necessary relationship to the validity of the argument. Those statements
which are assumed to be true make up the *hypothesis* (H) of a theorem.
That which we wish to establish is the *conclusion* (C) of the theorem.
Proving the theorem consists of showing the implication $H \to C$ is
true. It is quite possible to show by a valid argument that a false H
implies either a true or a false C. But if H is true, we can establish
$H \to C$ only for a true C. If H, although assumed true, happens to
be false the argument throws no light on C.

Consider the following.

Theorem 1

Hypothesis: (a)   All citizens of the United States are taxpayers.
(b)   Some citizens of the United States are penniless.
Conclusion: Some taxpayers are penniless.

Many taxpayers can vouch for the truth of this conclusion, but we are concerned with the validity of the argument. Is the conclusion justified from the hypothesis? Diagrams similar to Figure 2.1, known as Venn diagrams, are often helpful in testing the validity of an argument. They are comparable to the figures in geometric proofs.

Figure 2.1

All taxpayers are represented by the points within the large boundary. The citizens of the United States by Hypothesis (a) of Theorem 1 are in the total group of taxpayers. Hypothesis (b) demands that at least part of the United States citizen area also be in the region of the penniless. Therefore the hypothesis has forced us to place at least a part of the taxpayer region in the penniless region, and the argument is valid. Could the penniless region have been entirely within the taxpayer area? Entirely within the citizen area? When the word *some* is used in mathematics it does not mean "some, but not all," it means *at least one*.

Although it is more easily followed by using Venn diagrams the validity of the argument may be shown by a truth table. Let c represent citizens of the United States, t taxpayers, and p penniless persons. Hypothesis (a) is $c \rightarrow t$. Hypothesis (b) is not $c \rightarrow p$; this

Table 2.9

1	2	3	1	7	2	8	6	1	5	4	3	11	10	2	9	4	3
c	t	p	[(c	$\rightarrow$	t)	$\wedge$	$\sim$	(c	$\rightarrow$	$\sim$	p)]	$\rightarrow$	$\sim$	(t	$\rightarrow$	$\sim$	p)
T	T	T	T	T	T	T	T	T	F	F	T	T	T	T	F	F	T
T	T	F	T	T	T	F	F	T	T	T	F	T	F	T	T	T	F
T	F	T	T	F	F	F	T	T	F	F	T	T	F	F	T	F	T
T	F	F	T	F	F	F	F	T	T	T	F	T	F	F	T	T	F
F	T	T	F	T	T	F	F	F	T	F	T	T	T	T	F	F	T
F	T	F	F	T	T	F	F	F	T	T	F	T	F	T	T	T	F
F	F	T	F	T	F	F	F	F	T	F	T	T	F	F	T	F	T
F	F	F	F	T	F	F	F	F	T	T	F	T	F	F	T	T	F

would mean all citizens are penniless.   It is the negation of $c \rightarrow \sim p$; we deny that all citizens are not penniless.   Similarly, the conclusion is the negation of $t \rightarrow \sim p$.   We must show that the hypothesis $(c \rightarrow t) \wedge \sim(c \rightarrow \sim p)$ implies the conclusion $\sim(t \rightarrow \sim p)$.   This means that $[(c \rightarrow t) \wedge \sim(c \rightarrow \sim p)] \rightarrow \sim(t \rightarrow \sim p)$ is a tautology. Since only T appears in Column 11 the proposition is proved.

To return to the question: Is a valid conclusion true only if the hypothesis is true?   The question may be stated: Does the truth of the conclusion imply the truth of the hypothesis?   As an illustration that with a valid argument we may reach a true conclusion from a false hypothesis, consider the following.

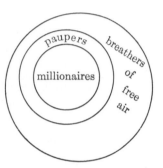

Theorem 2

Hypothesis: (a)   All millionaires are paupers.
                   (b)   All paupers breathe free air.
Conclusion: All millionaires breathe free air.

Here, the hypothesis (a) is false, yet we have reasoned correctly to a conclusion which we accept as true.   We cannot infer that a hypothesis is true merely because the reasoning is correct and the conclusion is true.

Figure 2.2

Do a true hypothesis and a true conclusion imply that the reasoning is valid?

Theorem 3

Hypothesis: (a)   All Tennesseans are residents of the United States.
                   (b)   All Nashvillians are residents of the United States.
Conclusion: All Nashvillians are Tennesseans.

Both hypothesis and conclusion are true. Yet the hypothesis forces us only to place Nashvillians in the area of the residents of the United States.   It does not force us to include Nashvillians among the Tennesseans. The reasoning is not valid.   Valid reasoning makes the conclusion inescapable.

If the reasoning is not valid we can make no inference as to the relative truth of hypothesis and conclusion.   It is possible to reach a true conclusion from either a true

Figure 2.3

or a false hypothesis. If a conclusion is reached which is accepted as true we can make no inference as to the truth or falsity of the hypothesis. Since a true hypothesis cannot lead by valid reasoning to a false conclusion, we may summarize by observing that with valid reasoning

(1) *a true hypothesis forces us to a true conclusion, and*

(2) *a false conclusion requires that the hypothesis also be false.*

However, a true conclusion does not require a true hypothesis nor does a false hypothesis require a false conclusion.

——————— E X E R C I S E S ———————

1. In Theorem 2, page 19, let m be "This person is a millionaire," let p be "This person is a pauper," and let a be "This person breathes free air." Write the theorem as a symbolic statement involving m, p, and a.

2. Show that the statement obtained in Exercise 1 is a tautology.

3. In Theorem 3, page 19, let t be "This person is a Tennessean," let u be "This person is a resident of the United States," and let n be "This person is a Nashvillian." Write the theorem as a symbolic statement involving t, u, and n.

4. Construct a truth table for the statement obtained in Exercise 3 and indicate from it why the theorem is not valid.

5. Is this statement true or false: Two statements that imply the same statement imply each other.

6. Draw a diagram to show the relationships among these three objects: cats, animals, tigers. Make all the statements you can about these objects on the basis of your diagram.

7. Follow the instructions of Exercise 6 for the relationships of these objects: places of amusement, places of business, movie theaters.

8. For each of the following, state the hypothesis, state the conclusion, and state whether the conclusion is or is not valid. Which conclusions do you consider true?

(a) Mr. Jones is a good man because he goes to church and all church-goers are good.

(b) Mr. Jones is an evil man since men are sent to prison for evil deeds and Mr. Jones has been in prison.

(c) Kind people are honest. Mr. Jones is unkind. Hence Mr. Jones is not honest.

(d) All men are intelligent animals. My dog Fido is an intelligent animal; therefore Fido is a man.

(e) Beautiful movie actresses smoke X-brand cigarettes, so if you smoke X-brand cigarettes you will be beautiful.

(f) Distinguished men drink X-brand liquor, so if you are distinguished you will drink X-brand liquor.

(g) Anyone who does not study cannot pass this course. Mary does study. Mary will pass this course.

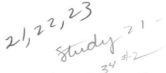

CONVERSE, INVERSE, AND CONTRAPOSITIVE

2.5   Usually, the hypothesis of a theorem consists of more than one assumption, from which we derive one or more conclusions. In its simplest form a deductive proof may consist of one hypothesis and one conclusion. We may write $H \to C$ to mean that hypothesis H implies conclusion C. In the case of a single hypothesis and single conclusion, the *converse* of a theorem is obtained by interchanging the hypothesis and the conclusion. If the direct theorem is $H \to C$, its converse is $C \to H$. More generally, a converse is obtained by interchanging one hypothesis with one conclusion.

All men are animals. "*A* is a man" implies that "*A* is an animal." But "*A* is an animal" does not imply that "*A* is a man." *The converse of a valid statement is not necessarily valid.*

If the direct theorem consists of

Hypothesis: (a)   All x's are y's.
           (b)   All y's are z's.
Conclusion: (c)   All x's are z's.

one possible converse may be obtained by interchanging (c) with (b). The converse is:

Hypothesis: (a)   All x's are y's.
           (c)   All x's are z's.
Conclusion: (b)   All y's are z's.

The Venn diagram in Figure 2.4(a) indicates that the direct theorem is valid, since the circle of x must be completely in the circle of y, which in turn must be completely in the circle of z. However, in Figure 2.4(b) we only place the x circle completely within the y circle and completely within the z circle. Parenthetically, we cannot appraise the truth or falsity of either hypothesis or either conclusion since x, y, z are not defined.

Symbolically, the direct theorem rests upon the fact that

$$[(x \rightarrow y) \wedge (y \rightarrow z)] \rightarrow (x \rightarrow z)$$

is a tautology. This is established in Section 2.8. The converse is logically equivalent to Exercise 4, Section 2.4.

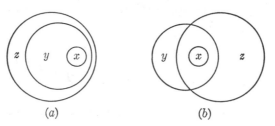

(a)   (b)

Figure 2.4. The converse of a valid theorem is not necessarily valid.

It happens that many valid statements do have valid converses. If a statement and its converse are both valid, this means that $H \leftrightarrow C$ (see page 15). If two sides of a triangle are equal, then the angles opposite these sides are equal. The converse of this theorem is: If two angles of a triangle are equal, then the sides opposite these angles are equal. This is an instance in which a theorem and its converse are both valid: equal angles imply equal sides, and equal sides imply equal angles. On the other hand, all right angles are equal but not all equal angles are right angles. That two angles are equal does not imply that they are right angles. Here is an inference that is not reversible.

The converse of a theorem is obtained by interchanging hypothesis and conclusion. The negation of both hypothesis and conclusion gives a theorem that is the *inverse* of the original. Consider a direct theorem: If the units digit of a natural number (positive whole number) is 5, then it is divisible by five. The converse is: If a natural number is divisible by five, then its units digit is 5. If we negate both the hypothesis and conclusion, we obtain the inverse: If the units digit of a natural number is not 5, then it is not divisible by five. The *contrapositive* of a theorem is obtained by both interchanging and negating hypothesis and conclusion. The hypothesis of the contrapositive is the negation of the conclusion of the original theorem and the conclusion of the contrapositive is the negation of the original hypothesis. The contrapositive of the original theorem is: If a natural number is not divisible by five, its units digit is not 5.

Direct Theorem: $H \rightarrow C$.
Converse: $C \rightarrow H$.
Inverse: $\sim H \rightarrow \sim C$.
Contrapositive: $\sim C \rightarrow \sim H$.

A theorem, $H \rightarrow C$, and its contrapositive, $\sim C \rightarrow \sim H$, are equivalent statements. They are both true or they are both false. Table 2.10 shows that the equivalence of the two conditionals $H \rightarrow C$ and $\sim C \rightarrow \sim H$ is a tautology.

Table 2.10   A theorem and its contrapositive are logically equivalent.

H	C	(H	→	C)	↔	(∼	C	→	∼	H)
T	T	T	T	T	T	F	T	T	F	T
T	F	T	F	F	T	T	F	F	F	T
F	T	F	T	T	T	F	T	T	T	F
F	F	F	T	F	T	T	F	T	T	F

Let us examine the above theorem and its contrapositive.

Direct Theorem
Hypothesis: Units digit five.
Conclusion: Divisible by five.

Contrapositive
Hypothesis: Not divisible by five.
Conclusion: Units digit not five.

The direct theorem requires that a number *must* be divisible by five if it ends in 5. It says nothing about the numbers ending in 0. The direct theorem is true. If the contrapositive were false, it would be possible for a natural number not to be divisible by five and yet have 5 as its units digit. Since this contradicts the true direct theorem, it is false that the contrapositive is false.

Note that the contrapositive may be obtained by taking either the inverse of the converse or the converse of the inverse.

If we consider the converse as the direct theorem we get:

Direct Theorem: $C \rightarrow H$.
Converse $H \rightarrow C$.
Inverse: $\sim C \rightarrow \sim H$.
Contrapositive: $\sim H \rightarrow \sim C$.

But this contrapositive is the original inverse. Then the converse and the inverse of a theorem are contrapositives and as such are logically equivalent.

—————————— E X E R C I S E S ——————————

1. Write the converse, the inverse, and the contrapositive of each of the following.
    *(a)   If it rains tomorrow my feet will hurt today.
    (b)   If a number is prime it is odd.
    *(c)   Lines perpendicular to the same line are parallel.
    (d)   If a person's parents are both blue eyed the person is blue eyed.
    *(e)   If two numbers are equal to the same number they are equal to each other.
    (f)   If x is an odd number, x^2 is an odd number.
    *(g)   If a number ends in 5 it is divisible by five.
    (h)   If a number ends in 7 it is an odd number.

2. Which statements in Exercise 1 are true?   Which converses?   Which contrapositives?   Which inverses?

3. Write the converse, inverse, and contrapositive of each of the following.
    *(a) $\sim p \to (q \vee \sim r)$ *(c) $\sim q \to \sim p$
    (b) $q \to \sim p$ (d) $\sim p \to q$

4. Construct a truth table for $(p \to q) \leftrightarrow (q \to p)$ and show that since it is not a tautology the converse of a true theorem need not be true.

5. Construct a truth table for $(q \to p) \leftrightarrow (\sim p \to \sim q)$ and show that the inverse and converse of a theorem are logically equivalent.

6. Assume the following is true: For Mr. Jones to be the murderer it is necessary that Mr. Brown be a bigamist.   Which of the following statements follow logically from this?
    *(a)   If Mr. Jones is not a murderer Mr. Brown is not a bigamist.
    (b)   If Mr. Brown is a bigamist Mr. Jones is a murderer.
    *(c)   If Mr. Brown is not a bigamist Mr. Jones is not a murderer.
    (d)   If Mr. Jones is a murderer Mr. Brown is a bigamist.

NECESSARY AND SUFFICIENT CONDITIONS

2.6   Frequently we see a proposition stated in the form: "B is true if and only if A is true" or "A is a necessary and sufficient condition for B." Both statements are merely other ways of specifying that both the proposition $A \to B$ and its converse $B \to A$ must be valid. We can accomplish the same thing by establishing the direct theorem $A \to B$ and its inverse $\sim A \to \sim B$.

If you studied plane geometry and recall locus problems, you will recognize this idea. The locus theorem required two things: (1) every point of the proposed locus must satisfy the given conditions, and

(2) either every point which satisfies the given conditions is a point of the locus (the converse) or every point not on the locus fails to satisfy the conditions (the inverse).

The example in Section 2.5, slightly modified and stated in the "if and only if" form, would be: A natural number is divisible by five if and only if its units digit is 0 or 5. The "if" part of the argument is established when we prove the direct theorem: units digit 0 or 5 → divisibility by five. The "only if" part calls for proving the inverse: units digit not 0 or 5 → not divisible by five. But if the converse is easier to prove, it is just as good.

If I have a dollar I can buy a loaf of bread. Having a dollar is a sufficient condition for the price of a loaf of bread, but it isn't necessary, since fifty cents is more than enough even at current prices. On the other hand, having one cent (for the tax) is a necessary condition, but it isn't sufficient.

If the above theorem were stated in the necessary and sufficient form, it would read: Having a units digit of 0 or 5 is a necessary and sufficient condition that a natural number be divisible by five. When we establish the direct theorem, units digit 0 or 5 → divisibility by five, we have shown the condition to be sufficient. Incidentally, a units digit either of 0 or of 5 constitutes a sufficient condition for divisibility by five, but neither one used alone is a necessary condition. The necessary condition requires that we prove either the inverse (failure to satisfy the condition of ending in 0 or 5 means failure to get the result of divisibility by five) or the converse (if the situation of divisibility by five is present, the condition of ending in 0 or 5 also has to be present).

ILLOGICAL BOOBY TRAPS

2.7   Many of the favorite errors of logic to which mathematics students are addicted are the result of misconceptions concerning the ideas we have been discussing. We shall call specific attention to some of them.

The idea that a theorem implies its converse. We wish to prove that $A \rightarrow B$. If we assume that B is true and can conclude that A must be also, that does not give us the right to say that $A \rightarrow B$. All we have shown is that $B \rightarrow A$. If this were permissible, we could "prove" that all odd numbers greater than 2 are prime by proving that all prime numbers greater than 2 are odd. (A prime is an integer greater than one, which has no exact divisors except itself and one; for example, the first five primes are 2, 3, 5, 7, and 11.) The best insurance against this mistake is to identify correctly the hypothesis, that which is given, and reason from it to that which is to be proved.

The idea that a statement which implies a true statement must be true. We have already pointed out that valid reasoning from a false hypothesis may yield a true conclusion. We can make no inference as to the truth or falsity of the hypothesis unless the conclusion is known to be false and we are sure the reasoning is valid. If a statement which implies a true statement had to be true, we could "prove" that $-4 = +4$. Assume that $-4 = +4$, then multiply each side of this "equality" by the "equal" quantities -4 and $+4$, and get $16 = 16$. We have reached a true conclusion; then we "conclude" that $-4 = +4$.

A variant of this is illustrated by the following.

Theorem

Hypothesis: If a number is divisible by six, it is divisible by three. Fifteen is divisible by three.

Conclusion: Fifteen is divisible by six.

Let p be "n is divisible by six," and let q be "n is divisible by three." Symbolically, the theorem requires that $[(p \to q) \land q] \to p$ is a tautology.

The truth table for the implication $H \to C$ (when H is $(p \to q) \land q$, and C is p) shows that $H \to C$ can be false even when q is true; for example, let $n = 15$.

Table 2.11

p	q	$[(p \to q)$	$\land$	$q]$	$\to$	p
T	T	T	T	T	T	T
T	F	F	F	F	T	T
F	T	T	T	T	F	F
F	F	T	F	F	T	F

Reasoning in a circle. This is assuming that which is to be proved. On its face, one might wonder how such a breach of logic could be made. However, this is probably the most deadly trap of all for the unwary. That is because the conclusion is often introduced in a disguised form.

The following is an example of reasoning in a circle. I wish to prove that all natural numbers are even. Let x equal any natural number. If it is even, then $x = 2y$, where y is a natural number. But if any natural number is doubled, the result is an even number. Therefore $2y$ is even. But $2y = x$, so x is even. Yet x is any number. Therefore, any number is even.

Substituting induction for deduction. This is not really an error in logic. It is evidence of lack of grasp of the meaning of deductive proof. In this connection, just as "some" in mathematics means "at least one," so "all" means "without a single exception." We can never prove that $A \rightarrow B$ by finding any number of special cases unless there is only a finite number of cases to be considered. But we can prove that $A \nrightarrow B$ (A does not imply B) by finding one case in which A fails to imply B. $A \rightarrow B$ means always, without exception; B follows logically from A. $A \nrightarrow B$ does not mean that A never implies B. It means that B does not need to follow from A, and all we must do is find one instance in which B fails to follow from A.

It should be observed that $A \nrightarrow B$ is not the inverse of $A \rightarrow B$. Let A represent quadrilateral and B represent parallelogram. $A \nrightarrow B$ means that a figure's being a quadrilateral does not imply its being a parallelogram: it does not have to be a parallelogram simply because it is a quadrilateral. The inverse of $A \rightarrow B$ means that if a figure is not a quadrilateral it cannot be a parallelogram.

Assuming that two statements that imply the same statement imply each other. It is quite possible for $A \rightarrow B$ and $C \rightarrow B$ to be true and yet for A and C to be unrelated. For example, if A is "n is a multiple of 6," B is "n is a multiple of 3" and C is "n is a multiple of 9."

————————— E X E R C I S E S —————————

1. Decide whether the given condition (stated first in the following) is necessary, sufficient, both necessary and sufficient, or neither necessary nor sufficient for the situation.
    (a) Being at least twenty-one years old — being President of the United States
    (b) Being a triangle — being a polygon
    (c) Being a polygon whose interior angles = 180° — being a triangle
    (d) Being blue eyed — getting married
    (e) Having ten dollars — having a good time
    (f) Answering this question — passing this course
    (g) Being sleepy — going to sleep
    (h) Being an odd number — being a prime number greater than 2

2. Point out the errors in logic of the following.
    (a) Doctor X's cancer cure is a sure cure for cancer because all five
         hundred patients he has treated have recovered.
    (b) Sweet milk and gunpowder is a sure cure for poison ivy because
         every person who has tried it has recovered from poison ivy.
    (c) Any number, x, equals any other number, y. Let $x + y = z$;
         then if $x = y$, $x + y = x + x = 2x = z$ and $x = z/2$. Therefore
         $z/2 + y = z$ and $y = z/2$. But, since $x = z/2$ and $y = z/2$, it
         follows that $x = y$.
    (d) If a man is sufficiently hungry he will steal. Therefore Jesse James
         was driven to crime by hunger.
    (e) Since nobody likes Santa Claus and Santa Claus is a fat man, it
         follows that nobody likes a fat man.
    (f) The product of two negative numbers is positive. The product
         $a \times b$ is positive. Therefore a and b are negative.
    (g) If wages increase, prices rise. Prices are rising. Therefore wages
         are increasing.

3. Compare the following with Exercise 2(e): Since nobody likes a fat man
    and Santa Claus is fat, nobody likes Santa Claus.

4. Let p stand for "This year is leap year" and q stand for "Mary Doe will
    get married this year." Write the following symbolically.
    (a) Mary Doe will not get married this year unless it is leap year.
    (b) If this is leap year Mary Doe will get married this year.
    (c) A sufficient condition for Mary Doe's marriage this year is that it
         be leap year.
    (d) A necessary condition for this to be leap year is that Mary Doe will
         not marry this year.
    (e) Mary Doe will not marry this year if and only if it is not leap year.
    (f) This is leap year if and only if Mary Doe marries this year.
    (g) Mary Doe's marriage this year is a necessary and sufficient con-
         dition for this to be leap year.

5. Let p be "It will rain today" and q be "The baseball game will be post-
    poned." Write out the following in the "necessary-sufficient" ter-
    minology.
    (a) $\sim q \to \sim p$ (c) $(p \to q) \wedge \sim (\sim p \to \sim q)$
    (b) $q \leftrightarrow p$ (d) $\sim p \leftrightarrow q$

6. Answer Exercise 5, using "if and only if" terminology.

7. "For an integer to be divisible by six it is necessary that the sum of its
    digits be divisible by three." Which of the following follows logically
    from this?
    (a) The sum of the digits of an integer is divisible by three if and only
         if the integer is divisible by six.
    (b) A digit sum not divisible by three is a sufficient condition that an
         integer not be divisible by six.
    (c) For the sum of the digits of an integer to be divisible by three it is
         necessary that the integer be divisible by six.

(d) For a number not to be divisible by six it is necessary that the sum of its digits not be divisible by three.

(e) If the sum of the digits of a number is divisible by three then the number is divisible by six.

(f) A number is divisible by six if and only if the sum of its digits is divisible by three.

8. Give a counterexample for each part of Exercise 7 that was not selected as following logically.

9. State and prove what is the necessary and sufficient condition that the product of two natural numbers be even.

10. If the product of two natural numbers is an odd number, is the condition that one of the factors be an odd integer a necessary condition? A sufficient condition? Explain.

DIRECT PROOF

2.8   Most deductive proofs consist of more than one step. Suppose we wish to prove the theorem $H \rightarrow C$. We are able to show that $H \rightarrow C_1$ — some conclusion other than C. We can also show that $C_1 \rightarrow C_2$, another conclusion different from C. We continue establishing implications until we finally reach the desired conclusion C. Do we now have a right to assert that $H \rightarrow C$ is true?

More simply, the question is: Does $p \rightarrow q \wedge q \rightarrow r$ imply $p \rightarrow r$? This is known as the *transitive* property. Is implication a transitive relation? It is, if and only if the statement $[(p \rightarrow q) \wedge (q \rightarrow r)] \rightarrow (p \rightarrow r)$ is a tautology. The truth table for this statement requires eight lines since we must provide for each possible combination of true or false for p, q, and r (Table 2.12).

Table 2.12

p	q	r	$[(p \rightarrow q)$	$\wedge$	$(q \rightarrow r)]$	$\rightarrow$	$(p \rightarrow r)$
T	T	T	T	T	T	T	T
T	T	F	T	F	F	T	F
T	F	T	F	F	T	T	T
T	F	F	F	F	T	T	F
F	T	T	T	T	T	T	T
F	T	F	T	F	F	T	T
F	F	T	T	T	T	T	T
F	F	F	T	T	T	T	T

Successive application of this principle permits a chain of implications of any desired length. If $p \rightarrow q$, $q \rightarrow r$, and $r \rightarrow s$, then $p \rightarrow s$, since $(p \rightarrow q) \wedge (q \rightarrow r)$ implies $p \rightarrow r$ and since $(p \rightarrow r) \wedge (r \rightarrow s)$ implies $p \rightarrow s$.

Our reasoning becomes: *If* the hypothesis is true, then the first implication must be; *if* the first implication is true, *then* the second must be; ... *if* the nth implication is true, *then* the conclusion must be. The assertion that the conclusion is true is not made. The assertion is: The conclusion must be true *if* the hypothesis is true.

Not all relationships are of this sort. A, the father of B, and B, the father of C, does not imply A, the father of C. Equality of numbers is such a relationship: if $A = B$ and $B = C$ then $A = C$. The principle holds for "greater than" with numbers. But it does not hold for "is not equal to" unless we specify that A, B, and C are all different, since $10 \neq 8$ and $8 \neq 10$ but $10 = 10$.

Direct proof consists of starting with a hypothesis, establishing a sequence of implications, and ending with the desired conclusion. Each individual step in the chain of implications must be justified in terms of the mathematical axioms, definitions, previously proved facts, and principles of logic.

The only difference between a formal and an informal proof is a difference of style. In the formal proof each step is clearly indicated and its justification specifically given. The informal proof is usually written in narrative style, only those reasons that might be obscure being given.

All too frequently mathematical proof is associated exclusively with geometric theorems. Whenever we "solve" an algebraic equation we are actually presenting a logical argument. Since the letters in an equation represent numbers, the properties of numbers may be applied.

Example 1   Solve the equation $5x - 13 = x - 1$.

$$5x - 13 = x - 1$$
$$5x = x + 12$$
$$4x = 12$$
$$x = 3$$

Here, the hypothesis is $5x - 13 = x - 1$ and the conclusion is $x = 3$. The solution of the equation differs from the usual geometry theorem in that the conclusion is not stated in advance. Stated in the usual "if-then" manner, the above would be: Prove that, if $5x - 13 = x - 1$, then $x = 3$.

Our chain of reasoning is: If $5x - 13 = x - 1$ is true, then by implication $5x = x + 12$ is also true. You will recognize the axiomatic basis of this step in the form "Equals added to equals give equals." Acceptance of this axiom is, in reality, acceptance of the truth of the implication "*If* two quantities are equal and *if* equal quantities are added to them, *then* the resulting sums are equal." If the first conclusion, $5x = x + 12$, is true, then by implication $4x = 12$ is also true, since we accept the truth of the implication "If equals are subtracted from equals then the remainders are equal." If the second conclusion, $4x = 12$, is true, then by implication $x = 3$ is also true, since we accept the implication "If equals are divided by equals (not zero) the quotients are equal." From the logical standpoint, the solution of the equation consists merely of establishing the proposition that *if* $5x - 13 = x - 1$ *then* $x = 3$ must be a logical consequence. We have *not* shown that if $x = 3$ then $5x - 13 = x - 1$. If we knew in advance that some number x will make $5x - 13 = x - 1$, we would then know that our hypothesis is true and that as a result our conclusion, $x = 3$, is also true. But we did not know this in advance; all we have established is that if there is any value of x which will make $5x - 13 = x - 1$, that value must be 3. We are in a position to assert that 3 is the only value x can possibly have; it is 3 or nothing (and we don't mean zero).

This may be shown most convincingly when we consider the contrapositive. The argument we have made establishes, by contraposition, the implication: *If* $x = 3$ is false, *then* $5x - 13 = x - 1$ is false. But $x = 3$ is false if x is anything but 3. Therefore any value of x other than 3 makes $5x - 13 = x - 1$ also false.

As we set out to find a value for x that does make $5x - 13 = x - 1$, the most obvious way to find out whether or not 3 is such a value is to try it and see. Another method is to establish the converse: if $x = 3$ then $5x - 13 = x - 1$. This could be done most easily by reversing the steps in the original argument. We divided by 4 to get $x = 3$, so the first step is to multiply by 4 and get $4x = 12$. This was obtained by subtracting x from both numbers; therefore we shall add x, getting $5x = x + 12$. The first step consisted of adding 13 to both sides, so we shall subtract 13 from both sides, getting $5x - 13 = x - 1$.

As long as we are certain that each step is a reversible one, of the form $A \rightarrow B$ and $B \rightarrow A$, we don't bother to verify the result by substitution or to establish the converse. However, it is a mistake to assume that all legitimate steps are reversible. If $a = b$, we may square both and get $a^2 = b^2$.   Now, if it is known that $a^2 = b^2 = 25$, we cannot infer that $a = b = 5$, because we could have $a = -5$ and $b = 5$, as we shall see when the number system is enlarged.   It is legitimate, though dangerous, to multiply both sides of an equation by zero — the results will certainly be equal since they are both zero. But the inverse step, division by zero, is meaningless.

Example 2   Solve the equation $\sqrt{x + 1} = \sqrt{x - 4} - 5$.

We square both sides to get $x + 1 = x - 4 - 10\sqrt{x - 4} + 25$

This simplifies to $-20 = -10\sqrt{x - 4}$

Or, dividing by -10, we get $2 = \sqrt{x - 4}$

Squaring again, we get $4 = x - 4$

And, adding 4 to both sides, we have $8 = x$

Our reasoning is: If there is any number x which will make $\sqrt{x + 1} = \sqrt{x - 4} - 5$ that number must be 8.   No number other than 8 can possibly do the trick.   However, when we substitute $x = 8$ we get $3 = -3$.   The difficulty lies, not in the fact that a mistake has been made, but rather in the fact that some nonreversible step has been taken.   The direct argument tells us that 8 is the only possibility and substitution tells us that it will not work.   Then we must conclude that there is no number x that will satisfy the equation $\sqrt{x + 1} = \sqrt{x - 4} - 5$.

Example 3   Solve the equation $\dfrac{2(x + 2)}{3} = \dfrac{4x}{6} - 2$.

Multiply both members by 6 $4(x + 2) = 4x - 12$

Apply the distributive law for multiplication $4x + 8 = 4x - 12$

Add 12 to both members $4x + 20 = 4x$

Subtract $4x$ from both members $20 = 0$

We have reasoned thus:

If $\dfrac{2(x + 2)}{3} = \dfrac{4x}{6} - 2$

then $4x + 8 = 4x - 12$

If $4x + 8 = 4x - 12$

then $4x + 20 = 4x$

If $4x + 20 = 4x$

then $20 = 0$

But we know that 20 does not equal 0. We have reached a false conclusion by valid reasoning. But we know that this can happen only if we start with a false hypothesis. Our result then tells us that there is no number x such that

$$\frac{2(x + 2)}{3} = \frac{4x}{6} - 2$$

On the other hand, consider the following.

Example 4 Solve the equation $(x + 4)^2 - 3 = x^2 + 16x + 5 - 8(x - 1)$.

The distributive law for multiplication gives
$$x^2 + 8x + 16 - 3 = x^2 + 16x + 5 - 8x + 8$$
Subtracting $x^2 + 8x$ we get $16 - 3 = 8x + 5 - 8x + 8$
Combining like terms, $13 = 13$

The reasoning is as follows:

If $(x + 4)^2 - 3 = x^2 + 16x + 5 - 8(x - 1)$

then $x^2 + 8x + 16 - 3 = x^2 + 16x + 5 - 8x + 8$

If $x^2 + 8x + 16 - 3 = x^2 + 16x + 5 - 8x + 8$

then $16 - 3 = 8x + 5 - 8x + 8$

If $16 - 3 = 8x + 5 - 8x + 8$

then $13 = 13$

We have reached a true conclusion which is independent of x. It makes no difference what value x takes; 13 certainly will equal itself. Furthermore, it makes no difference whether the hypothesis is true or not; 13 = 13. What, then, may we conclude from such a result? *If our steps are reversible, we may conclude that the hypothesis is true. If the steps are not reversible, we can make no inference regarding the truth or falsity of the hypothesis.* Why? But, assuming that they are reversible, we know our hypothesis is true. Yet the conclusion, 13 = 13, places no restriction on x. The hypothesis is true whenever 13 = 13. In other words, it is always true:

$$(x + 4)^2 - 3 = x^2 + 16x + 5 - 8(x - 1)$$

if x is any number.

If we multiply each side of the equation

$$x^2 = x$$

by zero, we get the obviously true statement, 0 = 0. Yet the original equation is not a true statement for all values of x. Neither is it false for all values of x; if $x = 0$ or $x = 1$, it is true.

——————————— E   X   E   R   C   I   S   E   S ———————————

1.   Determine the condition under which each of the following propositions
     is true.   State exactly what is done at each step and what the conclusion
     establishes.

(a) $\sqrt{x} = \sqrt{x+1} - 1$ (f) $(x+4)(x+1) - 4 = x(x+5)$

(b) $\dfrac{3}{x-2} = \dfrac{10}{2x-4}$ (g) $2x - 5 = x + 3$

(c) $\dfrac{3}{x-2} = \dfrac{5}{2+x}$ (h) $\dfrac{2}{x} + \dfrac{3}{2x} = \dfrac{1}{x}$

(d) $\sqrt{x-5} = 3$ (i) $5(x-6) + 3x = 18$

(e) $(x-1)(x-3) = 0$ (j) $\dfrac{2}{x+1} - \dfrac{1}{x} = \dfrac{1}{2x}$

2.   Prove that the product of two odd natural numbers is odd.   *Hint:* Any
     odd natural number may be expressed as $2n - 1$ where n is a natural
     number.

INDIRECT PROOF

2.9   The direct method of proof, establishing the implication
$H \to C$, is sometimes quite difficult.   Frequently, it is far easier to
establish the desired implication indirectly by establishing some other
implication that is logically equivalent to it.

Indirect proof rests upon the principle that we can reach a false conclusion by valid reasoning only if
the hypothesis is false.

If we examine the truth table for
$(p \to q) \wedge \sim q$ (see Exercise 10, Section 2.3) we find that the conjunction
is true only when p and q are both
false (Table 2.13).

Table 2.13

p	q	$p \to q$	$\wedge$	$\sim q$
T	T	T	F	F
T	F	F	F	T
F	T	T	F	F
F	F	T	T	T

If we assume $\sim q$ is true and can establish $p \to q$, we have reached
a false conclusion q.   The truth table shows that this can occur only
when p is false.

If $p \to q$ is true and q is false, then p is false.

The indirect method of proof is sometimes called *reductio ad absurdum* (the absurdity being that a statement and its negation are both true), or proof by contradiction.

We wish to prove indirectly $H \to C$. The most common form is $(H \wedge \sim C) \to \sim H$. That is, we assume the negation of the desired conclusion and show that its conjunction with the hypothesis implies the negation of the hypothesis. Now H is not "on trial." We are attempting to show that C is true under the assumption that H is. We therefore know that, in the context of the theorem, the conclusion $\sim H$ is false. Therefore the hypothesis $(H \wedge \sim C)$ is false. But, since H is true, $\sim C$ is false and C must be true. We should note that the original hypothesis H is probably the conjunction of a number of assumptions, $p \wedge q \wedge r$. We have established $\sim H$ when we have established the negation of any one of its component assumptions $\sim p$, $\sim q$, $\sim r$.

We may also show (Table 2.14) that $(H \wedge \sim C) \to \sim H$ is equivalent to $H \to C$ by establishing the tautology $[(H \wedge \sim C) \to \sim H] \leftrightarrow [H \to C]$.

Table 2.14

H	C	$[(H$	$\wedge$	$\sim C)$	$\to$	$\sim H]$	$\leftrightarrow$	$[H \to C]$
T	T	T	F	F	T	F	T	T
T	F	T	T	T	F	F	T	F
F	T	F	F	F	T	T	T	T
F	F	F	F	T	T	T	T	T

The indirect argument may also take other forms. The contrapositive, $\sim C \to \sim H$, as we have already shown, Table 2.10, is equivalent to $H \to C$. Still another variation is $(H \wedge \sim C) \to C$. Here again H is not "on trial"; we grant its truth. If C is false, we must accept the truth of the hypothesis $H \wedge \sim C$. But we know that an implication from true to false cannot be established. We must conclude, then, that C is true.

The essence of indirect proof consists in negating the desired conclusion and arriving at some contradiction. It is not necessary that H or C, either one, be contradicted. The contradiction may take the form of a result that is known to be false: If S is known to be true we can establish $H \to C$ by establishing $(H \wedge \sim C) \to (S \wedge \sim S)$. See Example 3, Section 2.8, for an illustration of this method.

A Classic Example   A beautiful example of indirect proof is Euclid's proof that there are no two natural numbers whose ratio equals $\sqrt{2}$. Now, we know that either there are two such numbers or there are not two such numbers.   We wish to prove that there are not.   Therefore we assume that there are, and proceed to establish a contradiction.

Assume that a, b exist such that $a/b = \sqrt{2}$; assume further that a, b have no factor in common.   This assumption is certainly justified for, if a and b have a factor in common, we may remove it by dividing a and b by all common factors and still have two integers whose ratio $= \sqrt{2}$.

$a/b = \sqrt{2} \rightarrow a = \sqrt{2}b$ (multiplying by b)

$a = \sqrt{2}b \rightarrow a^2 = 2b^2$ (multiplying equals by equals)

$a^2 = 2b^2 \rightarrow a^2$ is even   (definition of an even number)

a^2 is even $\rightarrow a$ is even   (if a were odd, $a \times a$ would be odd)

a is even $\rightarrow a = 2c$ (definition of an even number)

$a = 2c \rightarrow a^2 = 4c^2$ (multiplying equals by equals)

$a^2 = 4c^2 \rightarrow 2b^2 = 4c^2$ (numbers equal to the same number are equal)

$2b^2 = 4c^2 \rightarrow b^2 = 2c^2$ (division)

$b^2 = 2c^2 \rightarrow b^2$ is even   (definition of an even number)

b^2 is even $\rightarrow b$ is even   (if b were odd, $b \times b$ would be odd)

We have concluded that a and b are both even — they have the common factor 2, contrary to our assumption that they have no factor in common. Therefore the assumption, that a and b exist, $a/b = \sqrt{2}$, is false.   There are no natural numbers whose ratio equals $\sqrt{2}$.

If we write the theorem symbolically, H is $a/b = \sqrt{2}$ and C is "a, b are not natural numbers."   We have established that $(H \wedge \sim C) \rightarrow (S \wedge \sim S)$, S being the statement, "Any ratio of natural numbers can be expressed as a/b, where a, b have no common factors."

Another Example   The proof that there is an infinite number of primes is another interesting example of indirect proof. It is also ascribed to Euclid. We wish to prove there are infinitely many primes.   We assume the contradictory statement that there is only a finite number of primes.   Designate them $p_1, p_2, p_3, \ldots p_n$.   Multiply them all together and add 1.

$$p_1 \times p_2 \times p_3 \ldots p_n + 1$$

The three dots . . . are read "and so forth."   Now this number is either a prime or it is not a prime.   If it is a prime it is different from each of the first n primes.   Thus we contradict the assumption that there are only n primes.   If it is not a prime it has prime factors.   But when we divide by any one of the assumed n primes we get a remainder 1.   Therefore the number has prime factors different from the n primes which we assume to be all the primes.   Whether $p_1 \times p_2 \times p_3 \ldots p_n + 1$ is a prime or not, we are led to a contradiction, since there are at least $n + 1$ primes.

E   X   E   R   C   I   S   E   S

1. Use an indirect method to prove that if the product of two natural numbers is odd at least one factor is odd. *Hint:* What is the product of two even factors?

2. State the converse of Exercise 1. Is it true?

3. Prove that there are no two natural numbers the cube of whose ratio equals 2.

4. Where does the argument used on page 36 break down when we use it to prove that 4 has no rational square root (a rational number is a ratio of two integers).

5. What two things must we do to prove indirectly that a given whole number is less than 10?

6. Construct a truth table showing that $(H \wedge \sim C) \to C$ is equivalent to $H \to C$.

7. Construct a truth table showing that $\sim(H \wedge \sim C)$ is equivalent to $H \to C$.

8. In view of Exercise 7, how should $H \wedge \sim C$ be related to $H \to C$?

9. Construct a truth table demonstrating the equivalence of $(H \wedge \sim C) \to (S \wedge \sim S)$ and $H \to C$.

10. Write the symbolic form of the following indirect argument: If $ABCD$ is a rectangle it is a parallelogram; it is not a parallelogram; therefore it is not a rectangle.

11. Quite frequently indirect reasoning is used to show that two quantities a and b are equal by showing that a cannot be less than b, and a cannot be greater than b. This procedure is justified by the tautology $[(p \vee q \vee r) \wedge \sim(p \vee q)] \to r$. Verify this tautology.

12.* Use an indirect argument to prove that there are no two natural numbers the square of whose ratio is 3.

13.* Prove that the square of any odd number is one more than a multiple of 8.

14.* If you wished to use an indirect proof to show that some quantity x is less than 10, would it be sufficient to assume that $x = 10$ and reason to a conclusion which is a contradiction? Explain.

MATHEMATICAL INDUCTION

2.10   The infinity of primes argument is reminiscent of another type of proof, known as mathematical induction. Suppose we had assumed there were 100 primes. The infinity of primes argument yields a contradiction in that there must be at least 101 primes. We could repeat the argument, starting with the assumption that there are 101 primes, and show that there must be at least 102. This could be repeated indefinitely. We have shown that, no matter how many primes we assume there are, there is always at least one more.

Mathematical induction is a method that is applicable only when there is a succession of cases. There is a first situation, a second, a third, and so on. There is no next fraction after $\frac{1}{2}$, but there is always a next natural number after any specified one. Mathematical induction is still deductive reasoning.

Mathematical induction consists of two parts. We wish to prove that a statement involving the natural number n is true for *all* values of n. In Part 1 we show that it is true when $n = 1$. In Part 2 we show that if it is true for some number $n = k$ it must be true for the next number $n = k + 1$. In Part 2 we must show that the assumption of the truth of the proposition for $n = k$ implies its truth for $n = k + 1$. This does not assure us that it is ever true, but it does assure us that if we can find a value of n for which it is true it will be true for all greater values.

Let us use the method to show that the sum of the first n odd numbers equals n^2.

Part 1   If $n = 1$ the sum of the first n odd numbers is 1, but n^2 is also 1.

We should probably try more cases if we were trying to discover the relationship or if we wanted to convince ourselves that there is any point in trying to establish Part 2. But in so far as the proof is concerned this is unnecessary.

$$1 + 3 = 4 = 2^2$$
$$1 + 3 + 5 = 9 = 3^2$$
$$1 + 3 + 5 + 7 = 16 = 4^2$$

These relationships verify that the proposition is true when $n = 2, 3$, and 4, but they neither prove that the proposition holds for any n nor contribute anything to the proof.

Part 2   We assume that $1 + 3 + 5 + \ldots + (2k - 1) = k^2$ where $(2k - 1)$ is the kth odd number.

We must prove on the basis of our assumption that

$$1 + 3 + 5 + \cdots + (2k - 1) + (2k + 1) = (k + 1)^2$$

where $(2k + 1)$ is the next odd number after $(2k - 1)$: it is the $(k + 1)$th odd number.

This is our proposition:

If $\qquad\qquad 1 + 3 + 5 + \ldots + (2k - 1) = k^2$

then $\qquad 1 + 3 + 5 + \ldots + (2k - 1) + (2k + 1) = (k + 1)^2$

Proof:

If $\qquad\qquad 1 + 3 + 5 + \ldots + (2k - 1) = k^2$

then $\qquad 1 + 3 + 5 + \ldots + 2k - 1 + 2k + 1 = k^2 + 2k + 1$

because we added $2k + 1$ to both members of the equation.

But $\quad (k + 1)^2 = (k + 1)(k + 1) = (k + 1)k + (k + 1)1$
$$= k^2 + k + k + 1 = k^2 + 2k + 1$$

Then if we replace $k^2 + 2k + 1$ with its equal we get
$$1 + 3 + 5 + \ldots + (2k - 1) + (2k + 1) = (k + 1)^2$$
which is the required conclusion.

The technique used consists of adding the next term to the left member of the equation. This establishes the $k + 1$ situation on that side of the equation. We must add the same thing to the right member in order to preserve equality. The job then consists of showing that the right member is in fact also the $k + 1$ situation.

The proof accomplishes two things. It shows that if there is any value of n for which the proposition is true the proposition must be true for the *next* value of n also. This was Part 2.

Part 1 showed the proposition true for $n = 1$. Then if we apply Part 2 we know it is true for $n = 2$. Once we know that, we can apply Part 2 to $n = 2$ and infer its truth for $n = 3$. This step can be taken an indefinite number of times, showing the proposition true for all values of n.

Both parts of the argument by mathematical induction must be established, or we have proved nothing. It is easy to find examples of propositions that are true for $n = 1$ and for many other values of n, but Part 2 cannot be established. For instance, $n^2 - n + 41 = $ a prime number (see Section 2.11), or the sum of the first n integers is an odd number. The latter statement is true for $n = 1$, $n = 2$, $n = 5$, $n = 6, \ldots$.

It is also possible to find cases in which Part 2 but not Part 1 can be established. On the assumption that it is true for $n = k$, we can show that it must be true for $n = k + 1$ also, but we can find no value of n for which it is true. Consider the false proposition

$$\frac{1}{n} = \frac{1}{n + 1}$$

If this is true for $n = k$, we have

$$\frac{1}{k} = \frac{1}{k+1}$$

which implies that $k = k + 1$.   (Why?)   But $k = k + 1$ is precisely what we need, to make the induction.   If we substitute $k + 1$ for k in

$$\frac{1}{k} = \frac{1}{k+1}$$

we get

$$\frac{1}{k+1} = \frac{1}{k+1+1} = \frac{1}{k+2}$$

───────────   E   X   E   R   C   I   S   E   S   ───────────

1. In the first line below we have consecutive integers, in the second line we have consecutive odd integers.

1	2	3	4	5	...	n
1	3	5	7	9	...	

Try to discover what the nth odd integer is in terms of n.   When you think you have the correct answer, see whether you can prove it by mathematical induction.

2. By mathematical induction prove that
$$1 + 2 + 4 + \ldots + 2^{n-1} = 2^n - 1$$

3. Use the result of Exercise 2 to find how many grains of wheat are required if one grain is placed on the first square of a chessboard, two on the second and, on each succeeding square, the number is doubled.

4. Establish Part 2 of the proof of: The sum of the interior angles of a polygon of n sides $= 180\,n$ degrees?   Why cannot the proposition be proved?

5. If we wish to find the sum of all positive integers from one through 100 we could pair the first and last $(1 + 100)$ and the second and next to last $(2 + 99)$, and continue until we got 50 such pairs.   This suggests what formula for finding the sum of the first n integers?

6. Use mathematical induction to prove that the formula found in Exercise 5 is correct.

7. Prove by mathematical induction that the sum of the first n even positive integers is $n(n + 1)$.

INTUITION AND INDUCTION

2.11   It would be a mistake to think that intuition played no part in mathematics.   Intuition is of extreme importance in suggesting possibilities to be investigated.   Intuition furnishes us with leads, but it should never be substituted for proof.   All leads that are suggested by intuition do not prove fruitful.   Our intuition may tell us that there are more natural numbers than positive even numbers. Yet, as we shall see (Section 4.4), this is not the case.   Intuition is just an intelligent hunch; some people think of it as some extrasensory power.   Whether such exists or not, most of our intuitively held ideas are based on a certain amount of knowledge, observation, reasoning and, possibly, wishful thinking.   A vast number of mathematical intuitive beliefs subsequently have been proved.   Others have been disproved, and still others are open questions that have never been proved or disproved.   One of the assumptions on which the geometry of Euclid is based is: In a plane one and only one line can be drawn through a point not on a given line and parallel to the line.   The Greeks of Euclid's time had the intuitive notion that this statement could be proved, in other words, did not have to be assumed.   Mathematicians tried to prove it for nearly two thousand years, without success.   A little more than one hundred years ago it was proved that this statement had to be taken as an assumption.   The statement can be proved if we first make an alternative assumption.   This has been done in many ways.   As a matter of fact, the assumption quoted above is really an alternative to the assumption Euclid actually made. But that is begging the question.   Intuition was wrong.   But intuition was not a bad thing in this case, because much valuable mathematical research resulted from efforts to vindicate intuition.

Intuition tells mathematicians that it is possible to color any map with not more than four colors, so that no two adjoining areas shall have the same color.   Two areas with only a point in common are not considered to be adjoining in this problem.   To date, no one has been able to prove this or to disprove it.   All that it would take to disprove it would be to exhibit a map requiring more than four colors. In case you wish to try to draw one, it will be helpful to know that it has been proved that such a map will, if it exists, have more than 38 areas in it.   Intuition is very valuable in its place, but it should never be thought of as proof nor be substituted for proof.

The word *deduction* is often used rather loosely to mean "reaching a conclusion." We use the word in a much more precise way. A deduction is a conclusion that is reached by making logical inferences from a specific hypothesis. Deductive reasoning is often called "if-then" reasoning: *if* the hypothesis is satisfied, *then* the conclusion is inescapable. In so far as our logic is concerned, the truth or falsity of the hypothesis is of no concern whatever.

Hypothesis: (a)   All x's are y's.
                (b)   All y's are z's.
Conclusion: (a)   Some z's are x's.
                (b)   All x's are z's?

The above conclusions are valid. Are they true? They must be, if the hypothesis is true. But is the hypothesis true? That depends on what the x's, y's, and z's are. Suppose they are the undefined elements of our mathematical system (any mathematical system must have undefined elements). As long as we do not attempt to give a concrete interpretation of the undefined elements, it is rather pointless to consider the truth or falsity of the hypothesis.

Inductive reasoning is of the type that draws general conclusions from particular facts. It is observed from experiment that water contains two parts hydrogen to one part oxygen by volume, within the limitations of measurement. The experiment is repeated many times, with comparable results. We conclude that water always contains two parts hydrogen to one part oxygen by volume. This is inductive reasoning. Such conclusions are in the realm of *probable truth*. They are always subject to revision in the light of new evidence. If we consider "water" as including heavy water, this conclusion must be somewhat revised. The conclusions of induction are probably true and, by contrast, those of deduction are relatively true. Mathematical proof is based on deductive reasoning. This does not mean that induction has no place in mathematics — it is quite valuable in selecting plausible hypotheses — but inductive conclusions never constitute mathematical proof, except in situations involving a finite number of cases, all of which are established.

Consider the expression $x^2 - x + 41$. If $x = 0$, the expression equals 41, which is a prime number.

When $x = 1$, we get 41 again.
                   $x = 2$, $x^2 - x + 41 = 43$, a prime;
                   $x = 3$, $x^2 - x + 41 = 47$, a prime;
                   $x = 4$, $x^2 - x + 41 = 53$, a prime;
                   $x = 5$, $x^2 - x + 41 = 61$, a prime.

We may continue up to $x = 10$ and always get a prime. We may go on to $x = 20, 30, 40$ and always get a prime. By this time we should probably be ready to make the induction (generalization) that we always get a prime for any integral value of x. But this is not mathematical proof. We do not know that we will *always* get a prime. As a matter of fact, when we try $x = 41$ we get $41^2 - 41 + 41 = 41^2$, which is obviously not a prime.

We could surmise that the sum of the first n odd numbers equals n^2. We might verify this guess for all cases through $n = 100$. We should hardly be "jumping to conclusions" if we decided that it would always be true. But we haven't proved it. We cannot be sure that, no matter how many cases we have verified, the next case will hold.

——————— E   X   E   R   C   I   S   E   S ———————

1. Answer the following questions on the basis of intuition alone, then check your answer by computation.

   (a) A man sells two houses for $15,000 each. On one he gains 10 per cent of the cost, and on the other he loses 10 per cent. Does he lose, gain, or break even?

   (b) Company employees are given a 25 per cent cost-of-living raise, but they are told that when business drops off their salaries will be cut 25 per cent. Will their wages be higher, lower, or the same as before the raise?

   (c) Would you rather receive $100 the first day, $200 the second, $300 the third, and so on for a month, the amount received each day being $100 more than the preceding day, or 1¢ the first day, 2¢ the second, 4¢ the third, and so on for a month, the amount received each day being twice that of the preceding day?

   (d) If you place $100 at 100 per cent interest compounded annually, it would be worth $200 at the end of the year. If it is compounded semiannually it will amount to $225. Could the compounding interval be short enough for it to amount to $1,000 in one year?

   (e) One tin can is 5 inches tall and 4 inches in diameter. Another is 15 inches tall and 2 inches in diameter. Which can will hold more?

   (f) If one steel band is made to encircle the earth and another is made to fit over one-foot stakes which encircle the earth, how much longer is the second band?

   (g) Would you prefer a discount of 25 per cent, or a discount of 15 per cent followed by a second discount of 15 per cent on the remainder?

2.   How can you color the following map with not more than four colors such that no two adjoining areas will have the same color?

3.   Construct a map that cannot be colored with less than four colors.

4.   Since $1 \times 1 \times 1 + 2 \times 2 \times 2 = 3 \times 3$, what does intuition tell you (now, don't compute!) that $1 \times 1 \times 1 + 2 \times 2 \times 2 + 3 \times 3 \times 3$ equals?

5.   If you insisted on computing, we know that $1 \times 1 \times 1 + 2 \times 2 \times 2 + 3 \times 3 \times 3 = 6 \times 6$ and we can verify that $1 \times 1 \times 1 + 2 \times 2 \times 2 + 3 \times 3 \times 3 + 4 \times 4 \times 4 = 10 \times 10$. From this, what would you infer with regard to the sum of the first n whole numbers cubed (n cubed, written n^3, means $n \times n \times n$)?

6.   Is your answer to Exercise 5 an induction or a deduction?

7.   If it is impossible to prove "In a plane one and only one line can be drawn parallel to another line through a given point," is the statement false?

8.   How many possibilities are included in the negation of the statement in Exercise 7? What are they?

9.   Do you believe that $x^2 - x + 41$ is a prime number for all values of x which are not some multiple of 41?

10.   Is your answer to Exercise 9 a deduction, an induction, or intuition?

11.   A triangular number is one that can be represented by a triangular array of dots, for example ., ∴, ∴∴, ∴∴∴, indicate that the first four triangular numbers are 1, 3, 6, and 10. Derive a rule for finding triangular numbers. *Hint:* What do you add to the first to get the second? What do you add to the second to get the third?

12.   Find the sum of any two consecutive triangular numbers. What kind of number is the sum?

13.   Prove by mathematical induction
      $$1 + 2 + 3 + \ldots + n = n(n + 1)/2$$

14.   If the nth triangular number is $n(n + 1)/2$ what is the $(n + 1)^{\text{th}}$ triangular number?

15.   Prove the nth triangular number plus the $(n + 1)^{\text{th}}$ triangular number is equal to $(n + 1)^2$

16. The first triangular number is 1^2. The sum of the first two triangular numbers is 2^2. Does it follow that the sum of the first n triangular numbers is n^2?

17. Use the results of Exercise 14 to find the twentieth triangular number.

DO YOU KNOW

That 2 plus 2 does not always equal 4?

It is possible to multiply any two integers by doubling and halving alone?

We could use a number system which would require only three addition facts and three multiplication facts?

Why the numbers we use are superior to Roman numerals?

What an abacus is and what it had to do with the development of our present number system?

We have not always had the number zero?

What we mean when we say our system employs place value?

Why we could not have place value without a zero?

CHAPTER III

HOW WE WRITE NUMBERS

As is true of all technical achievements, mathematics did not spring into being full blown. Nor has it always been with us. It has reached its present state through a long, tedious, halting struggle. Our system of notation, which we take for granted, is one of the outstanding achievements of the human mind. As nearly as historians have been able to determine, the system was developed some time near the fifth century, and not until approximately the ninth century was it introduced into Europe. In order that we may appreciate the system more fully we shall examine some earlier systems to determine what characteristics make the present one superior.

ROMAN NUMERALS

3.1 The Roman system of notation is fairly familiar. We see Roman numerals used to number the chapters in a book, to mark the hours on a clock, to designate the dates on building cornerstones, and so on. There is really no reason to use them except in situations in which more than one set of numerals is required, for example, in detailed outlines.

Some interesting characteristics of Roman numerals may be noted. The consecutive integers, one through nine, are not represented by different symbols. We repeat the symbol for one to represent two, and we use the symbol for one three times to represent three. We have a distinct symbol for five and another distinct symbol for ten. The rest of the numbers below ten are combinations of these three symbols. Here we have an application of the additive principle and of the subtractive principle, VI being five plus one and IV being one less than five.

The meaning of the I in VI is different from its meaning in IV. Its meaning depends upon its position relative to V. However, the I represents a single element wherever it is found, not a single set of ten units or a single set of ten sets of ten units.

In the number XLVIII (48), the X (10) preceding the L (50) means that we take ten from 50; the V (5) following XL (40) means we add five to 40; the III (3) following XLV (45) means we add three ones to 45. We can get along fairly well with I, V, X, and L until we get to 90; then we have to invent another symbol, one to represent 100. As we proceed to larger and larger numbers we must continue to devise new symbols. This is no particular disadvantage as long as we have no need for large numbers, but if we are concerned with the number of electrons in a molecule or the size of the national debt it becomes very bothersome.

One can easily imagine how such a system evolved. We count one and make a single downward stroke thus, /; two, another downward stroke, //, very much as tally clerks do today. The origins of V and X are uncertain. One theory is that the Romans tallied ten, ////////, rather than the five we see nowadays, /////. The cross through the nine strokes counted as number ten and this was shortened to a mere cross: thus X was ten and half of X, or V, counted five. The C (100) and M (1,000) were probably derived from the first letters of the Latin words for 100 (centum) and 1,000 (mille). We should remember that early systems of notation were used primarily for recording results of counting or some other arithmetical operation. So, as long as the numbers did not become too involved this system could serve fairly well, even though it seems extremely awkward to us.

A really good system would make it possible to write a number as large as we please or as small as we please without the necessity of continually inventing new symbols, and it would lend itself to ease of computation. The Roman system seems to have some advantage over the present numerals when we consider the process of addition. Let us consider the addition of 127 and 58. In Roman numerals:

CXXVII
LVIII
———————
CLXXVVIIIII

We can merely bring down all the symbols in each addend; then if
we remember that five I's are written as V and two V's as X, the
answer becomes CLXXXV.   It is not necessary to know the addition
combinations such as 7 + 8 and 5 + 2.   However, the process is much
longer and more cumbersome.   But if we attempt to multiply or
divide, it is a different story.   Try multiplying 127 by 58, using Roman
numerals.   Civilizations that used early systems of notation did not
depend on their numerals for computation.   This was done with the
aid of an abacus, described on page 54.

Even addition and subtraction, however, become a bit tricky when
the subtractive principle is involved in the representation of the
number:

Example 1 Add: XCVII
                   LXIV
                   ‾‾‾‾‾
                   CLVVI = CLXI

Since the I in IV implies subtraction of I, it nullifies one of the I's in VII.
Similarly, since the X in XC implies subtraction of 10, it nullifies the X in
LX.

If there is no symbol in the other addend to compensate for one
which implies subtraction, then a conversion is necessary:

Example 2 Add: XCIV
                   LVI
                   ‾‾‾‾
                   CL

Here the two I's nullify each other, but there is no X to nullify the X in XC.
However, when we convert the two V's to X, we do have one.

The subtractive symbols may be handled rather neatly when we
are subtracting.   One of the properties of subtraction that is taught
in arithmetic is called the law of compensation.   The same number
may be added to (or subtracted from) both minuend and subtrahend
without changing the remainder.   For example, 125 − 87 = 128 − 90.

Example 3 Subtract: XCVII
                        LXIV
                        ‾‾‾‾‾

The problem is equivalent to subtracting LXXV from CVIII by the law
of compensation.

In subtraction we can eliminate symbols that are in a subtractive
position by placing them in the other number in an additive position.

———————————   E   X   E   R   C   I   S   E   S   ———————————

1.   The inscription on the cornerstone of a building reads MDCCCXCVIII.
When was it erected? (In Roman numerals I = 1, V = 5, X = 10,
L = 50, C = 100, D = 500, and M = 1,000.)

2.   What Roman numeral inscription would be placed on a building erected
this year?

3.   Add, without the aid of any other kind of notation: DXXI
XXVII
DCCCXXXVI

4.   Multiply the following, using Roman numerals. (You may have to "in-
vent" some multiplication tables as you go, for instance, X × V = L.)
CLXXXII
XXXV

Note: The Romans and their followers used a variety of schemes to
extend their notation beyond 1,000. In this problem, let it be agreed
that we shall use M as many times as necessary.

5.   Convert the numbers in the above exercise to our notation and compute.
Then convert the Roman numeral answer and compare.

6.   Subtract CXX from MCCXXXI without converting to another notation.

7.   Subtract, using Roman numerals: DCXLVI
CCCLVIII

8.   Add: CMXLVI
DCXIV

9.   Add: MCMLX
XCIV

10.   Subtract: XCLIV
LXXIX

11.   Subtract: DCCXLVII
CLIX

EGYPTIAN NUMERALS

3.2   The subtractive principle was a relatively late innovation of
the Roman system. From the mathematical standpoint its use is a
complication. It is a refinement only in the sense that it makes
notation more compact. The number 949 is written as DCCCC-

XXXXVIIII without the aid of the principle, and as CMXLIX with its aid.

The Roman system is basically a tens system, the basic symbols being I = 1, X = 10, C = 100, and M = 1000. The intermediate symbols V = 5, L = 50, and D = 500 are used to represent one half of the basic group size immediately larger. We never need use an intermediate symbol more than one time in expressing a number. Three hundred three is written CCCIII, but 165 = 3 × 50 + 3 × 5 is not written LLLVVV.

Without the refinements of intermediate symbols and the subtractive principle, the Roman system is structurally identical with a much older system, that of the ancient Egyptians. This system employs the additive principle exclusively. Distinct symbols are used to represent 1, 10, 100, 1,000, 10,000, 100,000 and 1,000,000.

I	∩	℮	↑	⌐	⌢	☥
1	10	100	1000	10,000	100,000	1,000,000

The ancient Egyptians used hieroglyphic (picture) writing. Hieroglyphic characters were used for numerals as follows: Numbers were sometimes written vertically, sometimes right to left, and sometimes in our present-day left-to-right fashion. A number was expressed by repeating each basic symbol the required number of times. For example:

$$1346 = ↑ ℮℮℮ ∩∩∩∩ IIIIII$$

The role of *ten* in this system is evident. We have a symbol for *one*, which is used additively to represent numbers through *nine*. We have a new symbol for *ten*. These two symbols are used in combination additively to represent numbers through *ninety-nine*. Then we need a new symbol for *one hundred*. No symbol is used in a number more than nine times.

——————— E X E R C I S E S ———————

1. Write the following in Roman numerals. In Egyptian numerals.
   (a) 546   (c) 1111
   (b) 3759   (d) 3003

2. How may zero be written in the Roman system? In the Egyptian system?

3. Convert the following to Roman numerals, then add.
    (a)   946 and 187   (b)   515 and 678   (c)   707 and 404

4. Repeat Exercise 3, using Egyptian numerals.

5. Convert the following to Roman numerals, then subtract.
    (a)   437 and 189   (b)   648 and 396   (c)   707 and 404

6. Repeat Exercise 5, using Egyptian numerals.

7. Multiply, using Egyptian numerals: ℮∩∩∩‖ by ∩∩‖‖‖‖‖

8. Convert Exercise 7 to Roman numerals.

9. Convert to Egyptian numerals and multiply: 504 by 23.

10. Repeat Exercise 9, using Roman numerals.

11. Although the Romans avoided the use of fractions, Roman numerals could be used to write common fractions. For example, $\dfrac{\text{III}}{\text{X}} = \dfrac{3}{10}$.

     Add the following: $\dfrac{\text{IV}}{\text{XV}} + \dfrac{\text{VII}}{\text{X}} + \dfrac{\text{XIII}}{\text{XX}}$.

12. Could either the Egyptian or the Roman system be used to write decimal fractions? Why?

THE GREEK SYSTEM

3.3   Many other schemes for writing numbers have been used in the past. The Ionic system of the Greeks is of considerable interest. The Ionic alphabet contained twenty-four letters. These, with the addition of three symbols from a former alphabet, were the basis of their number system. The first nine letters were used to represent the numbers 1 through 9; the next nine letters represented 10, 20, ... 90; the last nine stood for 100, 200, ... 900.

The twenty-seven symbols were used as follows:

A = 1, B = 2, Γ = 3, Δ = 4, E = 5, F = 6, Z = 7, H = 8, Θ = 9.
I = 10, K = 20, Λ = 30, M = 40, N = 50, Ξ = 60, O = 70, Π = 80,
Ϙ = 90.
P = 100, Σ = 200, T = 300, Υ = 400, Φ = 500, X = 600, Ψ = 700,
Ω = 800, ϡ = 900.

Three hundred and twenty-six would be written T KF: T for 300, K for 20, F for 6. This scheme enabled one to write numbers up to 999 without difficulty. Variations, such as placing a bar to the left of the letter, enabled the Greeks to extend their written numbers to extremely large ones. Archimedes successfully used this system to write a number greater than the number of grains of sand required to fill the universe.

The system, which is older than the Roman, approached one characteristic that is essential in our own system. *Different* symbols for successive numbers were employed, rather than the repetition principle common to the Egyptian and Roman systems. However, the real value of this idea escaped the Greeks; Δ was used only for 4 *ones*, not 4 *tens* or 4 *hundreds*. The addition and multiplication combinations had to be memorized and, what is worse, the task had to be done all over again for tens and hundreds. To learn that 5 × 6 = 30, the Greeks had to know that E · F = Λ; for 50 × 6 = 300, that N · F = T; and for 50 × 60 = 3,000, that N · Ξ = /Γ (the bar in front of Γ meaning thousands).

The Greeks usually placed a bar over the letters when they were used as numerals in order to avoid any possible confusion between a number and a word. The fact that the letters of a word had numerical equivalents led to a pseudo science called *gematria*, which has its adherents to this day. Probably the best known example of gematria is found in the last verse of chapter 13 of Revelation: "Here is wisdom. Let him that hath understanding count the number of the beast; for it is the number of a man; and his number is six hundred three score and six." This was probably a means of identifying a contemporary enemy of Christianity without calling him by name. Nevertheless, gematria addicts have been proving that their enemies had the number 666 for nearly two thousand years. A number of Popes, Martin Luther, and Adolph Hitler, all have been definitely established by somebody as bearing the number of the beast.

When a boy and girl have names whose corresponding numbers are the same, this is conclusive proof to the gematria addict that they are a perfect match.

——————   E   X   E   R   C   I   S   E   S   ——————

1. Using a modern adaptation of the Greek scheme, we have the following equivalents: $A = 1$, $B = 2$, $C = 3$, $D = 4$, $E = 5$, $F = 6$, $G = 7$, $H = 8$, $I = 9$, $J = 10$, $K = 20$, $L = 30$, $M = 40$, $N = 50$, $O = 60$, $P = 70$, $Q = 80$, $R = 90$, $S = 100$, $T = 200$, $U = 300$, $V = 400$, $W = 500$, $X = 600$, $Y = 700$, $Z = 800$, $\& = 900$. Complete the following.
    $$C + D = \qquad C + JD = \qquad C + SJD = \qquad TLD + UMG =$$

2.   Multiply the following, using the scheme given in Exercise 1:

$$\begin{array}{r} SJA \\ \underline{LC} \end{array}$$

3.   According to gematria, what sentence should the gun moll Kitty expect to get?

4.   If Ratha wants a happy marriage should she marry Tom, Dick, or Harry?

5.   Using the scheme in Exercise 1, would the beast mentioned in the quotation from Revelation more likely be a lion, a tiger, or a fox?

6.   Write the following numbers in the Ionic Greek system.
    (a)   MCMLXII
    (b)   DCCXXVIII   (c) ꟾꟾꟾ ∩∩∩∩∩ꟾ   (d) ⌅⌅ ℭ ℭ ℭℭ ∩∩ꟾꟾꟾꟾꟾ

7.   Find the following, using Greek numerals.
    (a)   ΣΝΓ plus ΧΖ plus ϒΚΕ
    (b)   ΦΟΔ minus ΡΚΓ
    (c)   ΛΔ times ΜΓ

THE ABACUS

3.4   As mentioned previously, the ancients did their computation with the aid of some sort of abacus. The abacus is still used by Oriental merchants. Many variations have been used, but the kind described below contains the basic features of all. It consists of a frame holding a series of wires on which are strung movable beads. Each wire is divided into an upper and a lower portion. The lower portion of each wire contains five beads; the upper portion, two beads.

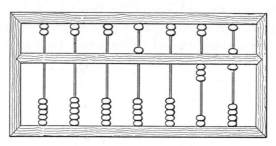

Figure 3.1   An abacus showing 5036 entered.

Each of the upper beads counts as five of the lower beads on the same wire. Any wire may be used to represent units, making the use of decimal fractions possible. If we confine our consideration to whole numbers, making the extreme right wire the unit's position, the abacus in Figure 3.1 denotes 5,036.   To enter a number, the beads are moved toward the divider.   One lower bead and one upper bead have been moved to the divider, indicating 6 units.   The three lower beads on the next wire indicate 3 tens.   None of the beads on the next wire have been used, indicating an absence of hundreds.   The upper bead on the next wire indicates 5 thousands.   If we now wish to add to or subtract from 5,036, we merely put in or take out the required amount. When all the lower beads on a given wire are used, they should be returned by bringing down one upper bead.   When the two upper beads have been used, they should be returned by bringing up one lower bead on the next wire.   Though the processes are considerably more complicated, the device may also be used to multiply and divide. Orientals attain amazing speed and accuracy with the abacus; their results compare favorably with those of an electrically driven computing machine.   But one shortcoming of the abacus is that at the end of the operation the only record remaining is the answer.

The abacus embodies the principle of place value: the value of a bead depends on its position, namely the wire on which it is located. Since the operator must record the result of his computation, it seems only natural that the result on each wire should be recorded in its relative position.   Once this notion is utilized, the desirability of different symbols for the first nine digits seems compelling.   The most important step of all was taken when someone hit upon the idea of using a symbol to indicate an empty space on the abacus.   Prior to the invention of a symbol for zero, the empty space was indicated merely by a blank, 5,036 being written 5 36.   Since this was before the day of printing, confusion and ambiguity were inevitable.   The inventor of zero doubtless had no idea of the transcendent importance of what he had done.   Its importance in the development of civilization is comparable to that of the invention of the wheel.   Originally a place holder for an empty spot, the zero in mathematics now has a far greater role.

There have been eminent mathematicians of the past who stoutly maintained that zero was not a number, being a symbol to indicate the absence of a number.   There will be more about this later.

The acceptance of our numerals came about after much difficulty. The algorithms (methods of performing the basic operations) first had to be developed.   Then there followed in Europe a bitter struggle between the advocates of the new algorithms and the old abacus.

Some countries actually passed laws forbidding the use of the new numerals. However, prohibition worked no better then than it did in the 1920's.

BABYLONIAN NUMERALS

3.5   The unknown Arab or Hindu who hit upon the idea of a symbol to represent the absence of a number was not the first to think of it.   If we go back to some of the earliest records that have been discovered, those of the Babylonians, we find the same idea. The Babylonians used the repetitive principle.   They did their writing by making impressions on tablets of clay.   These tablets were then baked to make permanent records.   A wedge-shaped stick (stylus) was used to make their cuneiform characters.   The numbers one through nine were made thus:

For 10, two strokes of the wedge, turned on its side, produced ◄ , and 100 was formed thus ⋎ ➤ .   We see here an approach to the notion of ten as a base, but no utilization of the concept of place value. However, their system contained a kind of place value, for the symbol ⋎ not only represented 1, but 60, 60 × 60, and so on.   From the standpoint of place value, 60 was the base.   We can thank the Babylonians for our sixty minutes to the hour, sixty seconds to the minute, and similar subdivisions of angular measure.   It was not always clear whether a single wedge was to mean 1, 60, $\frac{1}{60}$, or something else.

The Babylonians used a circle to indicate zero, but it was used only as an interior symbol, never at the end.   ⋎ ● ⋎ represented 3,601. The left wedge stood for 60^2 and the right wedge for 1.   But ⋎ ⋎ could mean 3,600 + 60, 60 + 1, or 1 + $\frac{1}{60}$, as well as 2.   Though this system contained some of the essential features of our system, it had grave shortcomings and was extremely cumbersome.

Numbers up to 59 were formed by using the additive repetitive principle.   These numbers could then be used to represent any number of ones, or sixties, or thirty-six hundreds, etc., depending on their positions.

Example   Express 6,165 in Babylonian notation.

$$6{,}165 = 3{,}600 + 2565 = 1 \times 60^2 \ + \ 42 \times 60 \ \ + \ \ 45$$

6,165 = Ｖ ＜＜＜＜ＶＹ ＜＜＜＜ＶＹＹ
                ＜   ＜   ＶＹ

NUMERALS OF THE AMERICAN INDIANS

3.6   The system of the Maya Indians apparently was developed independently of what was taking place in the rest of the world.   They used a system of dots and dashes; a dot represented 1 and a dash, 5. Their base was 20.   The first nineteen numbers were:

The Mayas had a highly developed concept of place value and a symbol for zero, ⊙.   As the individual symbols suggest, the Mayas wrote their numbers vertically.   Twenty was written ⊙̇, which is, reading down the column, "one-zero."   The single dot stood for a single group of twenty.   According to this plan, 50 would be ⁝⁚⎯⎯, for two twenties and a ten.   The importance of correct spacing is apparent when we compare this with the number 12, written ⎯•• .

The system had one peculiarity that greatly impaired its usefulness in computation.   In what is comparable to our tens digit, the symbols were used to represent quantities only from 1×20 to 17×20.   In all other positions 20 was used as base.   We should expect 425 to be written ⁝•⎯, the top dot representing 20×20, the middle dot 20, and the dash 5.   However, a dot in the third position represented 360 rather than 400, so 425 would be written ••• for $360 + 3 \times 20 + 5$. The principal use to which written numbers were put was in the recording of intervals of time.   The Mayas' year, consisting of 360 days, was subdivided into 18 intervals of 20 days each.   Thus 1 year, 3 "months," and 5 days would be written •••, or $360 + 3 \times 20 + 5$.

The peculiarity of the second position, the "18-month year," requires that the value of every digit number in the third or higher position have a factor 18.   Any symbol represents a number 20 times as great as the same symbol one position lower, except in position three; in this position it represents a number 18 times as great.

Example   Write 8,026 in Mayan numerals.

$$8{,}026 = 7{,}200 + 720 + 100 + 6 = 20 \times 18 \times 20 + 2 \times 18 \times 20$$
$$+ 5 \times 20 + 6$$

$8{,}026 = $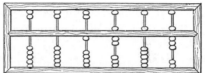

———————   E   X   E   R   C   I   S   E   S   ———————

1.   What number is represented on the abacus shown below?

2.   Describe how you would add 639 to the number on the abacus shown in Exercise 1.

3.   How would you subtract 495 from the number on the abacus shown in Exercise 1?

4.   Neither the Roman nor the Greek system provided a way of writing zero.   How can zero be represented on the abacus?

5.   Add the following Mayan numbers.

and

6.   Convert the numbers in Exercise 5 to present-day notation and check the answer.

7.   How long did a person live if his birth occurred on

and he died on

8.   Convert the numbers in Exercise 7 to Babylonian numerals and solve the problem.

9.   Compose an addition table for the numbers 1 through 10 in each of the following systems.
    (a)   Roman   (d)   Babylonian
    (b)   Egyptian   (e)   Mayan
    (c)   Greek

10.   Repeat Exercise 9, but with addition replaced by multiplication.

HINDU-ARABIC NUMERALS

3.7   Our system is called the Hindu-Arabic system because it was invented by the Hindus and transmitted to the Western world by the Arabs.   This system was not born overnight nor was it handed down from Mt. Sinai.   It evolved pretty much by accident and took at least a thousand years to reach its present state of perfection.   It is not positively known whether the Hindus or the Arabs contributed the zero.   But it is rather certain that the idea of a symbol for zero came considerably later than the use of the other nine symbols.   Without the zero we have just another system.   The extension of the basic idea to quantities less than unity, that is, the decimal fraction, was not made until approximately six hundred years after the system reached Europe.   The theory of decimal fractions was first explained in detail by the Dutch mathematician Simon Stevin in 1585.

Some of the features of our system are found in many other early systems, but each of the others had shortcomings which effectively blocked improvements.   Let us examine our system to see just what combination of features makes it superior to earlier efforts.   First, we do not employ the repetitive principle.   The symbol 1 can be used in a given number to represent the number "one" not more than once.   Similarly for the other symbols, we do not write 222 to represent six.   This requires that we have distinct symbols for the numbers one up to the base.   Thus 10 is not a simple symbol.   It is a compound symbol — the first symbol telling us that we have the base one time, and the second telling us that we have no units over and above the base.   If we write 235, the 2 tells us we have two times the base times the base, the 3 means we have in addition three times the base, and the 5 indicates still five more.   The subtractive principle is never employed.   We do not write nine as 110 (one less than ten) as the Romans did when they wrote IX.

We do employ an additive principle but not in the same sense as the Romans did. We would not write fifteen as 105, meaning ten plus five, whereas the Romans did this when writing XV for fifteen. Unfortunately for beginning algebra students, we do use this principle in the case of mixed numbers: $2\frac{3}{4}$ means two plus three quarters. However, this usage is not one of the virtues of our system. We use an additive principle in that the complete number is the sum of the numbers represented by each digit; thus 506.7 is the sum of 5 hundreds, no tens, 6 units, and 7 tenths of a unit. In addition to the fact that we have distinct symbols for each number up to the base, we have a symbol to represent the absence of a number and we utilize the principle of place value. Place value has been mentioned (page 55) in connection with the abacus. It means that the value of a symbol is determined by its place, or position, in the number. The symbol 7 always represents exactly seven, but exactly seven what? Whether it stands for seven units or seven trillions or seven hundredths depends upon its position in the complete number.

Along with the notion of place value and a base, one other idea should be stressed, namely, the exponential character of our positional notation.

EXPONENTS AND POWERS

3.8   Bear in mind that all our symbols mean what they do, in fact have any meaning at all, only by common agreement. When we write a^3 this means $a \cdot a \cdot a$ (another way of writing $a \times a \times a$). The superscript 3 is called an *exponent*. By definition, a *positive integral exponent* shows the number of times that the base (the number to which it is attached) is used as a factor.

Definition   If n is a positive integer, $a^n = a \cdot a \cdot a \ldots$ (for n factors).

By definition, $5^4 = 5 \times 5 \times 5 \times 5$. The expression 5^4 is read "five to the fourth power." The exponent is 4, but the *fourth power* of 5 is 625.

Since $a^3 = a \cdot a \cdot a$ and $a^2 = a \cdot a$, then $a^3 \cdot a^2 = (a \cdot a \cdot a) \cdot (a \cdot a)$. But, applying the same definition, $a \cdot a \cdot a \cdot a \cdot a = a^5$.

More generally, we have the rule:

Rule 1 $a^x \cdot a^y = a^{x+y}$ if x, y are positive whole numbers.

Proof:

$$a^x \cdot a^y = \underbrace{a \cdot a \cdot a \ldots}_{x \text{ factors}} \times \underbrace{a \cdot a \cdot a \ldots}_{y \text{ factors}} = \underbrace{a \cdot a \cdot a \ldots}_{x + y \text{ factors}}$$

But

$$\underbrace{a \cdot a \cdot a \ldots}_{x + y \text{ factors}} = a^{x+y}$$

When multiplying powers of the same base we add the exponents.

When we divide, applying the basic definition of an exponent and expressing the division as a quotient,

$$a^5 \div a^3 = \frac{a \cdot a \cdot a \cdot a \cdot a}{a \cdot a \cdot a} = \frac{a \cdot a \cdot a}{a \cdot a \cdot a} \cdot a \cdot a = 1 \cdot a \cdot a = a^2$$

indicates that we should subtract the exponent of the divisor from the exponent of the dividend.

Exponents other than positive whole numbers are meaningless under the definition on page 60. We cannot take a as a factor two thirds of a time. We might interpret a^0 as meaning that we take a as a factor no times, that is, we do not take a as a factor. We should then have no idea of its value, for we have merely stated what we do not do.

If the exponent of the divisor is greater than the exponent of the dividend, the above suggestion gives a meaningless result; in fact, it could not be carried through in the set of positive whole numbers.

We divide the following.

$$a^3 \div a^5 = \frac{a \cdot a \cdot a}{a \cdot a \cdot a \cdot a \cdot a} = \frac{a \cdot a \cdot a}{a \cdot a \cdot a} \cdot \frac{1}{a \cdot a} = 1 \cdot \frac{1}{a \cdot a} = \frac{1}{a^2}$$

This suggests that we should subtract the exponent of the dividend from the exponent of the divisor and place the base number raised to the indicated power in the denominator of a fraction with 1 as numerator.

These considerations suggest another rule.

Rule 2 $a^x \div a^y = a^{x-y}$ if x, y are positive whole numbers and $x > y$.
(The symbol $>$ is read "greater than".)
$a^x \div a^y = 1/a^{y-x}$ if x, y are positive whole numbers and $x < y$ (the symbol $<$ is read "less than").

The proof is a generalization of the above specific examples; it is left as an exercise.

We wish to extend our definition of exponents to include zero. We are at liberty to define the exponent zero in any way we please as long as no inconsistency is introduced. However, it is advantageous to select a definition such that Rules 1 and 2 will continue to apply if we relax the restriction on x and y so as to include zero among their possible values. Rule 2 does not specify what to do if $x = y$. If we subtract exponents, in this case $a^x \div a^y = a^{x-y} = a^0$, which is undefined. But we know that a number other than zero divided by itself equals *one:* $a^x \div a^x = 1$. This suggests a definition.

Definition   If $a \neq 0$ (a is not zero), then $a^0 = 1$. (We shall see later why we restrict a to numbers different from zero.)

With this definition we can now apply the first part of Rule 2 if $x \geq y$ (x greater than or equal to y). Furthermore, we may now apply either Rule 1 or Rule 2 even if x or y or both are zero.

Example $a^5 \cdot a^0 = a^{5+0} = a^5$ which is consistent with the definition of a^0

and
$$a^5 \cdot a^0 = a^5 \cdot 1 = a^5$$

$$a^5 \div a^0 = a^{5-0} = a^5$$

and
$$a^5 \div a^0 = a^5 \div 1 = a^5$$

$$a^0 \div a^5 = \frac{1}{a^{5-0}} = \frac{1}{a^5}$$

and
$$a^0 \div a^5 = 1 \div a^5 = \frac{1}{a^5}$$

If we apply the definition of an exponent to $(a^2)^3$ we get $(a^2)^3 = a^2 \cdot a^2 \cdot a^2$.

The rule for multiplication shows that
$$a^2 \cdot a^2 \cdot a^2 = a^{2+2+2} = a^6$$

Generalizing, we have the third rule.

Rule 3 $(a^n)^m = a^n \cdot a^n \cdot a^n \ldots$ (for m factors) $= a^{mn}$. *To obtain the power of a power we multiply the exponents.*

BASE TEN

3.9   In our exponential positional notation we must have some number for *base*. We use the number 10. Any number is expressed as the *sum* of multiples of powers of the *base*. Remember that $10^0 = 1$. The symbol in the unit's digit may be interpreted as that number times 10^0. The symbol in the tens digit represents that **number** times 10^1. Similarly for higher and higher **digits**.

Example   95,873 = (9 × 10⁴) + (5 × 10³) + (8 × 10²) + (7 × 10¹)
$$+ (3 \times 10^0).$$

Since $10^4 = 10,000$, $10^3 = 1,000$, $10^2 = 100$, $10^1 = 10$, and $10^0 = 1$, it follows that

$(9 \times 10^4) + (5 \times 10^3) + (8 \times 10^2) + (7 \times 10^1) + (3 \times 10^0)$
$$= (9 \times 10,000) + (5 \times 1,000) + (8 \times 100) + (7 \times 10) + (3 \times 1)$$
$$= 90,000 + 5,000 + 800 + 70 + 3$$
$$= 95,873$$

The scheme can be continued indefinitely; it enables us to write a number as large as we please without the necessity of inventing any new symbols.

This positional notation is such that a symbol always represents ten times as much as the same symbol in a position immediately to the right, and one tenth as much as the same symbol placed immediately to the left. This is universally true, regardless of where the symbol is located in the number.

The general notation for all positive whole numbers may be indicated

$$a_0\, 10^n + a_1\, 10^{n-1} + \ldots + a_n\, 10^0$$

where each a represents a digit from 0 through 9, except that $a_0 \neq 0$. The number contains $(n + 1)$ digits.

———————   E   X   E   R   C   I   S   E   S   ———————

1.   Simplify the following:

(a) $\dfrac{4^3 \cdot 4^4}{4^6}$

(i) $\dfrac{(4^2)^3}{(4^3)^2}$

(b) $10^2 \cdot 10^3$

(j) $(2^3)^3$

(c) $\dfrac{9x^2}{(3x)^2}$

(k) $7^5 \div 7^7$

(d) $(17\frac{2}{3}) \cdot (123)^0$

(l) $a^3 b^5 / a^6 b^2$

(e) $a^2 b^3 / a^2 b$

(m) $(3^2)^2$

(f) a^3 / b^0

(n) 3^{2^2}

(g) $a^3 b^0$

(o) $(3^2)^3$

(h) $(x^3 y)(x^2 y^2)$

(p) 3^{2^3}

2.   Show that $(b^3)^4 = (b^4)^3$.

3. Use the number 70,707 to illustrate the meaning of place value by showing what each of the 7's represents.

4. Expand 16,583 to show the value of each of its digit symbols.

5. Prove Rule 2, Section 3.8.

SUMS OF POWERS

3.10   The ability to write numbers as we do implies that it is always possible to express a number as the sum of powers of 10 without using any power of 10 more than nine times.   The number 115 is the sum of 10^1 taken eleven times and 10^0 taken five times, but it is also 10^2 taken one time plus 10^1 taken one time plus 10^0 taken five times. This fact seems rather obvious as long as we are talking about powers of 10.   It seems obvious because of our notation system, but the notation system is possible only because of this principle.   It is equally true but, possibly, not so obvious that the idea holds when we use a number different from 10.   Any number can be expressed as the sum of *powers* of *8* without using any power more than *seven* times.   Any number can be expressed as the sum of powers of 2 without using any power more than *one* time.   This last statement has many interesting and practical applications.   Here it is a case of take it or leave it. We can build the number by either using or not using each power of 2.

Let us examine the general idea: Any number may be expressed as the sum of powers of the number n without using any power more than $n - 1$ times.   To illustrate:

$$115 = 64 + 48 + 3 = (1 \times 8^2) + (6 \times 8^1) + (3 \times 8^0)$$

Here no power of 8 is used more than seven times:

$$115 = 64 + 32 + 16 + 2 + 1$$
$$= (1 \times 2^6) + (1 \times 2^5) + (1 \times 2^4) + (1 \times 2^1) + (1 \times 2^0)$$

and no power of 2 is used more than one time.

Let us see how we may find the correct powers other than by trial and error.   Suppose we wish to break 81 up into powers of 6.   If we divide by 6 we get 13 as quotient and 3 as remainder.   Then 81 is 3 more than a multiple of 6:

$$81 = (13 \times 6^1) + (3 \times 6^0)$$

If we divide 13 by 6, getting 2 for the quotient and 1 for the remainder, we may express 13 as $(2 \times 6^1) + (1 \times 6^0)$. Substituting this value for 13, we get

$$81 = [(2 \times 6^1) + (1 \times 6^0)]6^1 + (3 \times 6^0)$$
$$= (2 \times 6^2) + (1 \times 6^1) + (3 \times 6^0)$$

If we wish, we may think of dividing the quotient 2 by 6, getting the quotient 0 and the remainder 2. Then we may say that the number of times each power of 6 must be used is indicated by the remainders we get upon successive divisions by 6.

The above method is perfectly general: If we divide the number by the required base (the base being the number in terms of whose powers we wish to express the number), the remainder tells us the number of times we must use the base raised to the 0 power. If we divide the quotient by the base, the remainder tells how many times the first power of the base must be used. The process is continued until we reach a quotient 0. Note that each remainder must be less than the base since the base is the divisor. Note further that if at any time the remainder is 0 we need the corresponding power of the base zero times.

The necessary work may be conveniently arranged as in the following.

Example   Express 390 as the sum of powers of 7 where no power of 7 is used more than six times.

$$\frac{55}{7)390} \quad \text{remainder } 5, \therefore \text{ we need five } 7^0\text{'s}$$
$$(\therefore \text{ means ``therefore''})$$

$$\frac{7}{7)55} \quad \text{remainder } 6, \quad \therefore \text{ we need six } 7^1\text{'s}$$

$$\frac{1}{7)7} \quad \text{remainder } 0, \quad \therefore \text{ we need no } 7^2\text{'s}$$

$$\frac{0}{7)1} \quad \text{remainder } 1, \quad \therefore \text{ we need one } 7^3$$

Then $$390 = 1 \times 7^3 + 0 \times 7^2 + 6 \times 7^1 + 5 \times 7^0$$

Notice that the successive remainders appear in order from lowest to highest powers of the base, just the reverse of the order in which the digits of a number are read. To verify the above we observe that:

$$7^3 = 343 \text{ and } 1 \times 7^3 = 343$$
$$7^2 = 49 \text{ and } 0 \times 7^2 = 0$$
$$7^1 = 7 \text{ and } 6 \times 7^1 = 42$$
$$7^0 = 1 \text{ and } 5 \times 7^0 = 5$$
$$\text{Total } 390$$

BASES OTHER THAN TEN

3.11   You will recall that 10 has played an important role in all the notation systems we have examined, with the exception of the Maya system.   Though our system is decimal (base 10) it derives none of its superiority or usefulness from this fact.   Undoubtedly man has shown a preference for 10 because of the fact that he has ten fingers. The Mayas apparently went barefoot.   The foregoing paragraphs should suggest the possibility of using a base other than 10.   Although few would seriously advocate the abandonment of 10 as base, most mathematicians would agree that 10 actually is an unfortunate choice. It has two exact divisors, 2 and 5.   Obvious advantages would accrue if we used 12, whose divisors are 2, 3, 4, 6.   Other less obvious advantages would result if we used a prime number, such as 11.

Suppose we used 7 as our base.   The example on page 65 indicates how 390 would be written, namely 1065.   The individual symbols would indicate that we have the base raised to the zero power five times, plus the base to the first power six times, plus the base to the second power no times, plus the base to the third power one time. The symbol 10 (one-zero) would represent *not ten* but *seven*.   Ten would be written 13 (one-three).   One hundred would be 202 (two-zero-two), rather than 100, which would represent forty-nine.

Some writers prefer to assign new word names to numbers when a base other than 10 is used.   This would be highly desirable if we seriously proposed the abandonment of 10 as base, since the number names fit base 10 symbolism.   However, there is no logical necessity for doing so.   On the other hand, we could keep 10 for base and invent an entirely new set of names if we so desired.   In this text, we preserve the identity of the number by continuing to associate it with its current name.   The word "twelve" identifies the number corresponding to the following marks ////////////.   However, when we write the number "twelve" as 14_8, it should read "one-four, base eight." It should not be called "fourteen" or "fourteen, base eight," because "fourteen" is the name of another number that can be written in any base we choose, for instance 16_8.   The number name "fourteen" should be associated with the symbol 14 only when 10 is base.

Recall that we need a distinct symbol for each number from zero up to, but not including, the base.   If a number greater than 10 is used as base, new symbols must be invented.   Suppose we wish to use 12 as base.   We must then invent a symbol for 10, say t, and a symbol for 11, say e. Let us further adopt the convention that we indicate the base under consideration by a subscript *written in base 10*, otherwise the base would always appear as 10. If no subscript is used, base 10 is implied unless a statement to the contrary is made. Then 123_{12} means that the symbol 123_{12} is to be interpreted as a number in base 12. We have seen how a base 10 number may, by repeated division, be converted to any other base. However, one precaution needs attention. If the new base is greater than 10 we might get a remainder of 10 or more. In that case care should be taken to write the corresponding digit in the new notation. The following illustrates the idea.

Example   Convert 275_{10} to base 12 notation.

$$\frac{22}{12)275} \quad \text{remainder 11} \qquad \frac{1}{12)22} \quad \text{remainder 10}$$

$$\frac{0}{12)1} \quad \text{remainder 1} \qquad \therefore \quad 275_{10} = 1te_{12}$$

A number written in a different base may be converted to base 10 quite easily merely by expressing each digit in base 10 and adding.

Example   Convert 257_8 to base 10.

$$257_8 = (2 \times 8^2 + 5 \times 8^1 + 7 \times 8^0)_{10}$$
$$= (128 + 40 + 7)_{10} = 175_{10}$$

Finally, it is possible to move from any base to any other base by converting to base 10 and then to the new base:

Example   Convert 835_9 to base 5.

$$835_9 = (8 \times 9^2 + 3 \times 9^1 + 5 \times 9^0)_{10}$$
$$= (648 + 27 + 5)_{10} = 680_{10}$$

$$\frac{136}{5)680} \quad \text{remainder 0} \qquad \frac{27}{5)136} \quad \text{remainder 1}$$

$$\frac{5}{5)27} \quad \text{remainder 2} \qquad \frac{1}{5)5} \quad \text{remainder 0}$$

$$\frac{0}{5)1} \quad \text{remainder 1} \qquad \therefore \quad 680_{10} = 10210_5$$
$$\text{and finally } 835_9 = 10210_5$$

Changing base is merely a matter of repackaging. In the usual notation we express the number in packages of ten, or packages of ten packages of ten, or packages of ten packages of ten packages of ten, etc. If we change to base 7 we merely change the sequence of package sizes from ten to seven. For large numbers this method would be rather awkward, but we can change 24_{10} to base 7 by removing three items from one of the two packages of ten and placing it with the four extras. This gives us two packages of seven. If we now remove three items from the other package of ten, we have three packages of seven and three extras. Thus $24_{10} = 33_7$.

Any positive whole number greater than 1 can serve as a base of notation. Table 3.1 shows the representation of selected numbers in base 2, base 8, base 10, and base 12.

Table 3.1

Number	Base two	Base eight	Base ten	Base twelve
One	1	1	1	1
Two	10	2	2	2
Three	11	3	3	3
Four	100	4	4	4
Eight	1000	10	8	8
Nine	1001	11	9	9
Twelve	1100	14	12	10
One hundred and forty-four	10010000	220	144	100
Five hundred and twelve	1000000000	1000	512	368
One thousand	1111101000	1750	1000	6e4

——————   E   X   E   R   C   I   S   E   S   ——————

1. Write the following numbers in base 10.
   - (a) 144_{12}
   - (b) 362_7
   - (c) 3031_4
   - (d) $2et_{12}$
   - (e) 1010010_2
   - (f) 122_8

2. Express in base 2:
   - (a) 432
   - (b) 63
   - (c) 17

3. Find a value of b such that 342_b will be an odd number.

4. Can 131_b represent an even number? Can 31_b? If so, for what values of b? If not, why not?

5. What base of notation is used if $34 + 56 + 27 = 141$?

6. Is there a value of b for which 52_b is odd? For which 62_b is odd? Why?

7. Is there a base for which $5 \times 5 = 20$? $5 \times 5 = 61$? $5 \times 5 = 41$? If not, why not? If so, what is the base?

8.   Express in base 8:
     (a)   400   (b)   125   (c)   64
9.   Express in base 12:
     (a)   120   (b)   145   (c)   2364
10. Change $e73_{12}$ to base 11.
11. Change 736_8 to base 2.
12. Write each digit of 736_8 in base 2 and compare the result with the answer
     to Exercise 11.   Explain.

ARITHMETIC IN OTHER BASES

*3.12   It is not necessary to move through base 10 as was done in the
above example.   We can move directly from base 9 to base 5 by
dividing the base 9 number successively by 5.   But to do so we must
either have the addition and multiplication tables for base 9 before us
or make our conversions as we go along.   Following the latter procedure, the above example may be worked as follows:

$$\frac{161}{5)\overline{835}} \quad \text{remainder 0} \qquad\qquad \frac{30}{5)\overline{161}} \quad \text{remainder 1}$$

$$\frac{5}{5)\overline{30}} \quad \text{remainder 2} \qquad\qquad \frac{1}{5)\overline{5}} \quad \text{remainder 0}$$

$$\frac{0}{5)\overline{1}} \quad \text{remainder 1} \qquad\qquad \therefore 835_9 = 10210_5$$

This division looks odd because we are not accustomed to base 9
notation.   In the first step, we divide 5 into 8, getting quotient 1
remainder 3, then 5 into 33 (which is not thirty-three but $3 \times 9 + 3 =$
thirty) six times with no remainder, then 5 into 5 one time with
no remainder.

In the second division, we divide 5 into 16 $(9 + 6,$ or fifteen) three
times with no remainder, then 5 into 1 no times with remainder 1.

The third division is 5 into 30, but 30 means $3 \times 9 + 0.$ Therefore
5 into 30 goes five times with remainder 2.

Let us construct base 5 addition and multiplication tables (following
page).   We read the tables as follows.   To find 3×4 in Table 3.3, we
locate the number opposite 3 in the left margin and under 4 at the
top.   This number is 22; thus $3 \times 4 = 22.$ All cell entries are
obtained by finding the sum (Table 3.2) or the product (Table 3.3)

in the usual fashion and expressing the results in packages of five rather than the usual ten. For example, we cannot change the fact that $4 \times 4 = 16$. But when we package 16 by fives we get 3 packages of five and an extra 1; thus the 31 opposite 4 and under 4 in Table 3.3.

Table 3.2   Base 5 addition.

	0	1	2	3	4
0	0	1	2	3	4
1	1	2	3	4	10
2	2	3	4	10	11
3	3	4	10	11	12
4	4	10	11	12	13

Table 3.3   Base 5 multiplication.

	0	1	2	3	4
0	0	0	0	0	0
1	0	1	2	3	4
2	0	2	4	11	13
3	0	3	11	14	22
4	0	4	13	22	31

With the aid of the tables we may convert 10210_5 back to base 9 without the necessity of even thinking in base 10.

$$
\begin{array}{r}
300 \\
14)\overline{10210} \\
102 \\
\hline
10 \quad \text{remainder}
\end{array}
\qquad
\begin{array}{r}
13 \\
14)\overline{300} \\
14 \\
\hline
110 \\
102 \\
\hline
3 \quad \text{remainder}
\end{array}
\qquad
\begin{array}{r}
0 \\
14)\overline{13} \\
13 \ \text{remainder}
\end{array}
$$

When these remainders 13_5, 3_5, 10_5 are converted to base 9, we get $10210_5 = 835_9$.

Let us use b to designate our base and a_i to indicate some number from 0 to $(b - 1)$. The subscript i means any number from 0 to n. Then we may express a number in any base in a manner analogous to that used in Section 3.9:

$$a_0 b^n + a_1 b^{n-1} + \ldots + a_n b^0$$

Regardless of the base in which the number is written, it *can be* written in base b. If we divide the above expression by b,

$$a_0 b^n + a_1 b^{n-1} + \ldots + a_{n-1} b^1 + a_n b^0$$
$$= b(a_0 b^{n-1} + a_1 b^{n-2} + \ldots + a_{n-1} b^0) + a_n$$

our remainder is a_n and subsequent divisions will yield succeeding a's. Thus, to convert a number in any base to base b, merely divide the number successively by b. The remainders will give the required digits from lowest to highest, regardless of the base.

The mechanical procedure for all fundamental operations is identical with that used in base 10.   Let us do the following base 5 addition with the aid of the addition table.

Example   432
         140
         233
       ──────
        1410

These are our steps: (1) $2 + 3 = 10$ (the base).   Write 0 and carry 1. (2) $1 + 3 = 4, 4 + 4 = 13, 13 + 3 = 21$.   Write 1, carry 2.   (3) $2 + 2 = 4, 4 + 1 = 10, 10 + 4 = 14$.   Write 14.

Multiplication works in the same way.   We must use both Tables 3.2 and 3.3 in performing this multiplication.

Example   431
          243
        ──────
         2343
         3324
         1412
       ────────
        232333

Our steps are: (1) $3 \times 1 = 3$.   Write 3.   (2) $3 \times 3 = 14$.   Write 4. carry 1.   (3) $3 \times 4 = 22, 22 + 1 = 23$.   Write 23.   (4) $4 \times 1 = 4$, Write 4.   (5) $4 \times 3 = 22$.   Write 2, carry 2.   (6) $4 \times 4 = 31, 31 + 2 = 33$.   Write 33.   (7) $2 \times 1 = 2$.   Write 2.   (8) $2 \times 3 = 11$. Write 1, carry 1.   (9) $2 \times 4 = 13, 13 + 1 = 14$.   Write 14.   (10)   Draw down 3.   (11) $4 + 4 = 13$.   Write 3, carry 1.   (12) $1 + 2 = 3, 3 + 2 = 10, 10 + 3 = 13$.   Write 3, carry 1.   (13) $1 + 1 = 2, 2 + 3 = 10, 10 + 2 = 12$.   Write 2, carry 1.   (14) $1 + 4 = 10, 10 + 3 = 13$.   Write 3, carry 1.   (15) $1 + 1 = 2$.   Write 2.

We leave it as an exercise, to convert Examples 1 and 2 to base 10 and check on the correctness of our base 5 work.

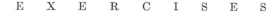

──────────   E   X   E   R   C   I   S   E   S   ──────────

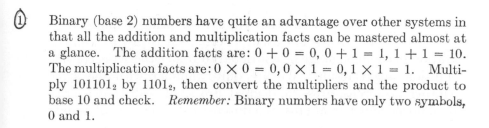

(1)   Binary (base 2) numbers have quite an advantage over other systems in that all the addition and multiplication facts can be mastered almost at a glance.   The addition facts are: $0 + 0 = 0, 0 + 1 = 1, 1 + 1 = 10$. The multiplication facts are: $0 \times 0 = 0, 0 \times 1 = 0, 1 \times 1 = 1$.   Multiply 101101_2 by 1101_2, then convert the multipliers and the product to base 10 and check.   *Remember:* Binary numbers have only two symbols, 0 and 1.

2.   Construct tables showing all the addition and multiplication facts needed to operate in base 4.

3.   Use the addition table constructed in Exercise 2 to add the following numbers which are written in base 4, and check your result by translating to base 10: $123 + 302 + 111 + 323$.

4.   Use the multiplication table constructed in Exercise 2 to find the following product — the numbers are written in base 4 — and check by translating to base 10: 320×102.

5.   Construct addition and multiplication tables necessary to operate in base 8.

6.   Use the addition table in Exercise 5 to add the following: $431_8 + 625_8 + 734_8$.   Check your result by translating to base 10.

7.   Use the tables in Exercise 5 to find the product of the following: $372_8 \times 104_8$.   Check your result by translating to base 10.

8.   Convert Example 1, page 71, to base 10 and solve.

9.   Convert Example 2, page 71, to base 10 and solve.

10.*   Prove that any number can be expressed as the sum or difference of powers of 3 where no power is used more than one time.

11.   Change $e8t_{12}$ to base 10.

12.   Change 578_9 to base 11 by first changing to base 10.

13.*   Change 578_9 to base 11 without going through base 10.

14.   Add the following base 8 numbers without the aid of the table: $175 + 363 + 732$.

15.   Prove that a base 10 number is divisible by 5 if it ends in 5 or 0.   Is the same true if the number is written in base 12?   Explain.

16.   Compare the factors of 36_{10} and 36_{12}.

17.   The symbol 13 represents a prime number if 10 is the base.   Does it represent a prime number regardless of the base?   Explain.

APPLICATIONS

3.13   The idea of a base other than 10 is utilized quite frequently although the notation is not used.   Perhaps it is just as well that the notation in common usage be restricted to 10.   Otherwise, considerable confusion might result.   We are quite familiar with the system of counting in dozens, gross, and great gross.   Recall that a gross is a dozen dozen and a great gross is a dozen gross.   This usage is definitely a utilization of the idea of base 12 (duodecimal).   The carpenter or cabinetmaker, though using duodecimals when working in feet and inches, reverts to base 2 when considering parts of an inch, halves, fourths, eighths, and sixteenths.   Written in the binary scale (base 2) these units would appear as 0.1, .01, .001, .0001.   Stockbrokers utilize base 8 when quoting stock prices in terms of eighths of a unit, and the rise or fall from the previous quotations as plus or minus so many eighths.   Mention has already been made of the fact that the common units of time and angle measure are applications of base 60 (called sexagesimals).   Speedometers, electric meters and the like, as well as many calculating machines utilize 10 as base by use of a sequence of gears with a ratio of 10 to 1.   However, the most recent high speed electronic computers utilize base 2.

Electronic computing machines are of two kinds, digital and analogue.   The abacus is a digital computer.   So are cash registers and ordinary adding machines.   On the other hand, clocks and slide rules (to be discussed later) are examples of analogue computers.   The analogue computer actually keeps track of one thing but is calibrated to read something else.   For instance, the speedometer of an automobile counts turns of the wheels but it *reads* miles per hour.

The digital computer uses binary numbers because a number may be obtained by either accepting or rejecting each power of 2.   Actually, some computers use bases other than 2, such as 4, 8, or 10, but they still employ the "take it or leave it" binary principle and obtain the desired base by ingenious systems of switching devices.

One of the simplest applications of the binary principle is the binary counter.   Let us suppose we have a bank of relays which are capable of transmitting a current of electricity over either of two routes.   We shall designate one output route as 0 and the other as 1. As long as a steady flow of current is being received the 0 or 1 state of the relay is unchanged.   When a pulsing current, or beat, is received, the condition of the relay is changed, 0 to 1 and 1 to 0.   If the relay is in condition 1 when it receives the beat, it changes its own output condition to 0 and transmits the beat to the next relay.   If the relay is in condition 0 when it receives a beat, it changes to condition 1 but transmits a steady flow of current to the next relay.   The first relay in the bank represents 2^0, the next 2^1, the next 2^2, and so on.   If a given relay is in condition 0, this means the corresponding power of 2 is not present; if its condition is 1, then that power of 2 is present.

Suppose we have counted up to 13. This would be recorded in the relay bank as indicated in Figure 3.2. Since relays number 1, 3, and 4 are in condition 1, we have recorded $2^0 + 2^2 + 2^3 = 13$.

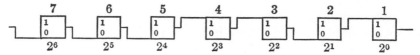

Figure 3.2 A binary counter, indicating a count of 13.

When the next beat signal is received, relay 1 transmits the beat to relay 2 and changes its own state to 0. Relay 2 transmits a steady current to the remainder of the bank but changes its state to 1. We now have recorded $2^1 + 2^2 + 2^3 = 14$, as indicated in Figure 3.3.

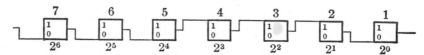

Figure 3.3 A binary counter, indicating a count of 14.

The next beat merely causes the first relay to change from condition 0 to condition 1, increasing the number by 2^0. On the following beat the first four relays will change to state 0 and convey a beat to the fifth relay, which will change to state 1. We then have recorded $2^4 = 16$.

One of the most marvelous things about the electronic digital computer is the fact that it performs its unbelievable feats largely by adding and "remembering." These machines have not eliminated the need for mathematicians. They have greatly increased the demand, since the machines have to be told what to do in order to solve a given problem.

Binary numbers have the obvious advantage of requiring a minimum of addition and multiplication facts. But we would lose much compactness if they were used. Compare 512_{10} with its equivalent, 1000000000_2. As has been mentioned, 12 has more exact divisors than 10 but, from the standpoint of divisibility, consider the convenience of 60. However, if 60 were the base we should need individual symbols for each number up to 59. Learning the multiplication combinations would become a formidable task. Ten is a pretty good compromise between compactness and divisibility on the one hand and the number of symbols and combination facts required on the other.   If a prime base were used, "basimal" fractions (analogous to decimal fractions) would always be in lowest terms.   For example, in base 11 the fraction .25 would mean $\frac{2}{11} + \frac{5}{121}$, which is not reducible.

We have considered bases other than 10, but their systems of notation are identical.   The difference between the base 10 notation we use and an earlier system, say the Roman, is analogous to the difference between a modern truck and a wheelbarrow.   But the difference between base 10 notation and base 12 notation is more comparable to the difference between a six-cylinder and an eight-cylinder motor.

——————   E   X   E   R   C   I   S   E   S   ——————

1. A druggist sells 3 gross, 5 dozen, and **7** bottles of Yip-Pe tonic in one month.   How many bottles did he sell?   Write the number in base 12 and in base 10.

2. A carpenter cuts a plank 11.7 feet long.   This number is written in base 12.   How many feet and inches long is it?

3. If a certain issue of stock is quoted at $125\frac{7}{8}$-$\frac{5}{8}$, how would this quotation be written in base 8?

4. Diagram the relay bank, described in Section 3.13, when 15 is recorded. Do the same for when 16 is recorded.

5. Let $\sqrt{}$, $\sim$, $\triangle$, $\square$ represent 1, 4, 16, 64 respectively in a repetitive additive system with base 4.   Express the following numbers in this system.
   (a)   125   (b)   70   (c)   85   (d)   400

6. Let $\sqrt{}$, $\sim$, $\triangle$, $\square$ represent 0, 1, 2, 3 respectively in an exponential positional number system with base 4.   Express the following numbers in this system.
   (a)   125   (b)   70   (c)   85   (d)   400

7. Construct the necessary addition and multiplication tables for operating in the system described in Exercise 6.

8. Use the tables constructed in Exercise 7 to find the following.
   (a) $\triangle\sim\square + \square\sqrt{} \sim \triangle$ (b) $\triangle\square \times \square\sim$

SUMMARY

3.14   We have seen in this chapter that the Hindu-Arabic system of notation is far more convenient than the ancient systems.   It enables us to write numbers as large as we please and as small as we please. No new symbols need be invented. The secret of its superiority lies in the use of the principle of place value, the complete utilization of which is impossible without a symbol for zero. The decimal nature of the system seems to be important only because of custom and familiarity; any other number could be used as base. We are apt to minimize the magnitude of this invention because of its simplicity. It should be remembered that the system had its beginning shortly after the advent of the Christian Era and did not reach completion until near the close of the sixteenth century. Thus it escaped the mentality of the nameless geniuses who were responsible for such accomplishments as the building of the Great Pyramids and the surveying of the Nile. It evaded such of the Greek intellectual giants as Euclid, Apollonius, and Archimedes.

Historians have been puzzled by this fact. Magnificent as was the Greek contribution to mathematical thought, many historians are convinced that their accomplishments were cut short of far greater heights for want of a decent numeration system. The Greeks were primarily preoccupied with geometry. Although there is considerable number theory in Euclid's monumental *Elements*, the treatment is essentially geometric. The same situation exists relative to algebra. Many algebraic identities are established in *Elements*, but they are stated and proved as geometric propositions.

Diophantus was the only algebraist of any consequence among the Greeks. He worked with the aid of practically no symbolism. Had he had the advantage of modern symbolism, the development of algebra probably would have been advanced many hundred years. Archimedes was at the very threshold of the calculus. The Greek failure to come to grips with the limit concept is indirectly related to their failure to develop a positional numeration system (see page 53). In Chapter VII you will find the idea utilized in the development of the real number system. Although positional notation is not essential for this development, it is quite helpful in grasping the idea of a limit.

It is ironical that the Greek preoccupation with geometry stemmed from their interest in mathematics as a system of logical thought. Yet the areas which they neglected, number theory, algebra, and analysis, are far more appropriate and more fruitful as examples of axiomatic deductive systems.

The value of a positional number system far transcends its value merely as an aid to computation, great though that is. In a very real sense it has opened innumerable mathematical doors. It has also had a significant bearing on the most recent technological advances. The present state of development of rocketry depends upon electronic computers. Corrections in the rocket's course are made by radio while the rocket is in flight. This is possible because, with unbelievable speed, the computer determines the correction from data obtained after the flight has begun. But the design of the computer utilizes the principles of a positional notation system.

DO YOU KNOW

There are as many even numbers as there are whole numbers?

The whole is not necessarily greater than any of its parts?

There is really just one fundamental operation of arithmetic?

How to tell at a glance whether 125, 938, 675, 416 is a perfect square?

Why our methods of multiplying and dividing work?

Many other methods of multiplying and dividing have been used?

How to tell at a glance whether or not a number is evenly divisible by 11?

How to tell whether two groups of objects are equal in number without counting either group?

How to prove that there are at least two men in New York City with exactly the same number of hairs on their heads?

CHAPTER IV

WHAT IS A NUMBER?

The following are symbols for numbers:

$$5, \; -\tfrac{7}{8}, \; \sqrt{3}, \; \Pi, \; \tfrac{1}{2}, \; i, \; a, \; x^2$$

Some, if not all, of them are probably familiar to you. The question posed in the chapter title does not refer to symbols. We can make a vocal sound for five, write the word *"five"* or the sign 5, or we may even hold up the fingers of one hand. All of these are symbols for a number. But what is the *number*, apart from these symbols?

In Chapter III we took several things for granted in developing the ideas concerning the way we write numbers. Most of what was said referred to a very particular kind of number. Now we shall examine some definitions and properties of number, some older ways of multiplying and dividing, and the concept of number congruence. As we pursue the answer to the above question, it is well to recall that we cannot define everything, and it might be the expedient course to take as undefined the positive whole numbers, or *natural numbers*, also called counting numbers. But even though we do just that, it is profitable to try to go a little deeper to see what underlies our notion of number.

ONE-TO-ONE CORRESPONDENCE

4.1 We are quite familiar with the notion of multiplication. Suppose we multiply 4 × 5. What are we finding? We are finding how many objects there are in four sets, each of which contains five elements. Generalizing, as long as the numbers are natural numbers, multiplication is equivalent to the addition of sets of equal numbers.

But what is addition?　When we add 5 + 4 we get the same result that we get from counting a set of five objects and counting on through another set of four objects.　Then addition is merely abridged counting.　But — let's be persistent — what is counting?

You have probably heard a four-year-old counting, "One, two, three, seven, five, ten. . . ."　The number names were there but they were not ordered properly.　The proper ordering of number names, as well as the names themselves, is a matter of common agreement. This agreement has developed gradually.　In fact, there is evidence in our language that man has not always been aware of the fact that two horses and two birds have the property of "twoness" in common. Span, pair, brace, and couple — these are a few words used to mean a special kind of two.　Although it is in the realm of conjecture, man probably made a tremendous stride forward when he realized that all sets of objects which contained five elements had something in common.　This something in common, this "same-as-ness," is the thing we call number.　Things may have the same shape, size, color, taste — many properties in common — and so may collections or sets of things, but sets may also have the property of containing the same number of members.　However, we cannot define number in terms of number and get anywhere.　"A number is a number is a number" may pass for poetry in some quarters, but it is not good mathematics.

If we give our imagination free play, we can guess how primitive man first counted.　Suppose he wished to count the sheep in his flock. He would make a mark on the ground or place a pebble in a pile as the sheep went by.　He knows that each mark or pebble "stands for" a sheep.　In the evening as the sheep return, a pebble may be removed from the pile or a mark rubbed out as each sheep goes by.　If all the pebbles or marks are used up, and there has been one to pair with each sheep, all the sheep are accounted for.　Here we have a "same as" relationship; the counters are the same as the sheep in that there is a counter to correspond to each sheep and a sheep to correspond to each counter.　If upon their return there are not enough sheep to account for each counter, our friend knows some sheep are missing (if he is sure no one has tampered with his counters).　In case sheep are still arriving after all counters have been used, either the counters have been disturbed or some new lambs have arrived.　In either case we do not have a "same as" relationship but a "less than" or "more than" situation.　This pairing off of sheep and counters is known as placing in one-to-one correspondence.

Definition   Two sets of things are in one-to-one correspondence when each member of the first set is paired with one member of the second, and each member of the second is paired with one member of the first.

In other words, each member has its partner in the other set, and no element in either set is without a partner. Any time two sets of things can be placed in one-to-one correspondence, the two sets have a "same as" relationship — they are equal in number. We do not necessarily have to know what the number is. If the members of a class enter a classroom and each sits in a separate chair, then the number of chairs is the same as the number of students, provided no empty chairs remain.

A CONVENIENT REFERENCE SET

4.2   Obviously, the primitive shepherd's scheme is too uncertain. It is too inconvenient to have to stand guard over the system of counters. It would be much better if we had a system of counters that is always with us. The fingers make an excellent frame of reference so long as our number requirements are small enough. Man ultimately hit upon the idea of a set of words as a frame of reference — then he could carry his counters with him in his mind. But we need more than just a set of words, unless we are always dealing with sets having the same number of objects. The set of words must be *ordered*. Why does seven "come before" eight and "come after" six? Merely because that is the arbitrarily agreed upon order of the arbitrarily agreed upon number names.

Then if we restrict our question "What is a number?" to natural numbers, we may say that the natural numbers are an ordered set of names. Two groups that have the "same as" relationship which is designated by the name *five* are two groups that may be placed in one-to-one correspondence with the ordered set of names *one, two, three, four, five.*

Similarly, for any other number. The number a designates a property that is common to all sets of objects which may be placed in one-to-one correspondence with the ordered set of number names ending with the number a. Since any two of these sets may be placed in one-to-one correspondence with the same set of number names, they may also be placed in correspondence with each other. Consequently, according to Section 4.1, they are equal in number.

COUNTING AND ORDERING

4.3   Natural numbers are used in two ways in the counting process. If we merely want to answer the question "How many elements in a set?" we place the members in the set to be counted, without regard to the order in which we use them, in correspondence with the ordered set of names (numbers).   Used in this way, the number of the set is a *cardinal* number.   If, however, the set to be counted is also ordered, each member of the set has an *ordinal* number.

The ordinal number of that member of the set which is counted last is the cardinal number of the set.   When two sets are equal in number they have the same cardinal number.

The children in a family are John, Mary, Bob, and Sue.   If John corresponds to one, Mary to two, Bob to three, and Sue to four, we conclude that there are four children in the family.   But the same result is obtained regardless of the order in which the names of the children are used.   On the other hand, if the above is the order of their ages, we may say John is *first*, Mary *second*, Bob *third*, and Sue *fourth*.   Here we have set up a correspondence and given each child an ordinal number.

In the first instance only the set of number names was ordered; in the latter, both sets were ordered.   Our concern is primarily with cardinal numbers.   If you want to count the number of states in the Union, it makes no difference which state is considered to be first, second, and so on.   We merely find the cardinal number of the set to be 50.   However, if we wish to rank them according to population, New York has the ordinal 1, California 2, and so on.   If they are ranked according to area, Alaska has the ordinal number 1; according to number of legal gambling houses, Nevada becomes 1.

COUNTING THE INFINITE

4.4   We have said that two sets have equal cardinal numbers when they can be placed in one-to-one correspondence.   Five chairs can be paired with five persons.   The states of the Union can be placed in correspondence with the first 50 number names.   But what of *all* the number names?   Here is a set that is said to be infinite.   For the moment we may think of this as meaning that the natural numbers are endless.   There is no last number.   The number of electrons in the entire universe has been estimated to be about 10^{79} (1 followed by 79 zeros).   This is a fair-sized number, yet it is finite.   The set of numbers from 1 to 10^{79} cannot be placed in one-to-one correspondence with all the natural numbers.   We might wonder whether any other set is as large as the set of natural numbers.   Since there is an odd number between any two consecutive even numbers, it seems reasonable to assume that there are half as many even numbers as there are natural numbers.   But wait!   If we stick to our statement that sets are equal in number if they can be placed in one-to-one correspondence, we must conclude that there are just as many even numbers as there are natural numbers.

$$1 \quad 2 \quad 3 \quad 4 \quad 5 \quad 6 \quad \ldots n \ldots$$
$$\updownarrow \quad \updownarrow \quad \updownarrow \quad \updownarrow \quad \updownarrow \quad \updownarrow \qquad \updownarrow$$
$$2 \quad 4 \quad 6 \quad 8 \quad 10 \quad 12 \quad \ldots 2n \ldots$$

In the above array, the natural numbers are on the top line and the even numbers are on the bottom line.   The double-headed arrows indicate how the elements of the two sets are placed in correspondence. The dots at the end of each line indicate that the process continues in the same manner endlessly.   If the sets to be placed in correspondence are finite, all the elements in each set may actually be used one and only one time, and every pair displayed.   However, if the sets are infinite, this obviously cannot be done.   If an infinite set is to be shown equal in number to the set of natural numbers, a method whereby the first set can be counted must be exhibited.   Such a set is said to be a *countably*, or *denumerably*, *infinite* set.   It is necessary that the set be ordered if it is to be counted.   The ordering can be in terms of magnitude.   This method was used with the even numbers: the *next* even number to be counted is always the *next larger* even number.   However, the order in which the elements of the set are to be counted need not be the order of size.   We merely have to show that the method of ordering ultimately includes all the elements and uses each one only once.   In a later chapter we shall see a countably infinite set which is ordered in a manner other than by magnitude.

This is the distinguishing feature of an infinite set, as opposed to a finite set.

Definition   An infinite set is a set which can be placed in one-to-one correspondence with a part of itself (one of its proper subsets; see page 233).

This may be upsetting to those of you who learned in geometry that the whole is equal to the sum of its parts, because here the whole is equal to a part of itself.   When dealing with infinite sets, we simply reject the axiom that the whole is equal to the sum of its parts — after all, we cannot prove it.   We had to assume it in geometry.   We have just as much right to make the counterassumption in reference to infinite sets.   We can make any assumptions we wish, as long as they are not contradictory.

It may seem to you that all infinite sets are equal in number.   But this is not the case.   It can be shown that there are more points on a one-inch line than there are natural numbers.   We shall return to the arithmetic of the infinite in a later chapter.

——————————   E   X   E   R   C   I   S   E   S   ——————————

1.   Prove that there are as many multiples of three as there are even numbers.

2.   Place the two following sets in one-to-one correspondence in as many ways as possible.   *Set 1:* glod, bint, talw, sming; *Set 2:* apple, dog, biscuit, horse.

3.   Without counting either set, determine which is the greater.   *Set 1:* red, green, purple, blue, black, white; *Set 2:* Monday, Tuesday, Wednesday, Thursday, Friday, Saturday, Sunday.

4.   If you count the months of the year, what two sets have been placed in one-to-one correspondence?

5.   Prove there are as many natural numbers greater than 100 as there are natural numbers.

6.   In the following, which numbers are used ordinally?   Which are used cardinally?
     (a)   Six months from now the calendar will show month 9.
     (b)   The Smiths are a family of four living at 24 North Main.
     (c)   When Don Juan added telephone number XY-2-0002 to his collection, this made twelve.
     (d)   When a man is in his fortieth year he has had thirty-nine birthdays.
     (e)   Channel 16 showed three murder mysteries four days in a row.
     (f)   He is all feet, he wears a 14 shoe and a 6 hat.
     (g)   It was a fourteen-page assignment, ending on page 156.

7.   What vocabulary evidence is there which indicates that the ordinal and cardinal concepts of number evolved independently?   Which do you think evolved first?   Why?

8.   Prove there are as many unit fractions (fractions with numerator 1) as there are natural numbers.

9.   Does it follow from Exercise 8 that there are more fractions between zero and one than there are natural numbers?   Discuss.

ADDITION IS COUNTING

4.5   Now that we have agreed on what counting is, if the count of one set is the number a and the count of a second set is the number b, then the count of a set obtained by combining the two is $a + b$.   The operation of obtaining the count of the combined sets we shall call addition, and indicate the operation with the sign $+$.   This putting together of the two sets does not have to be done in a physical sense. In fact, it usually is not done; it is sufficient to combine them mentally. When the grocer is taking inventory he does not bother to put all the cans of beans in one pile.   He probably counts the cases in the storeroom and from this count, by multiplication, finds the number of cans there; then counts the cans in the back row on the shelf, counts the cans in the front row on the shelf, and adds.   Although it is not essential, we can extend the basic notion of addition to any number of sets; we can think of combining set a, set b, and set c into one set whose count is $a + b + c$.   We are usually taught the addition combinations by two, thus $7 + 8 = 15$, not $7 + 8 + 9 = 24$.   Addition is a *binary* operation, one which combines only two numbers.   When more than two are to be combined the operation is repeated.   However, we could be taught the sum of three or more numbers as a single fact, and frequently we do recognize at a glance the sum of more than two.

Suppose the grocer found that he had 240 cans in the storeroom, 24 on the back row of the shelf, and 16 on the front row.   He could add 24 to 240, and 16 to this sum.   We indicate this by $(240 + 24) + 16$, the parentheses showing that $240 + 24$ are combined first. However, he is more likely to combine the 24 and 16, then add the sum to 240.   This would be indicated by $240 + (24 + 16)$.   Incidentally, if we use no parentheses and write $240 + 24 + 16$, we imply the order of the operation first mentioned, so in $(240 + 24) + 16$ the parentheses are used merely for emphasis.   In any event, the number of cans of beans is the same.   We indicate this by writing $(240 + 24) + 16 = 240 + (24 + 16)$.   We may verify by as many examples as we like that the sum is unaffected by this *regrouping*. This property is known as the *associative law for addition*.

A_1 Addition is associative: $(a + b) + c = a + (b + c)$, where a, b, c are natural numbers.

(The axioms about natural numbers will be indicated by the letter A, with a subscript denoting its number, as A_1 above.)

The law is called associative because we *associate a* with b and their sum with c in the first case. But the elements are associated in a different manner in the second case; b and c are associated together and this sum is associated with a. The associative property provides a convenient check on addition. Different addition combinations are usually required when we obtain the sum by different associations.

Addition also obeys the *commutative law*. To commute means to reverse, to change.

A_2 Addition is commutative: $a + b = b + a$.

The two operations are not identical. The roles of the a and the b have been interchanged. On the left side we are to add b to a but on the right side we add a to b. Adding a dollar to a million dollars is easier than adding a million dollars to a dollar, even though both are out of reach for most of us. But if we are lucky enough to do either one, we have the same amount of money in either case.

If the hardware merchant sells his hexagon-headed, $\frac{3}{16}$-inch bolts for the same price as square-headed bolts of the same size, he merely needs to know how many $\frac{3}{16}$-inch bolts he has in taking inventory. He doesn't want to dump them together and count them, since they would have to be re-sorted. He can count the hexagon bolts and keep right on counting through the square bolts. But he can count the other way: square bolts, then hexagon bolts. This is the commutative property. The order in which the elements are used in addition is immaterial in so far as the sum is concerned.

MULTIPLICATION IS ADDITION

4.6   We have been talking about counting the elements in sets of things. We also can count the number of sets. Let us see how many sets of cans of beans the grocer was counting. Those in the storeroom were one set, those in the back row on the shelf were a second set, and those in the front row were a third set. Of course, when he had finished his count he had combined them (mentally) into one set. Suppose those in the storeroom were in cases, each case containing 24 cans. He would think you were rather silly if you suggested opening each case and counting the individual cans. There was a time in man's development when that would have been the accepted procedure. Some time in the distant past, an unusually observant person saw that if groups were of the same number, the same number of groups always gave the same result. Our grocer merely counts the ten cases and since he knows each case holds 24 cans he knows he has 240 cans in the storeroom. Now, the set of cans in the storeroom consists of ten sets of cans, the ten cases. So the grocer counts the set of cases in order to find the size of the set of cans. He could have added the ten sets, each containing 24 cans, and reached the same total of 240 cans. The process of finding the total count of a number of like-sized sets we shall call multiplication. The natural number b multiplied by the natural number a means the same as $b + b + b + \dots$ until we have added b, a times. You are probably familiar with three ways of indicating multiplication: they are the $\times$ sign as used in arithmetic, the raised dot $\cdot$, just like the English decimal point, and juxtaposition, or placing next to each other, without a sign. Thus

$$a \times b \qquad a \cdot b \qquad ab$$

all indicate b multiplied by a, or a times b. Notice the difference in the wording b *multiplied by* a and a *times* b; both mean that we add together sets whose count is b and we have a such sets. We are agreeing that in the multiplication symbolism the first factor tells how many sets we add and the second factor tells how large each set is. None of the three ways of indicating multiplication is completely satisfactory. The $\times$ can be confused with the letter x used to indicate any one of a set of numbers, just as we have used a and b above. The raised dot can be confused with a decimal point. Juxtaposition can never be used with specific numbers, because of our notation. We cannot let 56 mean five times six because we have already decided to let it mean $(5 \times 10^1) + (6 \times 10^0)$. At this point we shall adopt for most purposes the convention of indicating multiplication by means of the raised dot, as $5 \cdot 3$ for five times three, when using numbers. We shall omit the sign when using letters to stand for numbers, as ab for a times b, or when we use a letter and a number, as $5a$ for five times a.

A_3 Multiplication is associative: $a(bc) = (ab)c$.

The left side of the equality means the product bc is added a times:

$$bc + bc + bc + bc + \ldots \text{for } a \text{ terms}$$

The right member means the number c is added ab times:

$$c + c + c + c + \ldots \text{for } ab \text{ terms}$$

The numbers to be multiplied together are called *factors*; the result of the multiplication is called the *product*. The names should be distinguished from the names employed in addition; the numbers added are *terms*, and the result is a *sum*. The names chosen are purely arbitrary but their distinction should never be lost; as we shall see later, *terms* and *factors* do not always behave alike.

The associative law for multiplication does not seem quite as obvious as did that for addition. Suppose a packing carton, Figure 4.1, is

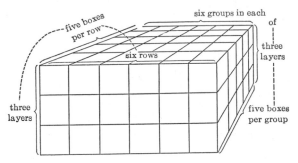

Figure 4.1 Multiplication is associative: $3 \cdot (6 \cdot 5) = (3 \cdot 6) \cdot 5$.

deep enough to hold three layers of smaller boxes, and each layer contains six rows of boxes, five boxes to the row. We can count the boxes in each row (5) and the number of rows (6); then by multiplication we have $6 \cdot 5 = 30$ boxes per layer. Then we know, since there are 3 layers, that there are $3 \cdot 30 = 90$ boxes per carton. This is symbolized as $3 \cdot (6 \cdot 5)$. We could also think of the boxes as consisting of sets of 5, 6 such sets in each of 3 layers. The total number of sets of 5 is then $3 \cdot 6 = 18$, and the total number in the 18 sets of 5 is $18 \cdot 5 = 90$ boxes per carton. This is symbolized as $(3 \cdot 6) \cdot 5$. Here we have *associated* the factors in two different ways, parentheses being used to indicate the manner in which the association is made.

Addition is associative, multiplication is associative, but we cannot change the association when both are involved. We cannot say $3 + (5 \cdot 6) = (3 + 5) \cdot 6$. Suppose we write $3 + 5 \cdot 6$. We might infer that in the absence of signs to show how the numbers are associated we perform the operations in the order in which they appear. This would mean we add $3 + 5 = 8$, then multiply by 6, giving 48. This happens not to be correct.   Any time parentheses are not present to indicate how the numbers are to be associated, the correct procedure is to perform all indicated multiplications (and divisions) in the order in which they appear *first*, then all indicated additions (and subtractions) in the order in which they appear.   This cannot be proved. It is one of the rules of mathematical grammar.   It is by common agreement that we must make the above interpretation.   When we write $3 + (5 \cdot 6)$, the parentheses serve merely to emphasize the fact that we are to multiply 6 by 5 and add the product to 3.

A_4 Multiplication is commutative: $ab = ba$.

The left side of the equality means

$$b + b + b + b \dots \text{for } a \text{ terms}$$

while the right side means

$$a + a + a + a \dots \text{for } b \text{ terms.}$$

In counting the boxes in the carton we said we had 6 rows, 5 boxes to the row.   We could look at it the other way and call the same array 5 rows, 6 boxes per row.   In the first instance we are adding six 5's — $5 + 5 + 5 + 5 + 5 + 5$ — when we find $6 \cdot 5$.   In the second case we are adding five 6's — $6 + 6 + 6 + 6 + 6$ — when we find $5 \cdot 6$.

------------   E   X   E   R   C   I   S   E   S   ------------

1.   Which of the following is associative?
  (a)   (Hot water + tea leaves) + ice
  (b)   Ground beef + (salt + pepper)
  (c) $(100 \div 10) \div 5$
  (d) $(100 \div 10) \div 1$

2.   Which of the following is commutative?
  (a)   Brushing your teeth and combing your hair
  (b)   Putting on your shoes and your socks
  (c)   Reaching second base and reaching third base
  (d)   Putting cream and sugar in your coffee
  (e)   Loading a gun and pulling the trigger

3.   What is the difference in the meaning between the two expressions $5a$ and $a5$?

4. Frequently, in adding a column of figures, one adds up the column, then as a check adds down the column. What is the justification for this check?

5. Use A_2 to prove $a + b + c = c + b + a$.

6. State a generalization of A_2 to any number of terms.

7. Use A_1 to prove $[(a + b) + c] + d = a + [b + (c + d)]$.

8. Prove $[(a + b) + c] + d = c + [d + (b + a)]$.

9. If $a = 2$, $b = 3$, $c = 4$, $d = 5$, evaluate each side of the equation in Exercise 8.

10. Prove $a \cdot b \cdot c = c \cdot b \cdot a$.

11. Prove $[(a \cdot b) \cdot c] \cdot d = a \cdot [b \cdot (c \cdot d)]$.

12. How are the proofs of Exercises 10 and 11 related to those of Exercises 5 and 7 respectively?

THE DISTRIBUTIVE PRINCIPLE

4.7   The natural numbers obey another law known as the *distributive law*. This law combines addition and multiplication.

A_5 Multiplication is distributive with respect to addition: $a(b + c) = ab + ac$.

Here the factor a distributes itself over the terms of the other factor $(b + c)$, giving us two terms, ab and ac, each of which contains two factors, a and b, and a and c.

We know that $3 \cdot (4 + 5) = 3 \cdot 9 = 27$ and that $3 \cdot 4 + 3 \cdot 5 = 12 + 15 = 27$. If the prevailing price of apples is 3 dollars per bushel and Farmer Jones brings 4 bushels of apples to the produce merchant and an hour later his son brings 5 bushels, they will receive $3 \cdot 4 = 12$ dollars plus $3 \cdot 5 = 15$ dollars, or 27 dollars for the apples. However, if they arrive at the same time, the merchant pays Mr. Jones $3 \cdot (4 + 5) = 27$ dollars for the apples. Notice that neither $3 \cdot (4 + 5)$ nor $3 \cdot 4 + 3 \cdot 5$ is identically the same as $3 \cdot 9$ but both are equal to it and to each other.

The distributive principle is familiar to algebra students as *removing parentheses* when reading from left to right,

$$\overrightarrow{a(b + c)} = ab + ac$$

and as *factoring out* in reading from right to left,

$$\overleftarrow{a(b + c)} = ab + ac.$$

RULES OF THE GAME

4.8   The associative, commutative, and distributive properties are the "rules of the game" in manipulating natural numbers.   Other rules concerning equality, some of which we might almost unconsciously use, follow.

A_6 Substitution: A number may be replaced by its equal.   If $a = b$ and $b = c$, then $a = c$.

A_7 Identity: A number is equal to itself. $a = a$.

A_8 Symmetry: An equality may be read in either direction.   If $a = b$, then $b = a$.

A_9 Addition: Equal numbers added to equal numbers give equal numbers. If $a = b$ and $c = d$, then $a + c = b + d$.

A_{10} Multiplication: Equal numbers multiplied by equal numbers give equal numbers.   If $a = b$ and $c = d$, then $ac = bd$.

We must keep in mind that at this point we are talking about natural numbers only, and only the operations of addition and multiplication.   Any new numbers we admit we shall define in terms of what we have at that time.   We shall also define any new operations. Assumptions, in addition to those already made, will be indicated at the appropriate places.

One other property of the natural numbers should be mentioned. It, too, is an assumption.   But first we need the definition:

Definition   A set is *closed* with respect to an operation if, when any two members of the set are combined by the operation, a member of the set is produced.

If we add two natural numbers the sum is always a natural number. If we multiply two natural numbers the product is always a natural number:

Closure   The natural numbers are closed under addition and multiplication.

A_{11} If a, b are natural numbers and $a + b = c$, then c is a natural number. If a, b are natural numbers and $ab = d$, then d is a natural number.

Notice that this assumption would be ridiculous if the natural numbers were not infinite.   The set of numbers from one to ten is not closed with respect to addition because, although $5 + 4$ does equal a number between one and ten, $8 + 7$ does not.

We know that
$$a(b + c) = (c + b)a$$

which seems to be a new assumption, but it actually need not be. This equality can be derived from the properties already given:

$a(b + c) = (b + c)a$	Multiplication is commutative	(A$_4$)
$(b + c)a = (c + b)a$	Addition is commutative	(A$_2$)
$a(b + c) = (c + b)a$	Substitution	(A$_6$)

Where is the closure property involved?   This same relationship may also be derived as follows:

$a(b + c) = ab + ac$	Distributive property	(A$_5$)
$ab + ac = ac + ab$	Addition is commutative	(A$_2$)
$ac + ab = a(c + b)$	Distributive property	(A$_5$)
$a(c + b) = (c + b)a$	Multiplication is commutative	(A$_4$)
$a(b + c) = (c + b)a$	Substitution	(A$_6$)

One might feel that the last step is actually three substitution steps. The substitution axiom may be stated: *Numbers equal to the same number are equal to each other.*   Our chain of steps could be linked like this:

$$a(b + c) = ab + ac = ac + ab = a(c + b) = (c + b)a$$

If addition were distributive with respect to multiplication, this would mean
$$c + (ab) = (c + a)(c + b)$$

We refuse to make this assumption because it is contrary to our experience with natural numbers:

$$7 + (3 \cdot 4) = 7 + 12 = 19$$
but
$$(7 + 3)(7 + 4) = 10 \cdot 11 = 110$$

We can prove that a statement is false if we can find a single exception, but we cannot prove it is true by finding any finite number of cases where it is verified if there are infinitely many possible cases. This is why we insist that we have merely assumed the properties listed.   Our experience with natural numbers tells us that they are true.   But we have not proved them.

However, we should not conclude that all of these properties must be assumed.   All of the properties of the natural numbers can be derived from five axioms, known as Peano's postulates.   This was

done by the Italian mathematician Giuseppe Peano.   Thanks to his
work, we may feel secure in our liberality with regard to axioms.   We
can assume as much as we like provided we are sure our axioms imply
no contradictions.

——————————   E   X   E   R   C   I   S   E   S   ——————————

In these exercises *number* means natural number or zero.

1.   We have assumed the natural numbers are closed under addition and
     multiplication.   Which of the following sets are closed?
     (a)   The even numbers under addition   *yes*
     (b)   The odd numbers under addition   *no*
     (c)   The even numbers under multiplication   *yes*
     (d)   The odd numbers under multiplication   *yes*
     (e)   Gases under chemical combining   *no*
     (f)   Words under rearrangement of letters   *no*

2.   State the principle by which each of the following is justified.
     (a) $4 + 12 = 12 + 4$ *comm. of add.*
     (b) $a \cdot b + c = b \cdot a + c$ *comm. of mult.*
     (c) $x(y + z) = xy + xz$ *distrib.*
     (d) $(a + b)(x + y) = (a + b)x + (a + b)y$ *distrib.*
     (e) $m + (n + 6) + 3 = (m + n) + (6 + 3)$ *assoc. of add.*

3.   Since $3 + 9 \cdot 4 = 3(9 + 4) = 39$, does it follow that $a + b \cdot c = a(b + c)$?   Explain.

4.   Bear in mind that our assumptions with regard to the commutative
     property referred to only two terms, $a + b = b + a$ and $ab = ba$.   The
     associative properties are assumptions relating only three terms: $(a + b) + c = a + (b + c)$ and $a(bc) = (ab)c$.   The distributive property con-
     cerns only three numbers and, furthermore, the factor to be distributed
     precedes the other factor.   We assume $a(b + c) = ab + ac$; we have not
     assumed $(b + c)a = ba + ca$.   Prove the following, justifying each step.
     (a) $a(b + c) = (b + c)a$
     (b) $(m + n) + p = (m + p) + n$
     (c) $(b + c)a = ba + ca$
     (d) $(x + y) + z = (z + y) + x$
     (e) $(a + b) + (c + d) = (a + d) + (b + c)$
     (f) $a(b + c + d + e) = ab + ac + ad + ae$

5.   Find two other sets of values for a, b, c which will satisfy the equation in
     Exercise 3.

6.   Some of the axioms of this chapter are implications that we accept as
     valid.   In each such case identify p and q in the implication $p \rightarrow q$.

7.   Prove $a(b + c + d) = ab + ac + ad$. State a generalization of this result.

8.   If addition and multiplication are interchanged in any one of the axioms except A_5 the resulting statement will be one of the axioms. Verify this.

9.   Interchange addition and multiplication in A_5. Prove the resulting statement is false.

10.   If addition were distributive over multiplication, what would $3 + (4 \times 5)$ equal?

11.   Let the operation $*$ be defined by the equation $a * b = a \times b + b$. Is $*$ commutative? Associative?

UNDOING WHAT HAS BEEN DONE

4.9   Throughout mathematics we find the notion of inverses, inverse operations, inverse elements, and inverse functions. The inverse of an operation is another operation which "undoes" the first. If we operate on a number with a second number, then perform the inverse operation with the second number, the result is the first number; the two inverse operations put us right back where we started.

The inverse of addition is subtraction. If a and b are natural numbers, the following equations define subtraction:

Definition 1 $a - b = x$ if and only if $b + x = a$.

We may think of it this way: $a - b$ represents the thing we are attempting to define. What does this new operation $(-)$, operating on the two elements a and b, mean? We designate its meaning by the symbol x. The second equation tells us what x is, namely, the number which added to b gives a. We have defined subtraction in terms of addition, an operation we have already accepted. Under this definition, what does $5 - 8$ mean? It means that number which, when added to 8, will produce 5. But since 5 precedes 8 in our ordered set of number names, we cannot hope to get back to 5 by proceeding to count on beyond 8. Then we can properly say there is no number x which we can add to 8 to get 5. Then we are forced to conclude that, without further definition, $5 - 8$ is meaningless. You learned in arithmetic that you cannot subtract a larger number from a smaller one. Nothing that you learned in algebra contradicts this, because in arithmetic you were restricted to positive numbers.

We have succeeded in defining the inverse of addition, but as long as we are restricted to natural numbers the inverse is not always possible.   It is possible only if $a > b$.   The natural numbers are not closed under the operation of subtraction.   Is subtraction associative?   Is it commutative?   Does multiplication distribute itself over subtraction?

The inverse of multiplication is *division*.   Since we have thought of multiplication as the addition of equal sets, we could think of the inverse as the subtraction of equal sets.   This concept of division, that is, repeated subtraction, is inherent in our method of division. But let us define division in terms of multiplication without worrying about what multiplication means.   We define the division of two natural numbers a and b, written $a \div b$, by the equations:

Definition 2 $a \div b = x$ if and only if $b \cdot x = a$.

The symbol x defines the expression $a \div b$.   The second equation, $b \cdot x = a$, defines x.   Put into words, the two equations state that $a \div b$ means that number which, when multiplied by b, gives the product a.   Under this definition, what does $5 \div 3$ mean?   It means that number which, when multiplied by 3, gives the product 5.   But when we realize that $3 \cdot 1 = 3$ and $3 \cdot 2 = 6$, and that any greater number multiplied by 3 gives more than 6 — can you say how we know this?— we are forced to admit that there is no natural number which we can multiply by 3 to get 5.   Therefore $5 \div 3$ does not mean anything until further definitions are made, and we must conclude that the natural numbers are not closed with respect to division.   Is division commutative or associative?   Does division distribute over addition? Over subtraction?

NAME FOR AN EMPTY SET

4.10   The ancients were much disturbed about whether *zero* and *one* are numbers; they felt that *one*, unity, is the source of number, that from which number is derived.   Since we find *zero* first being used to indicate the absence of number, how can no number be a number?   The approach we have used leaves little room for argument as to whether *one* is a number.   But the case of zero is different.   Zero is not a natural number.   If we are counting to find the cardinal number of a set, there is no member of the set before the first one. We shall take the position that zero is to be a number simply because we want it, and need it as a member of the family of numbers.   When the farmer's wife gathers the eggs it is convenient for her to have a number for how many eggs the hens have laid.   Just such a convenience as this is what motivated man to create numbers.   It is equally convenient to have a number to represent the cardinal number for the set of eggs laid on a day that all the hens took a vacation.   So we create the number zero for just this purpose.   From this point of view zero still means "nothing," no eggs.   For the present we shall let the matter rest there; the fact that zero does not always mean "nothing" will be taken care of in due time.   We shall define zero in terms of the natural numbers and the two basic operations of addition and multiplication.   The following equations define the number zero.

Definition 3 $a + 0 = a$ and $a \cdot 0 = 0 \cdot a = 0$, where a is a natural number.

This is in conformity with our earlier interpretations of addition and multiplication as well as with the notion that zero means "nothing," the cardinal number of an empty set.

In the case of $a + 0 = a$, we count through a set containing a elements and continue to count through a set that has no elements. In other words, we count the first set.   This is exactly the situation when we find how many eggs there are in two baskets, the first basket containing two dozen eggs and the second basket being empty.   No difficulty is encountered when we apply the commutative axiom $0 + a = a$.   The first basket is now the empty one.   The associative axiom also continues to apply: $(a + b) + 0 = a + (b + 0) = a + b$. No difficulty is encountered when we think of two empty baskets:

$$0 + 0 = 0$$

This enables us to remove the restriction that a be a natural number, at least in so far as the first of the defining equations is concerned.   We may consider a as being any number of our enlarged system of numbers, the natural numbers and zero.

Multiplication is subject to similar interpretations.   The equation

$$a \cdot 0 = 0$$

may be interpreted as $0 + 0 + 0 + 0 + \ldots$ for a terms.   We add together a empty sets.   This is similar to asking how many oranges there are in twelve empty orange crates.   At this point we encounter a fundamental difficulty, when we consider the commutative axiom. What can $0 \cdot a$ possibly mean?   We are here concerned with sets, each of which contains a elements, but we add none of these sets together.   How many eggs are there in no egg crates if each crate contains thirty dozen eggs?   If there are no crates, how can we talk about the number of eggs this absence of crates will hold?   This apparent difficulty really isn't a difficulty at all.   Up to this stage our major emphasis has been on the physical interpretation of our system.   Actually, the mathematical system is in no way dependent on its physical counterpart.   For the present, since it will not contradict our physical interpretation of the number system, we simply require that zero obey the commutative axiom for multiplication,

$$a \cdot 0 = 0 \cdot a = 0$$

and specifically $$0 \cdot 0 = 0$$

Once we accept the commutative axiom for multiplication, the associative and the distributive axioms offer no difficulty:

$$(ab) \cdot 0 = 0$$

but by the associative axiom

$$(ab) \cdot 0 = a(b \cdot 0) = a \cdot 0 = 0$$

Similarly, $$0(a + b) = 0$$

but the distributive axiom gives

$$0(a + b) = 0 \cdot a + 0 \cdot b = 0 + 0 = 0$$

also $$a(0 + b) = a \cdot 0 + ab = 0 + ab = ab$$

Observe that 0 does the same for addition that 1 does for multiplication, namely, leaves the other number unchanged:

$$a + 0 = a \text{ and } a \cdot 1 = a$$

They are called the *identity elements* for addition and multiplication respectively.

Let us examine the effect the inclusion of zero has on the inverse operations.   We have $a - 0 = a$, because we must add a (the difference) to zero to get a (the number we started with).   Hence, we may say that zero is the subtraction identity also, just as one is the division identity, $a \div 1 = a$.

Formerly we were restricted to the subtraction of a smaller number from a larger.   Now $a - a = 0$, since we must add zero to the second a in order to get the first a.   We can now subtract a number from itself, but still cannot subtract a larger number from a smaller.

The analogy with one continues to hold, since $a \div a = 1$ because we must multiply the second a by 1 in order to get the first a for product.

ZERO IN DIVISION

4.11   Zero in division is not so simple.   Let us examine three cases:

(1) $0 \div b$ (2) $b \div 0$ (3) $0 \div 0$,   where $b \neq 0$

Case 1, $0 \div b$, requires an answer which, when multiplied by b, produces zero.   We know that regardless of what b may equal the other factor must be zero if the product is zero: $0 \div b = 0$ because $b \cdot 0 = 0$. Case 2 requires that we multiply zero by something and get b which is not zero.   But we know that, regardless of what we multiply zero by, the product must be zero.   Then we are in the dilemma of changing the definition of division or of not accepting that part of the definition of zero which requires that any number times zero give zero. Case 3 requires that we find a number which, upon multiplication by zero, gives the product zero.   In this case any number whatever will do.   Case 2 forces us into a contradiction and Case 3 does not permit a unique (single) result.   We avoid these two situations by banishing division by zero.   *Division by zero is undefined,* and we need have no fear that it will be.   It is undefined because it cannot be defined in an acceptable manner.

Note that Case 1 does not involve division by zero; it involves division of zero by a number different from zero.   Case 1 is defined.

At this point we shall state two more axioms of equality:

A_{12} Subtraction: Equal numbers subtracted from equal numbers give equal numbers.   If $a = b$ and $c = d$ where $c \leq a$ and $d \leq b$, then $a - c = b - d$.

(The $\leq$ restriction will later be removed.)

A_{13} Division: Equal numbers divided by equal numbers different from zero are equal.   If $a = b$ and $c = d \neq 0$, then $a \div c = b \div d$.

We have accepted zero as a number which has the same properties as have the natural numbers, with one restriction: we can *never use zero as a divisor*.   If we adhere to this restriction, zero will behave in exactly the same way as a natural number.

──────────   E   X   E   R   C   I   S   E   S   ──────────

1.   Although the concept of an inverse is common to mathematics, not all operations have inverses.   Which of the following have inverses?
     (a)   Putting on one's shoes
     (b)   Dying

(c) Scrambling eggs
(d) Falling in love
(e) Falling out of a fifteenth story window
(f) Reading a book

2. If subtraction is associative, $(a - b) - c = a - (b - c)$. Evaluate $(10 - 7) - 3$ and $10 - (7 - 3)$. Is subtraction associative? *no*

3. Since $5 - 2 \neq 2 - 5$, we cannot say subtraction is commutative. Neither is it associative, since $10 - (5 - 2) \neq (10 - 5) - 2$. Find three numbers, a, b, c, such that $a - (b - c) = (a - b) - c$.

4. If division is distributive with respect to addition, then $a \div (b + c) = a \div b + a \div c$. If division is commutative, then $a \div (b + c) = (b + c) \div a$. As a result of this and Exercise 4(c), Section 4.8 $(b + c) \div a = b \div a + c \div a$. Which, if any, of the above equalities are correct?

5. If division is associative, $(a \div b) \div c = a \div (b \div c)$. Evaluate $(64 \div 8) \div 4$ and $64 \div (8 \div 4)$. Is division associative?

6.* Prove that multiplication is distributive with respect to subtraction, that is, that $a(b - c) = ab - ac$, where $b - c$ is a natural number or zero. *Hint:* Let $b - c = x$; then by definition of subtraction $c + x = b$. Now multiply both sides by a.

7. Insert parentheses to make each of the following expressions correct.
(a) $60 \div 4 \cdot 3 - 2 = 3$
(b) $60 \div 4 \cdot 3 - 2 = 43$
(c) $60 \div 4 \cdot 3 - 2 = 15$
(d) $60 \div 4 \cdot 3 - 2 = 6$

8.* Prove that $a - (b - c) = a - b + c$, where $a > b > c$. *Hint:* Use the definition of subtraction and the associative principle. This justifies the rule that when removing parentheses preceded by a minus sign we must change the signs of the terms within the parentheses.

9.* The exponent zero was defined by the equation $a^0 = 1$, $a \neq 0$. Why is the restriction placed on a? *Hint:* Why was this definition of the exponent zero chosen? (See Section 3.8.)

10. What is wrong with the following proof that $2 = 1$?

If $a = b$
then $a^2 = ab$ (multiplying both sides by a)
$a^2 - b^2 = ab - b^2$ (subtracting b^2 from both sides)
$(a + b)(a - b) = b(a - b)$ (distributive law)
$a + b = b$ (division axiom)
$b + b = b$ (substitution)
$2b = b$ (addition)
$2 = 1$ (division)

11. Zero plays the same role in addition that 1 plays in multiplication. Does zero play the same role in multiplication that 1 plays in addition? Why?

12. When we subtract by the "borrow and pay back" method, we add ten to the units digit of the minuend and add one to the tens digit of the subtrahend; for example, in 83 − 59, we find 13 − 9 = 4 for the units digit, and 8 − 6 = 2 for the tens digit.   Justify this procedure.

13. What property is involved when we "carry" in addition?

14. Show that the distributive axiom is employed when we multiply 137 by 4.

15. We frequently add up a column of figures, then add down as a check. What number properties are involved in this?   Illustrate.

THE ALGORITHMS

4.12   An algorithm is a schematic method for performing a mathematical operation.   Whenever we add or multiply two one-digit numbers we merely state the result from memory, but for more complicated computations we may resort to the aid of an algorithm.   The algorithm enables us to carry through the operation without having to know from memory any combination in which the numbers to be combined contain more than one digit.   Our system of notation makes the algorithms possible.   The algorithms that we use are by no means the only ones which could be used.   In fact, there are a number of earlier and cruder methods which we shall want to examine.   The slow acceptance of the Hindu-Arabic numerals was due in part to the absence of good algorithms.

One of the earliest methods of multiplying and dividing is fairly well adapted to any kind of number system.   It was used by the ancient Egyptians, as indicated in the Ahmes Papyrus, written about 1650 B.C.

To multiply, the Egyptians used a process of doubling.   The process is illustrated below.

Example   Multiply 158 by 27.

*1	158
*2	316
4	632
*8	1264
*16	2528
	4266

In the left-hand column we begin with 1 and double until the next step exceeds the multiplier, 27.   The other factor, 158, is doubled the same

number of times.   The numbers marked with asterisks in the left column
sum to 27.   The right column numbers that correspond to the checked
numbers in the left column are added, giving the desired product.   In
division the Egyptians used doubling and halving.

Example   Divide 247 by 19.

1	19*
2	38
4	76*
8	152*

Here we select those numbers in the right column whose sum is the dividend,
247.   The sum of the corresponding numbers in the left column
$(8 + 4 + 1 = 13)$ is the desired quotient.

Division which yields a fractional quotient may become complicated.   The Egyptians used unit fractions, that is, fractions whose
numerators are 1, almost exclusively.   If we use for divisor a power
of 2, the extension can be made rather easily.

Example   Divide 87 by 16.

1	16*
2	32
4	64*
$\frac{1}{2}$	8
$\frac{1}{4}$	4*
$\frac{1}{8}$	2*
$\frac{1}{16}$	1*

Since we must add $16 + 64 + 4 + 2 + 1$ to get the dividend 87, we
add the corresponding numbers $1 + 4 + \frac{1}{4} + \frac{1}{8} + \frac{1}{16} = 5\frac{7}{16}$ to get the
quotient.

Methods similar to these frequently have been found in use among
primitive peoples.   An interesting variant of this, somewhat more
sophisticated, is known as Russian Peasant multiplication.

Example   Multiply 137 by 73.

137	73
274	36
548	18
1096	9
2192	4
4384	2
8768	1
10001	

Here we double one factor and halve the other, dropping all fractions in the halved column. Numbers in the column of doubles that correspond to even numbers in the halved column are discarded. The sum of the remaining numbers in the column of doubles is the desired product.

If we recall how a number may, by division by two, be expressed in the binary scale, the justification of the procedure is evident. In the halved column we divided 73 and the succeeding quotients by 2. Those divisions which gave a remainder 1 indicated the corresponding power of 2 that was needed. Those divisions which gave a remainder zero indicated powers of 2 which were not needed. But the even numbers correspond to the latter case: $73 = 1001001_2$. Then each term in the column of doubles which is used is 137 times one of the powers of 2 needed in expressing 73 in binary notation. In the final addition we have added

$$137 \times 2^0 + 137 \times 2^3 + 137 \times 2^6 = 137 \ (2^0 + 2^3 + 2^6) = 137 \times 73$$

A method of multiplying that was popular at the time of the discovery of America was known as the "lattice" or "gelosia" method. We shall use this method to multiply 457 by 138.

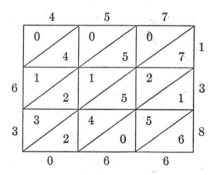

The factors are placed at the top and at the right of the gridwork. In each square we place the product of the numbers that are at the top and to the right, the units below the diagonal, and the tens above. The answer is obtained by adding along the diagonals, "carrying" where necessary to the next diagonal.

One form of abacus which differed considerably from that previously described was a sandboard. The computer wrote in the sand sprinkled on the board and as his numbers were used they were removed by smoothing over the sand. This form of abacus led to a popular algorithm known as "the scratch method." The numbers

were scratched out as they were used. We shall multiply 37 by 28
by this method.

```
8
6  4            10
   37            9 3
   28            8 8
                 6 46
                 37
                 28
```

             Step I   Step II

In Step I we place the units digit of one factor, 28, directly beneath
the highest digit (the extreme left) of the other factor, 37. Multiply
2 by 3 to obtain 6. Then multiply 8 by 3. The 24 is entered as 4
over the 3, and 2 is added to 6, which is then scratched, to give the 8
over the scratched 6. It is scratched when no longer needed. In
Step II the factor 28 is shifted one place to the right. The product of
2 times 7 is entered by replacing the 4, which is then scratched, by
the 8 over it. The 1 is entered by replacing the 8 over the scratched
6 with 9. The final factor 8 times 7 is entered by placing 6 over the
7, adding the 5 to 8 in the next column, which gives 3, and changing
the 9 in the next column to 10.

In practice the two steps were combined into one. Each number
is scratched when it is no longer needed.

The complete solution looks as follows:

```
10
 9 3
 8 8
 6 4 6
   3 7
 2 8 8
   2
```

Another of the most popular division algorithms also was a scratch
method. It was also called "the galley method" because the work
takes the shape of a ship. We shall use the method to divide 43,900
by 321.

```
                          1                    2
                                               0
                                               1 4
                     2 7                     2 7 6
1 1 8            1 1 8 7              1 1 8 7 4
4 3 9 0 0  | 1   4 3 9 0 0  | 13    4 3 9 0 0  | 136
3 2 1            3 2 1                3 2 1
```

       Step I   Step II   Step III

In Step I, 321 is subtracted from 439. In Step II, 3 times 321 is subtracted from 1,180. In Step III, 6 times 321 is subtracted from 2,170. The 3 and the 6 are obtained by trial, just as in the customary algorithm.

Combining the steps, the complete solution is as follows:

$$
\begin{array}{r}
2 \\
\emptyset \\
\cancel{1}\ 4 \\
2\ 7\ \cancel{6} \\
\cancel{1}\ \cancel{1}\ 8\ 7\ 4 \\
\cancel{4}\ \cancel{3}\ \cancel{9}\ \emptyset\ \emptyset \\
\cancel{3}\ \cancel{2}\ \cancel{1}\ \cancel{1}\ \cancel{1} \\
\cancel{3}\ \cancel{2}\ 2 \\
\cancel{3}
\end{array}
\;\Big|\;136
$$

The quotient is 136 with remainder 244.

───────── E   X   E   R   C   I   S   E   S ─────────

1. Some calculating machines use the following method in performing subtraction.

$$
\begin{array}{r}
735 \\
276 \\
\hline
1{,}458
\end{array}
$$

We add the complement to 9 of each digit in the subtrahend. The complement of 6 is 3 (6 + 3 = 9), so we add 3 to 5, getting 8 in the units digit. The complement of 7 is 2 (7 + 2 = 9); then we add 2 + 3 = 5 for the tens digit. The complement of 2 is 7; then we add 7 + 7 = 14 for the hundreds digit. The extreme left digit in the answer, which will always be a 1, is removed and added to the units digit. This gives the correct difference, 459. Use the above method to find 8,653 − 4,276.

2.* Explain why the method employed in Exercise 1 works.

3. Use the Egyptian method to find 740 ÷ 16.

4. Use the Russian Peasant method to find 136 × 73.

5. Rework Exercise 4 with the roles of the two factors reversed.

6. Use the gelosia method to multiply 836 by 279.

7. Multiply 538 by 327, using the scratch method.

8. Use the galley method to divide 4,321 by 157.

9.* With Roman numerals our algorithms are of no value. But we could change our base from 10 and they would work just as well in the new base. Use the gelosia method to multiply 635_8 by 213_8.

10.   Multiply 147_8 by 63_8, using the Russian Peasant method.

11.   Convert the factors in Exercise 10 to base 10 and multiply by the same method.

12.   Use the Russian Peasant method to find $234_5 \times 43_5$.

13.   Convert the factors in Exercise 12 to base 10 and multiply by the same method.

14.   Use the scratch method to find $374_8 \times 261_8$.

15.   Convert Exercise 14 to base 10 and check the result.

THE CHECK OF NINES

4.13   When we make a computation with an abacus the only number remaining at its conclusion is the answer.   This makes review of the steps of our operation impossible.   Consequently, some kind of check on the correctness of a computation is almost essential to the abacist. Many elaborate checks have been devised.   One of the favorites is the check of nines.   It may be applied to any of the fundamental operations.   We shall use examples to show how it works.

> *Example 1*   Add: $7937 \rightarrow 26 \rightarrow 8$
> $\; 2816 \rightarrow 17 \rightarrow 8$
> $\; 4359 \rightarrow 21 \rightarrow 3$
> $\; 1182 \rightarrow 12 \rightarrow 3$
> $\; 6065 \rightarrow 17 \rightarrow \underline{8}$
> $30 \rightarrow 3$

Here we add the digits of each number, add the digits of that sum, and continue until we get a one-digit number.   Across the top line we add the digits $7 + 9 + 3 + 7 = 26$, the sum of whose digits is 8.   If our one-digit sum happens to be 9 we exchange it for 0.   When the digits of each number have been summed we add these sums.   In the above example we have added $8 + 8 + 3 + 3 + 8 = 30$ and then $3 + 0 = 3$.   This final one-digit sum of digits should be the same that we get when we add the digits of the answer.   The completed addition and check follow:

$$7937 \rightarrow 26 \rightarrow 8$$
$$2816 \rightarrow 17 \rightarrow 8$$
$$4359 \rightarrow 21 \rightarrow 3$$
$$1182 \rightarrow 12 \rightarrow 3$$
$$\underline{6065} \rightarrow 17 \rightarrow 8$$
$$22359 \qquad\qquad \overline{30} \rightarrow 3$$
$$\updownarrow$$
$$2 + 2 + 3 + 5 + 9 = 21; 2 + 1 = 3$$

The only change to be made when checking subtraction is to subtract the digit sums rather than add them:

Example 2   Subtract: $83726 \rightarrow 26 \rightarrow 8$
$\underline{52914 \rightarrow 21 \rightarrow 3}$
$30812 \qquad\qquad \overline{5}$

$$3+0+8+1+2 = 14; 1+4 = 5$$

We may have a subtrahend with a larger digit sum than that of the minuend. In that case add 9 to the digit sum of the minuend and proceed as before:

Example 3   Subtract: $53605 \rightarrow 19 \rightarrow 10 \rightarrow 1 \rightarrow 10$
$\underline{24830 \rightarrow 17 \rightarrow \qquad\quad 8 \rightarrow \quad 8}$
$28775 \qquad\qquad\qquad\qquad\qquad 2$

$$2+8+7+7+5 = 29; 2+9 = 11; 1+1 = 2$$

We check multiplication by multiplying the digit sums of the factors and comparing this with the digit sum of the product:

Example 4   Multiply: $385 \rightarrow 16 \rightarrow \ 7$
$\underline{156 \rightarrow 12 \rightarrow \ 3}$
$\overline{2310} \qquad\qquad \overline{21} \rightarrow 3$
1925
385
$\overline{60060}$
$$6+0+0+6+0 = 12; 1+2 = 3$$

The usual inverse operation check for division — quotient times divisor plus remainder equals dividend — may be used with the check of nines. We merely perform the inverse step with the digit sums rather than with the numbers themselves:

Example 5   Divide 87562 by 376.

$\underline{232}$
$376)\overline{87562}$ $2+3+2 = 7$ (quotient digit sum)
$\underline{752}$
$\overline{1236}$ $3+7+6 = 16; 1+6 = 7$ (divisor digit sum)
1128
$\overline{1082}$ $3+3+0 = 6$ (remainder digit sum)
$\underline{752}$
$\overline{330}$ $8+7+5+6+2 = 28$
$\qquad\qquad 2+8 = 10; 1+0 = 1$ (dividend digit sum)

Then quotient 7 times divisor 7 gives 49, which sums to $4 + 9 = 13$, $1 + 3 = 4$. Then this 4 plus remainder 6 gives 10, which sums to $1 + 0 = 1$. But since the digit sum of the dividend is 1 the check holds.

─────────── E X E R C I S E S ───────────

1. Add and check by the check of nines: $3792 + 8643 + 10932 + 5776$.
2. Subtract and check by the check of nines.
   (a) $4336 - 1702$ (b) $8254 - 7641$
3. Multiply and check by the check of nines: 43765×8731.
4. Divide and check by the check of nines: $87346 \div 435$.

NUMBER CONGRUENCES

4.14 Number congruence is a very convenient concept if we attempt to prove the correctness of the methods described in Section 4.13. The idea, though simple, is a very important one in number theory. It was first used by the great German mathematician Karl Friedrich Gauss.

If it is now 3 o'clock, what time will it be 15 hours from now? We could find out by starting at 3 on the face of a clock and counting around the face clockwise for 15 steps. This "addition on the clock" would give $3 + 15 = 6$. If we did not get too bored with the process, we could in the same way find that it would be 7 o'clock 100 hours from now, $3 + 100 = 7$. We may get the same results by observing that $3 + 15 = 18$ and $18 - 12 = 6$ in the first case, and that $3 + 100 = 103$ and $103 - 8 \cdot 12 = 7$ in the other case. When two numbers have the same remainder upon division by 12, we express this relationship by saying that they are *congruent*. A moment of reflection will indicate that any natural number is congruent to one of the numbers 0 through 11, for the numbers less than 12 are their own remainders when divided by 12.

The idea of congruence is not confined to the face of the clock. We could replace 12 with any other natural number. We call the number so chosen the *modulus*. The generalized idea is stated in the following:

Definition Two natural numbers A and B are congruent with respect to the modulus M if they have the same remainder upon division by M.

This relationship is symbolized as

$$A \equiv B, \text{mod } M \text{ (read, } A \text{ is congruent to } B, \text{ modulo } M)$$

which implies that

$$A = pM + R$$

and

$$B = qM + R \quad (p, q \text{ natural numbers or zero; } R < M)$$

Otherwise stated, if

$$A \equiv B, \text{mod } M$$

their difference is a multiple of M:

$$A - B = kM \quad (A > B; k \text{ a natural number or zero})$$

From the definition of congruence it is evident that any natural number A is congruent, modulo M, to one of the numbers from 0 to $(M - 1)$.

We wish to prove the theorem:

Theorem

If $\qquad\qquad A \equiv a, \text{mod } M \quad (A > a)$
and $\qquad\qquad B \equiv b, \text{mod } M \quad (B > b)$
then $\qquad A + B \equiv a + b, \text{mod } M$

Proof: $\qquad\quad A \equiv a, \text{mod } M, \text{ implies } a + kM = A$
$\qquad\qquad\quad B \equiv b, \text{mod } M, \text{ implies } b + lM = B$
$A + B = a + kM + b + lM = a + b + (k + l)M$

But the last expression is certainly congruent to $a + b$, modulo M; hence our conclusion.

The theorem merely asserts that if two numbers A and B are divided by the modulus M the sum of the remainders is congruent to the remainder of the sum.

Illustration $\qquad\qquad\qquad\qquad 40 \equiv 5, \text{mod } 7$
$\qquad\qquad\qquad\qquad\qquad\qquad\quad 63 \equiv 0, \text{mod } 7$
$\qquad\qquad\qquad 40 + 63 = 103 \equiv 5, \text{mod } 7$

The property may be established for subtraction by evaluating $A - B$.

The same property applies to multiplication:

Theorem

If $\qquad\qquad\qquad\qquad A \equiv a, \text{mod } M$
and $\qquad\qquad\qquad\qquad B \equiv b, \text{mod } M$
then $\qquad\qquad\qquad\quad AB \equiv ab, \text{mod } M$

Proof: $A \equiv a$, mod M, implies $a + kM = A$
                   $B \equiv b$, mod M, implies $b + lM = B$
$$AB = (a + kM)(b + lM)$$
$$= (a + kM)b + (a + kM)lM$$
$$= ab + bkM + alM + kMlM$$
$$= ab + (bk + al + kMl)M \equiv ab, \text{ mod } M$$

With the aid of the addition and multiplication theorems we can show that any natural number

$$a_0 10^n + a_1 10^{n-1} + \ldots + a_n$$

is congruent to the sum of its digits, modulo 9. First we observe that

$$10 \equiv 1, \text{ mod } 9$$

and by the multiplication theorem

$$10^n \equiv 1^n = 1, \text{ mod } 9 \qquad (n \text{ any natural number})$$

With the multiplication theorem again

$$a_i 10^{n-i} \equiv a_i, \text{ mod } 9 \qquad (i \text{ any number from 0 to } n)$$

Finally, if we apply the addition theorem,

$$a_0 10^n + a_1 10^{n-1} + \ldots + a_n \equiv a_0 + a_1 + \ldots + a_n, \text{ mod } 9$$

Illustration $372 = 3 \cdot 10^2 + 7 \cdot 10 + 2$
$$\equiv 3 \cdot 1^2 + 7 \cdot 1 + 2 = 12 \equiv 1 + 2 = 3, \text{ mod } 9$$

All the checks of Section 4.13 are now immediately apparent in the light of the fact that when congruent numbers are added, subtracted, or multiplied the results are congruent.

Many interesting number facts can be established easily with the aid of congruence. A *perfect square* is a natural number which is obtained by multiplying a natural number by itself. Every natural number is congruent to one of the numbers 0 through 8, modulo 9. Then every perfect square must be congruent to the square of some number 0 through 8.

$$0 \cdot 0 \equiv 0, \text{ mod } 9$$
$$1 \cdot 1 \equiv 1, \text{ mod } 9$$
$$2 \cdot 2 \equiv 4, \text{ mod } 9$$
$$3 \cdot 3 = 9 \equiv 0, \text{ mod } 9$$
$$4 \cdot 4 = 16 \equiv 7, \text{ mod } 9$$
$$5 \cdot 5 = 25 \equiv 7, \text{ mod } 9$$
$$6 \cdot 6 = 36 \equiv 0, \text{ mod } 9$$
$$7 \cdot 7 = 49 \equiv 4, \text{ mod } 9$$
$$8 \cdot 8 = 64 \equiv 10 \equiv 1, \text{ mod } 9$$

From the above it is evident that any perfect square has a remainder 0, 1, 4, or 7 when divided by 9. Notice the systematic order in which the remainders occur. This is not an absolute check on whether or not a given number is a square. If the number is not congruent to 0, 1, 4, or 7, we know it is not a square. On the other hand, if it is congruent to one of these numbers, it *may be* a perfect square. The number 93,548,674 is congruent to $9 + 3 + 5 + 4 + 8 + 6 + 7 + 4 = 46 \equiv 10 \equiv 1$, mod 9; therefore it *may* be a square. But 873,426 is congruent to $8 + 7 + 3 + 4 + 2 + 6 = 30 \equiv 3$, mod 9, and *cannot* be a square.

By finding the third power of each of the remainders 0 through 8 we can show that any perfect third power must be a multiple of 9, one more than a multiple of 9, or one less than a multiple of 9. We leave this as an exercise.

Since any natural number is congruent to one of the numbers 0 through 6, modulo 7, the sum or the product of any two natural numbers will be also. Tables for addition and multiplication, modulo 7, of the numbers 0, 1, 2, 3, 4, 5, 6 can serve to show to what any natural number sum or product will be congruent.

Table 4.1   Addition, modulo 7

	0	1	2	3	4	5	6
0	0	1	2	3	4	5	6
1	1	2	3	4	5	6	0
2	2	3	4	5	6	0	1
3	3	4	5	6	0	1	2
4	4	5	6	0	1	2	3
5	5	6	0	1	2	3	4
6	6	0	1	2	3	4	5

Table 4.2   Multiplication, modulo 7

	0	1	2	3	4	5	6
0	0	0	0	0	0	0	0
1	0	1	2	3	4	5	6
2	0	2	4	6	1	3	5
3	0	3	6	2	5	1	4
4	0	4	1	5	2	6	3
5	0	5	3	1	6	4	2
6	0	6	5	4	3	2	1

Table 4.1 is obtained by finding the sum of the number in the left column opposite a given space and the number at the top of the table over this space. In this space we do not enter the sum, but the remainder when the sum is divided by 7. For example, in the space opposite 4 and under 5 we find 2 because $4 + 5 = 9$ and $9 \div 7$ will have 2 for remainder. Table 4.2 is obtained in a similar way. In the space opposite 3 and under 6 we find 4 because 3×6 has 4 for remainder when divided by 7.

We may illustrate the uses of the tables by the following examples.

Example The sum of any number congruent to 5, modulo 7, plus any number congruent to 6, modulo 7, is congruent to 4, modulo 7.   We know this because Table 4.1 shows $5 + 6 = 4$.

$$40 \equiv 5, \text{ mod } 7$$
$$\underline{76 \equiv 6, \text{ mod } 7}$$
$$116 \equiv 4, \text{ mod } 7$$

Example The product of any number congruent to 4, modulo 7, times any number congruent to 3, modulo 7, is congruent to 5, modulo 7, because Table 4.2 shows $4 \times 3 = 5$.

$$46 \equiv 4, \text{ mod } 7$$
$$\underline{17 \equiv 3, \text{ mod } 7}$$
$$782 \equiv 5, \text{ mod } 7$$

-------------------- E X E R C I S E S --------------------

1. Write a number of several digits. Rearrange them to form a second number. Subtract the smaller of the two from the larger. Cancel all but one digit (the uncanceled digit must be not a zero). If you state what digits were canceled, the uncanceled digit can be determined from this. Explain how it is done.

2. Multiply 583 by 427 by the gelosia method and check by the check of nines.

3. Divide 4,371 by 287 by the galley method and check by the check of nines.

4.* Multiply the following in base 12. Check your work in a manner analogous to the check of nines in base 10; that is, add digits until a result of 11 or less is reached: $831_{12} \times 173_{12}$.
Why will this check work in base 12?

5.* Find four numbers that are congruent to the following.
(a) 5, mod 7   (b) 3, mod 13   (c) 1, mod 2

6.* Verify the addition theorem of Section 4.14 with the following congruencies.
$68 \equiv 3, \text{ mod } 13$ $140 \equiv 10, \text{ mod } 13$

7.* Verify the multiplication theorem of Section 4.14 with the following.
$99 \equiv 3, \text{ mod } 12$ $20 \equiv 8, \text{ mod } 12$

8.* Find four values for x that will satisfy the following relationships.
(a) $25 + x \equiv 3, \text{ mod } 8$ (c) $16 + x \equiv 0, \text{ mod } 5$
(b) $73 + x \equiv 5, \text{ mod } 9$ (d) $33 + x \equiv 6, \text{ mod } 7$

9. In this section we have proved that A_9 and A_{10} are true if we replace "equal" with "congruent." Prove that A_6, A_7, and A_8 are also true when this replacement is made.

10. Show that the commutative, associative, and distributive properties hold when "equal" is replaced with "congruent."

4.15   When is a number divisible by two?   We are apt to say, "When it is even."   But when is a number even?   When it is divisible by two?   It does not make a great amount of difference which of the terms "even" and "divisible by two" is defined in terms of the other, as long as we do not define *each* in terms of the other.   However, let us say that a number is even if it is divisible by 2.   We determine divisibility by 2 by examining the units digit.   If the units digit is divisible by 2 so is the number; otherwise it is not.   We have to remember merely that 0, 2, 4, 6, and 8 are one-digit multiples of 2.   It may never have occurred to you to wonder why this is the case.   It isn't true of all one-digit numbers.   We cannot say that a number whose units digit is a multiple of 3 is divisible by 3.   As a matter of fact, if we change our base from 10, the principle may not even work for 2.   Consider 13_{17} and 22_5.

Tests for divisibility are dependent upon the base of notation.   If we write the number

$$a_0 10^n + a_1 10^{n-1} + a_2 10^{n-2} + \ldots + a_{n-1} 10 + a_n$$

in the form

$$(a_0 10^{n-1} + a_1 10^{n-2} + a_2 10^{n-3} + \ldots + a_{n-1}) 10 + a_n$$

we are emphasizing the fact that the number is some multiple of 10 plus the units digit.   The only factors of 10 are 2 and 5.   This assures us that we can divide $(a_0 10^{n-1} + a_1 10^{n-2} + \ldots + a_{n-1}) 10$ by either 2 or 5.   Then the original number is divisible by 2 (or 5) if and only if the units digit is.

Four is not a factor of 10 but it is a factor of 100.   The test for divisibility by 4 is: *A number is divisible by 4 if and only if the number represented by the tens and units digits is divisible by 4.*   This can be shown, in a way analogous to the above argument, for 2.   We may also establish the rule for 8 in this way: *A number is divisible by 8 if and only if the number represented by the units, tens, and hundreds digits is divisible by 8.*

We may infer from Section 4.13 that *a number is divisible by 9 if and only if the sum of its digits is divisible by 9.*   The proof of this statement follows immediately from Section 4.14.   We may also show, using the method of Section 4.14, that *a number is divisible by 3 if and only if the sum of its digits is divisible by 3.*

A number is divisible by 6 if and only if it is divisible by both 2 and 3.

This takes care of all one-digit divisors except 7. We shall show a test in the next section which is quite interesting, though impractical — it is easier to divide by 7 than to apply the test.

TESTS FOR DIVISIBILITY (CONTINUED)

*4.16 This section really does not deserve its star rating except for the fact that a minimum knowledge of negative numbers is required. Although we shall shortly extend the concept of number to include the negative integers, for the present we shall assume a few of their properties.

We have said, in Section 4.14, that

$$10 \equiv 1, \bmod 9$$

means that 10 is one more than a multiple of 9. In the same manner we can say that

$$10 \equiv (-1), \bmod 11,$$

to express the fact that 10 is 1 *less than* a multiple of 11. Parenthetically, we developed congruence in Section 4.14 in terms of natural numbers only. The idea may easily be extended to the integers, the positive and negative whole numbers. We confined ourselves to natural numbers because they are the only kind of numbers the existence of which we have officially admitted. If you will accept the facts that minus times minus gives plus, and plus times minus gives minus, then for the present we shall ask no more of these strange creatures that seem to be "less than nothing." We can now establish the following sequence of congruencies:

$$10^2 \equiv (-1)^2 = 1, \bmod 11$$
$$10^3 = 10^2 \cdot 10 \equiv 1(-1) = -1, \bmod 11$$
$$10^4 = 10^3 \cdot 10 \equiv (-1)(-1) = 1, \bmod 11$$
$$10^n = 10^{n-1} \cdot 10 \equiv (-1)^{n-1}(-1) = (-1)^n = \pm 1, \bmod 11$$

(The double sign means "plus or minus.")

Since the congruence of each power of 10 is obtained from that of the preceding power by multiplying by (-1), it is evident that the congruences of succeeding powers are alternately minus and plus. From the above and the two theorems of Section 4.14 we have

$$a_0 10^n + a_1 10^{n-1} + \ldots + a_{n-1}10 + a_n$$
$$= a_0(-1)^n + a_1(-1)^{n-1} + \ldots + a_{n-1}(-1) + a_n(+1)$$

Stated verbally, this means: A number is congruent, modulo 11, to the sum of its odd-placed digits, units, hundreds, ten thousands, etc., minus the sum of its even-placed digits, tens, thousands, hundred thousands, etc. If this difference of sums is zero or some other integral multiple of 11, then the number is a multiple of 11.

Illustration The number 95,943,628 is a multiple of 11 because
$$8 + 6 + 4 + 5 - 2 - 3 - 9 - 9 = 0$$
But $8,362,817 \equiv 23 \equiv 1$, mod 11, because
$$7 + 8 + 6 + 8 - 1 - 2 - 3 = 23 \quad \text{and} \quad 3 - 2 = 1$$
Therefore 8,362,817 has a remainder 1 when divided by 11.

In case we have a number like
$$934,271 \equiv -14 \equiv -3, \text{ mod } 11$$
our interpretation is that we were 3 short of a multiple of 11, which means that we are 8 more than the next lower multiple of 11.

The test for divisibility by 7 may be obtained by observing that

$$10 \equiv 3, \text{ mod } 7$$
$$10^2 \equiv 3^2 = 9 \equiv 2, \text{ mod } 7$$
$$10^3 = 10^2 \cdot 10 \equiv 2 \cdot 3 = 6 \equiv (-1), \text{ mod } 7$$
$$10^4 = 10^3 \cdot 10 \equiv (-1) \cdot 3 = (-3), \text{ mod } 7$$
$$10^5 = 10^4 \cdot 10 \equiv (-3) \cdot 3 = (-9) \equiv (-2), \text{ mod } 7$$
$$10^6 = 10^5 \cdot 10 \equiv (-2) \cdot 3 = (-6) \equiv 1, \text{ mod } 7$$
$$10^7 = 10^6 \cdot 10 \equiv 1 \cdot 3 = 3, \text{ mod } 7$$

We then have $\qquad 10^7 \equiv 10, \text{ mod } 7$
and it is evident that the cycle of congruences will be repeated.

This suggests the following rule for divisibility by 7. If and only if 1 times the units digit plus 3 times the tens digit plus 2 times the hundreds digit minus 1 times the thousands digit minus 3 times the ten-thousands digit minus 2 times the hundred-thousands digit plus 1 times the millions digit, etc., is equal to an integral multiple of 7, then the number itself is also.

Illustration $\quad 173,824 = 10^5 + 7 \cdot 10^4 + 3 \cdot 10^3 + 8 \cdot 10^2 + 2 \cdot 10 + 4$
$$\equiv (-2) + 7(-3) + 3(-1) + 8(2) + 2(3) + 4$$
$$= -2 - 21 - 3 + 16 + 6 + 4 = 0$$

Therefore 173,824 has 7 as a factor. On the other hand:
$$173,284 = 10^5 + 7 \cdot 10^4 + 3 \cdot 10^3 + 2 \cdot 10^2 + 8 \cdot 10 + 4$$
$$\equiv (-2) + 7(-3) + 3(-1) + 2(2) + 8(3) + 4$$
$$= -2 - 21 - 3 + 4 + 24 + 4 = 6$$

Therefore 173,284 has the remainder 6 when divided by 7.

We devise a similar test for divisibility by 13.

$$10 \equiv (-3), \bmod 13$$
$$10^2 \equiv (-3)^2 = 9 \equiv (-4), \bmod 13$$
$$10^3 = 10^2 \cdot 10 \equiv (-4)(-3) = 12 \equiv (-1), \bmod 13$$
$$10^4 = 10^3 \cdot 10 \equiv (-1)(-3) = 3, \bmod 13$$
$$10^5 = 10^4 \cdot 10 \equiv 3(-3) = (-9) \equiv 4, \bmod 13$$
$$10^6 = 10^5 \cdot 10 \equiv 4(-3) = (-12) \equiv 1, \bmod 13$$
$$10^7 = 10^6 \cdot 10 \equiv 1(-3) = (-3), \bmod 13$$

Then we add the units digit multiplied by 1, the tens by (-3), hundreds by (-4), thousands by (-1), ten thousands by 3, hundred thousands by 4, millions by 1, etc. If this sum is a multiple of 13, the number is also.

Illustration
$$2{,}457 = 2 \cdot 10^3 + 4 \cdot 10^2 + 5 \cdot 10 + 7$$
$$\equiv 2 \cdot (-1) + 4 \cdot (-4) + 5 \cdot (-3) + 7 = -26$$
$$\equiv 0, \bmod 13$$

Therefore 2,457 has the factor 13.

$$76{,}348 = 7 \cdot 10^4 + 6 \cdot 10^3 + 3 \cdot 10^2 + 4 \cdot 10 + 8$$
$$\equiv 7 \cdot 3 + 6 \cdot (-1) + 3(-4) + 4 \cdot (-3) + 8 = -1 \equiv 12, \bmod 13$$

Therefore 76,348 has the remainder 12 when divided by 13.

──────────── E X E R C I S E S ────────────

1. Use tests for divisibility to determine whether each one-digit number greater than 1, except 7, is a factor of each of the following numbers. Determine the remainder when it is divided by each nonfactor, 6 and 7 excepted.
   (a) 436,812   (b) 39,645   (c) 43,611   (d) 9,816

2. Since a number is divisible by 6 if and only if it is divisible by both 2 and 3, why can we not say that a number divisible by both 2 and 4 is divisible by 8?

3.* Prove that a number is divisible by 3 if and only if the sum of its digits is divisible by 3.

4. Is a base 12 number divisible by 5 if it ends in zero or 5? Explain.

5. How would you test a base 12 number for divisibility by 4?

6.* Use the method of Section 4.16 to devise a test for divisibility by 4.

7.* Show that the result of Exercise 6 is equivalent to the test given in Section 4.15.

DO YOU KNOW

The difference between algebra and arithmetic?

Why medieval barbers called themselves "algebristas"?

There is more than one algebra?

The difference between an identical equation and a conditional equation?

The difference between a field and a group?

Why we have numbers other than the natural numbers and zero?

Why we do not add fractions like this one?

$$\frac{a}{b} + \frac{c}{d} = \frac{a+c}{b+d}$$

Why you invert the divisor and multiply when dividing fractions?

CHAPTER V

WHAT IS ALGEBRA?

In this chapter we shall attempt to see algebra as an application of logic and not as the blind manipulation of symbols. In order to do this we must learn what, from the mathematical viewpoint, a field is. This will require the extension of number so as to get the positive and negative integers and the rational numbers into the picture.

FROM ARITHMETIC TO ALGEBRA

5.1   One answer to the question, "What is algebra?" is "It is generalized arithmetic." There are two main distinctions between arithmetic and elementary algebra. First, in arithmetic we are concerned with special cases, whereas in algebra we are concerned with generalizations of special cases.

The statement

$$2(5 + 8) = 10 + 16$$

is a special relationship involving *these* numbers, 2, 5, 8, 10, and 16. This is an application of arithmetic.

But the statement

$$a(b + c) = ab + ac$$

is a statement applying to *all* numbers (that is, all numbers of the algebra under consideration). Here we have used a, b, and c to represent any number. This is an application of algebra.

Also,

$$a - b = 5$$

is an algebraic statement, but it applies to *some* numbers. The distinction between these two basically different algebraic statements is important and will be further elaborated presently.   But for now we see one distinguishing characteristic of algebra, the extension of arith-- metic from relationships involving specific numbers to those involving either the whole set of numbers of our algebra or a part of the set.

When we say that

$$a(b + c) = ab + ac$$

we are asserting that this relationship is true for any three numbers of our set; a, b, and c are not necessarily distinct.   We have complete freedom in choosing each of them.   Each letter represents any number.

On the other hand, in the expression

$$a - b = 5$$

we do not have complete freedom of choice.   If our set of numbers consists of the natural numbers and zero, then a may be anything equal to or greater than 5.   But paired with each value a may take, there is just one value for b.   In this case there are infinitely many ordered pairs of values which a and b may take simultaneously.

In either event, the letters are used to represent any one of a set of numbers.   They are called *variables*.

Definition   A variable is a symbol that represents any one of a set of elements.

Letters may also be used to represent a single number, as in the equation

$$5x - 6 = x + 18$$

The x in the equation given above is called the *unknown* because the solution of the equation consists of finding all values of x (and there is just one in this case) which make a true statement of the proposition that $5x - 6$ and $x + 18$ are equal.   We may think of this one value as a set which has just one element in it.   A letter may also be used to represent a single number in a different sense.   It may be used to stand for a number the value of which we know, as π for the ratio of circumference to diameter of a circle.   Or we may not particularly care what its value is as long as we know it does not change.   For example, if we think of x as the unknown in the equation

$$ax - 6 = x + 18$$

the solution consists of finding the value of x which satisfies the equation.   But we can only find x in terms of a.   If a has a single value we can find a single value for x.   When letters are used in this manner they are called *constants*.

Definition   A constant is a symbol which represents the element of a set which contains just one element.

The second major difference between algebra and arithmetic concerns the kind of numbers with which we deal.   In the arithmetic of the elementary school we work with whole numbers, which we have called natural numbers, and fractions, which we shall call rational numbers.   On the other hand, the elements of algebra (the most common variety of algebra) are complex numbers.   We have not as yet defined complex numbers, but we shall do so (Chapter VII).   Our first extension of number will be to the integers, which will give us the negative numbers.   In the arithmetic of positive numbers there is no such thing as 8 − 12, but as soon as we complete our first extension of number, 8 − 12 will be a number just as truly as 8 + 4 is.

ALGEBRA — THEN AND NOW

5.2   Algebra derived its name from the title of an Arabic book, *Hisâb al-jabr wâl-muquabalah*, by a famous mathematician of the eighth century, al-Khowârizmî.   The title has been translated to mean "restoration and opposition."   These words refer to mechanical steps in the solution of equations.   We "restore" negative terms and "oppose" positive terms in order to evaluate the unknown.   Al-Khowârizmî's text was translated into Latin and used in Europe. It became known simply as *Algebra*, which was derived from the second word of the title, *Al-jabr*.   An algebrista was a restorer of broken bones.   In those days the barber was also the bonesetter and bloodletter.

Algebra, as the science of solving equations, was pretty well completed during the seventeenth century.   During the past century, however, algebra has come to take on a much broader meaning.   As it is now conceived, algebra is the study of mathematical systems. In Section 1.5 a mathematical system was described as consisting of undefined terms, axioms, definitions, and theorems.   An algebra may consist of (1) undefined *elements*, (2) two binary *operations*, usually denoted + and × (a binary operation is one combining two elements), (3) a set of *axioms* which specify assumed relationships between the elements and operations, (4) certain *definitions* as, for example, the definitions of the inverse operations, and (5) *theorems*.   Every time we solve an algebraic equation we are actually proving a theorem.

A given algebra may have a number of different applications, provided we can find more than one suitable interpretation of the undefined
elements and the operations.   However, it is in a different sense that
we say there are many algebras.   When we use another set of postulates we get a new algebra, even though we may not even bother to
find any interpretation of the undefined terms.

5.3   One of the most basic systems in modern algebra is the *group*.
It is important in many branches of mathematics, both pure and
applied.

> *Definition*   A set of elements $a, b, c \ldots$, combinable under a binary
> operation o, is called a group with respect to o if the following properties are
> satisfied:
>
> G_1 Closure: If a, b are any two elements (not necessarily distinct) of the
> set, then aob is an element of the set.
>
> G_2 Associativity: If a, b, c are any three elements (not necessarily distinct)
> of the set, then $(aob)oc = ao(boc)$.
>
> G_3 Identity: There is an element I such that, for any element a of the set,
> $aoI = Ioa = a$.
>
> G_4 Inverse: For each element a of the set there is an element a' such
> that $aoa' = a'oa = I$.

We have not said that the elements must be numbers, or how
many elements there must be.   The elements may be numbers, or
rotations, or permutations — to name a few possibilities.   In fact,
they may remain undefined provided we can show that the four
properties are satisfied.   The set of elements may be finite or infinite.

We have not stated that the operation must be either addition or
multiplication.   It, too, may remain undefined.   But the result of
combining each two elements must be well defined if we are to verify
that G_1 to G_4 are satisfied.

From the point of view of a group as an abstract system, the set of
elements and the operation are undefined. G_1 to G_4 are our axioms.
We must define the combinations in such manner that the axioms
G_1 to G_4 are satisfied.

Closure, G_1, and associativity, G_2, are the familiar properties which
we assumed for the natural numbers in Chapter IV.   We recognize 1

as the identity for the multiplication of natural numbers.   We created 0 in order that the natural numbers might have an addition identity. G_4, the inverse property, we do not find among the properties of the natural numbers: there is no natural number that we can add to 7 to get 0, and no natural number we can multiply by 7 to get 1.

Consider three undefined elements a, b, c and the undefined operation o.   The combinations are defined by Table 5.1.

Table 5.1

	a	b	c
a	a	b	c
b	b	c	a
c	c	a	b

The table is read in the usual way.   To find boc locate b in the left column and c at the top.   The space opposite b and under c contains a.   Then $boc = a$, which means that if we combine b and c in that order the result is a.

The closure property is satisfied because each space in the table contains an a, a b, or a c.

Examination of the first row and the first column verifies that a is the identity element, since this row and column are repetitions of the sequence of elements across the top of the table and down the left side.

If each element is to have an inverse, there must be some element with which we can combine it to produce the identity a.   The table shows that a is its own inverse, since $aoa = a$, and that b and c are inverses, since $boc = cob = a$.   In terms of the notation in G_4, we say $b' = c$, $c' = b$, and $a' = a$.

The associative property is a little more troublesome.   In order to prove that it will always hold we should have to verify twenty-seven separate possibilities, since the three elements are not necessarily distinct.   Representative samples of the possibilities are:

(1) $(aoc)ob = ao(cob)$
(2) $(cob)ob = co(bob)$
(3) $(bob)ob = bo(bob)$

To verify (1) we find from the table that $aoc = c$ and $cob = a$; then (1) becomes $cob = aoa$.   But the table verifies that each of these operations yields a.

There is a much easier way of establishing the associative property, which we shall examine presently. For the moment, if we grant this property always holds, we know that the set of elements a, b, c with the operation o is a group.

The group we have described has form without content. It is a pure abstraction. If we assign meaning to the elements a, b, c and the operation o in such manner that Table 5.1 gives consistent results, we then have a model for the abstract system.

Consider an equilateral triangle, vertices 1, 2, 3, center 0. If we rotate the triangle clockwise about 0 through 120° (one third of a complete circle), vertex 1 will go to the original position of 2, vertex 2 to the original position of 3, and 3 to the original position of 1. If we rotate 240° (two thirds of a complete circle), vertex 1 will go to 3, 2 will go to 1, and 3 will go to 2. If we rotate 360° (a full circle), each vertex will go back to its original position: 1 to 1, 2 to 2, and 3 to 3.

Let us define the element a as a 360° rotation, b as a 120° rotation, and c as a 240° rotation. We further define the operation o thus: aob means to rotate 360° and then rotate 120°. We could call the operation "add," "multiply," "followed by," or whatever name happens to appeal to us. But it means that we perform the rotation indicated by the first element and continue rotating the amount indicated by the second element.

We can verify that under this interpretation Table 5.1 is correct. For example, $boc = a$ means that a rotation of 120° followed by a rotation of 240° is equivalent to a single rotation of 360°.

We have closure, since if we carry out any one of these rotations and follow it by any one of them, the end result will be equivalent to some one of them. For example, if we rotate 240°, vertex 1 will go to 3, 2 will go to 1, and 3 will go to 2. If we follow this by another 240° rotation, vertex 1 will go from 3 to 2, 2 will go from 1 to 3, and 3 will go from 2 to 1. But if we rotate 120° from the initial position, vertex 1 will go to 2, 2 will go to 3, and 3 will go to 1. Then $coc = b$.

The identity element is a, a rotation of 360°, for it will carry each vertex back to its position before the rotation.

We have inverses: 360° is its own inverse, and 120° followed by 240° or 240° followed by 120° is equivalent to 360°, so that 120° and 240° are inverses

If in Table 5.1 we replace a by 0, b by 1, and c by 2, we get Table 5.2.

Table 5.2

	0	1	2
0	0	1	2
1	1	2	0
2	2	0	1

This is the table for addition, modulo 3. The system of rotations which we have just described and addition, modulo 3, are abstractly identical. Such a relationship is called an *isomorphism*.

Definition   Two groups are isomorphic if there is a one-to-one correspondence of elements which is preserved under the group operation.

For example, the correspondence $a \leftrightarrow 0$, $b \leftrightarrow 1$, and $c \leftrightarrow 2$ is preserved when elements are combined:

$$boc = a \text{ and } 1 + 2 = 0$$

The idea of isomorphism is not restricted to groups. The literal meaning of the word is "same form." We employ the idea when we check a computation in base 8 by converting to base 10 and computing. The answers must correspond in the same manner as do the two representations of each number in the computation.

We can now show that the associative property is satisfied in Table 5.1. Since a, b, c can be interpreted as $0, 1, 2$, modulo 3, it is sufficient to show that modulo addition is associative.

Let A, B, C be any three natural numbers and a, b, c their respective remainders when divided by the modulus. We know that $(A + B) + C = A + (B + C)$. Being equal, they must be congruent:

$$(A + B) + C \equiv A + (B + C)$$

But $(A + B) + C \equiv (a + b) + c$ and $A + (B + C) \equiv a + (b + c)$. Therefore $(a + b) + c \equiv a + (b + c)$.

––––––––––   E X E R C I S E S   ––––––––––

1.   Prove that the set of numbers 0, 1, 2, 3, 4 is a group with respect to modulo 5 addition.

2.   Prove that the set of numbers 1, 2, 3, 4 is a group with respect to modulo 5 multiplication.

3. Prove that the set of numbers 1, 2, 3 is not a group with respect to modulo 4 multiplication.

4. Consider the set of rotations of a square about its center which will rotate vertices into vertices. Is this a group?

5. Construct the combination table for Exercise 4.

6. Show that the groups of Exercise 2 and Exercise 4 are isomorphic. *Hint:* Reconstruct the table, Exercise 2, with 3 and 4 interchanged.

7. Construct a table of multiplication, modulo 12, for 1, 5, 7, 11. Show that this is a group.

8. Is the group in Exercise 7 isomorphic to the group in Exercise 4?

9. Construct a table of addition, modulo 6, for 0, 1, 2, 3, 4, 5. Is this a group?

10. Construct the table of multiplication, modulo 6, for 1, 2, 3, 4, 5. Is this a group?

ABELIAN GROUPS

5.4 All of the groups we have examined have, in addition to the properties G_1 through G_4, still another property in common. They all satisfy the commutative property $aob = boa$.

Definition A group is an Abelian or commutative group if it satisfies the axiom:

G_5 Commutativity: If a and b are any elements of a group, $aob = boa$.

The name "Abelian" is in honor of Niels Henrik Abel, the young Norwegian who, with Evariste Galois, did pioneering work in group theory in the early nineteenth century. The latter was the originator of the theory. His career was cut short by a pointless duel, just before his twenty-first birthday.

To establish the commutative property of the groups we have examined, it is sufficient to note that the table entries are symmetrically placed relative to the upper left to lower right diagonal. For example, in Table 5.1 we see, along the diagonal, a, c, b in that order. In all other cases we find the same element in any two spaces symmetrically located relative to the diagonal. To find cob we locate the space opposite c in the left column and under b at the top. But to find boc we interchange column for row: we find the space opposite b in the left column and under c at the top. An interchange of column

with row will always lead to a position symmetric to the original
position relative to the upper left to lower right diagonal.

Not all groups are Abelian.   Consider the triangle described on
page 122.   The element a, which is a 360° rotation, caused each vertex
to assume its original position.   This can be represented as $\begin{pmatrix} 123 \\ 123 \end{pmatrix}$,
the top row indicating the initial position of the vertices, and the
bottom row their final position.   Similarly, the element b, a 120°
rotation, may be indicated $\begin{pmatrix} 123 \\ 231 \end{pmatrix}$, meaning that vertex 1 goes to position 2, vertex 3 to position 1, and vertex 2 to position 3.   The same
rotation is indicated by $\begin{pmatrix} 213 \\ 321 \end{pmatrix}$ or any other arrangement of 1, 2, and
3 on the top row.   The important point is that 2 must be under 1,
3 under 2, and 1 under 3.

In similar fashion, element c may be indicated as $\begin{pmatrix} 123 \\ 312 \end{pmatrix}$.   These
new symbols signify *permutations* of the elements 1, 2, 3.   A permuta-
tion of a set of things is simply an arrangement of the things in a
definite order.   But, as we have already indicated, our concern here
is not with the number of ways the elements 1, 2, 3 can be arranged;
it is rather with the number of ways the elements 1, 2, 3 can be replaced
by the elements 1, 2, 3.   One or more of the elements can, of course,
be replaced by itself.   By $\begin{pmatrix} 123 \\ 321 \end{pmatrix}$ we mean that 1 is replaced by 3, 2
is replaced by 2, and 3 is replaced by 1.

To find the *product* of two permutations it is necessary merely to
find a single permutation which is equivalent to the first followed by
the second.   To find $\begin{pmatrix} 123 \\ 312 \end{pmatrix} \cdot \begin{pmatrix} 123 \\ 231 \end{pmatrix}$ we note that 1 goes to 3 by the
first permutation and 3 goes to 1 by the second; then the product
sends 1 into 1.   Similarly, we have 2 into 1 and 1 into 2, or 2 into 2.
Finally 3 goes to 2 and 2 to 3, or 3 into 3.   Then the product is

$$\begin{pmatrix} 123 \\ 312 \end{pmatrix} \cdot \begin{pmatrix} 123 \\ 231 \end{pmatrix} = \begin{pmatrix} 123 \\ 123 \end{pmatrix}$$

We now have still another interpretation for the group on page 121.

If $\qquad\qquad a = \begin{pmatrix} 123 \\ 123 \end{pmatrix}, b = \begin{pmatrix} 123 \\ 231 \end{pmatrix}, c = \begin{pmatrix} 123 \\ 312 \end{pmatrix}$

then Table 5.1 is the multiplication table for the permutations a, b, c.

If we consider the arrangement $\begin{pmatrix}123\\ \_\_\_\end{pmatrix}$ we can see that the first blank can be filled in any one of three ways (with 1, 2, or 3). With any of these three choices, the middle blank can be filled in two ways. With any of the six choices for the first two blanks, the final one can be filled in just one way. The six possible permutations are

$$a = \begin{pmatrix}123\\123\end{pmatrix}, \; b = \begin{pmatrix}123\\231\end{pmatrix}, \; c = \begin{pmatrix}123\\312\end{pmatrix}, \; d = \begin{pmatrix}123\\132\end{pmatrix}, \; e = \begin{pmatrix}123\\321\end{pmatrix}, \; f = \begin{pmatrix}123\\213\end{pmatrix}$$

Permutations d, e, and f also have meaning in terms of the equilateral triangle. A 180° rotation about the altitude through vertex 1 is equivalent to d. That is, 1 is replaced by 1, 2 is replaced by 3, and 3 is replaced by 2. Similarly for e and f with altitudes through vertices 2 and 3 respectively.

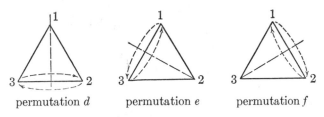

permutation d permutation e permutation f

The six elements a, b, c, d, e, f are a group with respect to permutation multiplication.

The closure property is fulfilled because, after any permutation and therefore after any sequence of two permutations, each vertex is in one and only one of the original positions of the vertices. Furthermore, every possible rearrangement of the vertices is represented by the six permutations.

There is an identity element, $a = \begin{pmatrix}123\\123\end{pmatrix}$. We shall let j, k, l represent some arrangement of the numbers 1, 2, 3:

$$\begin{pmatrix}123\\jkl\end{pmatrix} \cdot \begin{pmatrix}123\\123\end{pmatrix} = \begin{pmatrix}123\\jkl\end{pmatrix}$$

That is, 1 is replaced by j, and j is replaced by itself; 2 is replaced by k, and k is replaced by itself; 3 is replaced by l and l is replaced by itself.

Also

$$\begin{pmatrix}123\\123\end{pmatrix} \cdot \begin{pmatrix}123\\jkl\end{pmatrix} = \begin{pmatrix}123\\jkl\end{pmatrix}$$

Each element has an inverse: a is its own inverse, b and c are inverses of each other.   The reader should verify that each of d, e, and f is its own inverse.

The associative property is satisfied.   Let any three permutations be represented by $\begin{pmatrix} 123 \\ klm \end{pmatrix}$, $\begin{pmatrix} klm \\ pqr \end{pmatrix}$, and $\begin{pmatrix} pqr \\ stu \end{pmatrix}$, when each of the triples (k, l, m), (p, q, r), and (s, t, u) represents some specific arrangement of $(1, 2, 3)$.

The associative property requires that

$$\left\{ \begin{pmatrix} 123 \\ klm \end{pmatrix} \cdot \begin{pmatrix} klm \\ pqr \end{pmatrix} \right\} \cdot \begin{pmatrix} pqr \\ stu \end{pmatrix} = \begin{pmatrix} 123 \\ klm \end{pmatrix} \cdot \left\{ \begin{pmatrix} klm \\ pqr \end{pmatrix} \cdot \begin{pmatrix} pqr \\ stu \end{pmatrix} \right\}$$

Performing the multiplication within the braces on either side of the equality, we get

$$\begin{pmatrix} 123 \\ pqr \end{pmatrix} \cdot \begin{pmatrix} pqr \\ stu \end{pmatrix} = \begin{pmatrix} 123 \\ klm \end{pmatrix} \cdot \begin{pmatrix} klm \\ stu \end{pmatrix}$$

But these products give

$$\begin{pmatrix} 123 \\ stu \end{pmatrix} = \begin{pmatrix} 123 \\ stu \end{pmatrix}$$

All four group properties are fulfilled, but the resulting group is not Abelian.   This may be demonstrated by comparing $d \cdot b$ and $b \cdot d$:

$$b \cdot d = \begin{pmatrix} 123 \\ 231 \end{pmatrix} \cdot \begin{pmatrix} 123 \\ 132 \end{pmatrix} = \begin{pmatrix} 123 \\ 321 \end{pmatrix} = e$$

but

$$d \cdot b = \begin{pmatrix} 123 \\ 132 \end{pmatrix} \cdot \begin{pmatrix} 123 \\ 231 \end{pmatrix} = \begin{pmatrix} 123 \\ 213 \end{pmatrix} = f$$

Table 5.3 is the complete table for this non-Abelian group.

Table 5.3

	a	b	c	d	e	f
a	a	b	c	d	e	f
b	b	c	a	e	f	d
c	c	a	b	f	d	e
d	d	f	e	a	c	b
e	e	d	f	b	a	c
f	f	e	d	c	b	a

The table can be verified by carrying through the multiplications.

We have already seen that a, b, c form a multiplication group.   A subset of a group's elements, which is itself a group, is called a subgroup.   Can you find any other subgroups in the table?

——————————— E X E R C I S E S ———————————

1. Demonstrate with diagrams the interpretation of $e \cdot d = b$ and $d \cdot e = c$ when applied to the rotations of an equilateral triangle.

2. Multiply the following permutations.
    (a) $e \cdot f$ (b) $c \cdot d$ (c) $f \cdot e$

3. Number the vertices of a square 1, 2, 3, 4. Interpret the following permutations in terms of rotations about the center of the square.

    (a) $\begin{pmatrix} 1234 \\ 2341 \end{pmatrix}$ (b) $\begin{pmatrix} 1234 \\ 3412 \end{pmatrix}$ (c) $\begin{pmatrix} 1234 \\ 4123 \end{pmatrix}$ (d) $\begin{pmatrix} 1234 \\ 1234 \end{pmatrix}$

4. Construct the multiplication table for the permutations in Exercise 3. Is this a multiplication group? An Abelian multiplication group?

5. Interpret the following permutations in terms of the vertices of a square.

    (a) $\begin{pmatrix} 1234 \\ 1234 \end{pmatrix}$ (b) $\begin{pmatrix} 1234 \\ 2143 \end{pmatrix}$ (c) $\begin{pmatrix} 1234 \\ 4321 \end{pmatrix}$ (d) $\begin{pmatrix} 1234 \\ 3412 \end{pmatrix}$

6. Construct the multiplication table for the permutations in Exercise 5. Is this a group? If so, is it isomorphic to the group in Exercise 4?

7. Is the addition, modulo 6, group (see Exercise 9, Section 5.3) isomorphic to the permutation group on page 127?

8. There are six distinct permutations of 1, 2, 3, 4 in Exercises 3 and 5. Do these six permutations form a group? If so, is it Abelian?

9. What is the smallest number of elements a group can have?

10. Do the odd natural numbers form a multiplication group? Why?

11. Why are the natural numbers not a subtraction group?

FIELDS

5.5   A group involves only one operation. There are a number of algebraic systems involving two operations. Our immediate concern is with a system known as a *field*.

> *Definition*   A set of elements that is an Abelian addition group, whose nonzero elements are an Abelian multiplication group, and which obey the distributive property is a *field*.

We have seen examples of modulo systems which are addition groups and whose nonzero elements are multiplication groups. Modulo 5 is such an example. Table 5.4 gives the modulo 5 addition facts for the numbers 0, 1, 2, 3, 4.   Table 5.5 gives the modulo 5 multiplication facts for the numbers 0, 1, 2, 3, 4.

Table 5.4 Addition, modulo 5.

	0	1	2	3	4
0	0	1	2	3	4
1	1	2	3	4	0
2	2	3	4	0	1
3	3	4	0	1	2
4	4	0	1	2	3

Table 5.5 Multiplication, modulo 5.

	0	1	2	3	4
0	0	0	0	0	0
1	0	1	2	3	4
2	0	2	4	1	3
3	0	3	1	4	2
4	0	4	3	2	1

We have closure with respect to each operation, since the spaces in each table contain 0, 1, 2, 3, or 4.

We may verify from Table 5.4 that 0 is the addition identity, since for any element a, $a + 0 = 0 + a = a$.   Similarly, from Table 5.4 we see that 1 is the multiplication identity.

The symmetry of the entries in each table relative to the upper left to lower right diagonals assures us that both addition and multiplication are commutative.

We may verify from Table 5.4 that $0 + 0 = 0$, $1 + 4 = 4 + 1 = 0$, and $2 + 3 = 3 + 2 = 0$.   Therefore each element has an additive inverse.

From Table 5.5 we see that $1 \cdot 1 = 1$, $2 \cdot 3 = 3 \cdot 2 = 1$, and $4 \cdot 4 = 1$.   Thus each nonzero element has a multiplicative inverse.

It remains only to show that, with respect to any modulus, the associative and distributive properties hold.

(1) $(a + b) + c \equiv a + (b + c)$

(2) $(a \cdot b) \cdot c \equiv a \cdot (b \cdot c)$

(3) $a(b + c) \equiv a \cdot b + a \cdot c$

We established (1) on page 123.   We can establish (2) in exactly the same way merely by replacing the addition signs with multiplication signs.

To establish (3), let A, B, C be any three natural numbers, and a, b, c their respective remainders upon division by the modulus. Then $A(B + C) \equiv AB + AC$ because the two expressions are equal and therefore must be congruent.   But $A(B + C) \equiv a(b + c)$ since $A \equiv a$, $B \equiv b$, and $C \equiv c$ and we may add and multiply congruences (page 108).   Similarly, $AB + AC \equiv ab + ac$.   Then, by substitution, $a(b + c) \equiv ab + ac$.

Not all modulo systems are fields. Tables 5.6 and 5.7 give the addition and multiplication facts, modulo 4, for 0, 1, 2, 3.

Table 5.6   Addition, modulo 4.

	0	1	2	3
0	0	1	2	3
1	1	2	3	0
2	2	3	0	1
3	3	0	1	2

Table 5.7   Multiplication, modulo 4.

	0	1	2	3
0	0	0	0	0
1	0	1	2	3
2	0	2	0	2
3	0	3	2	1

This system is not a field, on two counts. The nonzero elements are not a multiplication group because (1) they are not closed ($2 \times 2 = 0$) and (2) there is no inverse for the element 2.

In this system, 2 is said to be a *divisor of zero*, since $2 \times 2 = 0$, $0 \div 2 = 2$. In a field there are no divisors of zero. We saw, page 96, that if zero is a factor the product must be zero. It is not necessary to assume this property in a field.

Theorem $a \cdot 0 = 0$.

We know that $a + 0 = a$; then multiplying by a gives

$$a(a + 0) = a \cdot a$$
$$a \cdot a + a \cdot 0 = a \cdot a$$

If we add the additive inverse of $a \cdot a$ to both sides we get $a \cdot 0 = 0$.

It is also true of a field that, if a product is zero, at least one factor must be zero.

Theorem   If $a \cdot b = 0$ and $a \neq 0$, then $b = 0$. If $a \neq 0$ it has a multiplicative inverse a'.

If $a \cdot b = 0, \ a \neq 0$

then $a' \cdot a \cdot b = a' \cdot 0$
$$1 \cdot b = 0$$
$$b = 0$$

——————   E   X   E   R   C   I   S   E   S   ——————

1.   A field must have at least two elements, the addition identity 0 and the multiplicative identity 1. Construct the addition and multiplication tables for 0, 1, modulo 2. Is this a field?

2.   Let E represent even numbers and O represent odd numbers.   Construct addition and multiplication tables for E and O, showing how even and odd numbers combine.   Is the result isomorphic to the result of Exercise 1?

3.   Show that multiplication of the numbers 1, 2, modulo 3, is isomorphic to the addition of 0, 1, modulo 2.

4.   Do 0, 1, 2, 3, 4, 5 form a field under modulo 6 addition and multiplication?   If not, what properties are not fulfilled?

5.   Do 0, 1, 2, 3, 4, 5, 6 form a field under modulo 7 addition and multiplication?   If not what properties are not fulfilled?

6.   Construct tables for base 4 addition and multiplication.   Compare these with Tables 5.6 and 5.7.

7.   Find the divisors of zero in multiplication, modulo 12.

8.   If the modulus is a prime number can there be divisors of zero?   Explain.

9.   If the modulus is not prime must there be divisors of zero?   Explain.

10.   In the light of Exercises 8 and 9 state what you consider a necessary and sufficient condition that a modulo system be a field.

INVERSE ELEMENTS

5.6   The significance of the existence of inverse elements lies in the fact that they make the set closed with respect to the inverse operation.   Since, Table 5.4, each element has an addition inverse, we can always subtract.

Example   Find $2 - 4$, modulo 5.

Since by definition of subtraction $2 - 4$ means that which we must add to 4 to get 2, we merely find 2 in Row 4: it is in Column 3.   Therefore $2 - 4 = 3$ because $4 + 3 = 2$.
However, the inverse of 4 is 1, and $2 + 1 = 3$.

In a similar fashion we may verify that $1 - 3$ equals $1 + 2$ (2 is the inverse of 3).   This suggests that subtracting an element is equivalent to adding its additive inverse.

Theorem   If b' is the additive inverse of b, then $a - b = a + b'$.

By definition of subtraction: $a - b = a + b'$ if and only if $b + a + b' = a$.
But $b + a + b' = a + b + b' = a + 0 = a$.

In modulo 5 we can always divide by nonzero elements.

Example   Find $3 \div 4$, modulo 5.

By the definition of division, $3 \div 4$ equals that by which we must multiply 4 to get 3. We locate 3 in Row 4; it is in Column 2. Therefore $3 \div 4 = 2$, because $4 \times 2 = 3$.

However, 4 is its own inverse, and $3 \times 4 = 2$.

In a similar way we can demonstrate that $4 \div 2 = 4 \times 3$ (3 is the inverse of 2). We may divide by a nonzero element by multiplying by its multiplicative inverse.

Theorem   If b' is the multiplicative inverse of b, then $a \div b = a \cdot b'$.

By definition of division: $a \div b = a \cdot b'$ if and only if $b \cdot a \cdot b' = a$.
But $b \cdot a \cdot b' = a \cdot b \cdot b' = a \cdot 1 = a$.

The addition identity, zero, is not required to have a multiplicative inverse. In fact, in a field it is impossible for zero to have one. Assume that the inverse of 0 is some element x. Then $a \div 0 = a \cdot x$ and, since the field is closed to multiplication, $a \cdot x$ is an element of the set. But this contradicts the fact that division by zero cannot be defined.

We see, Table 5.7, that 2 does not have a multiplicative inverse in modulo 4 multiplication. We cannot, therefore, guarantee division by 2. If we attempt to find $3 \div 2$ we cannot multiply 3 by the inverse of 2, since it has none. When we attempt to find the quotient directly we must find an element that we can multiply by 2 to get 3 for product. When we look in Column 2 for a 3 we find none there. There is no element by which we may multiply 2 to get product 3. Then $3 \div 2$ does not exist.

On the other hand, if we attempt to find $2 \div 2$, the answer may be either 1 or 3, since $2 \times 1 = 2$ and $2 \times 3 = 2$. In this case the division is not unique; that is, we do not get a single result.

———————   E X E R C I S E S   ———————

1. Use Tables 5.4 and 5.5 to find the following:
    (a) $2 - 4$ (c) $1 - 3$ (e) $2 \div 4$ (g) $4 - 1$
    (b) $3 \div 4$ (d) $1 \div 3$ (f) $4 \div 2$

2. Use Tables 5.4 and 5.5 to demonstrate that the distributive property holds for $3(4 + 2)$.

3. Evaluate the following, modulo 5, by performing the inverse operation with the inverse element. Check your results by performing the direct operation.
    (a) $4 + 2$ (b) $3 - 1$ (c) $2 \div 3$ (d) 4×2

4. Verify the following, modulo 5.
    (a) $(4 + 3) + 2 = 4 + (3 + 2)$ (d) $3 - 4 = 3 + 1$
    (b) $(3 \cdot 2) \cdot 4 = 3 \cdot (2 \cdot 4)$ (e) $2 \div 3 = 2 \cdot 2$
    (c) $2(4 + 3) = 2 \cdot 4 + 2 \cdot 3 = (3 + 4)2$

5. Explain the meaning of $3 \div 4 = 2$, modulo 5.

6. Verify the following, modulo 4.
    (a) $2(3 + 1) = 2 \cdot 3 + 2 \cdot 1$
    (b) $(3 + 2) + 3 = 3 + (2 + 3)$
    (c) $(2 \cdot 3) \cdot 2 = 2 \cdot (3 \cdot 2)$

7. In modulo 5, which is the greater: $2 + 2$ or $3 + 4$? In what respect do these numbers differ from the natural numbers?

8. Use Table 5.3 to find the following. Explain why, although $b \div f = d$, $b \div d$ does not equal f.
    (a) $b \div f$ (b) $b \div d$

9. Explain why, although e is not the multiplicative identity in Table 5.3, $e \div e = e \times e$. What element in modulo 5 multiplication has this same property?

THE NATURAL NUMBERS NOT A FIELD

5.7 A field was defined, page 128, in terms of groups. We now list the field properties without reference to groups.

F_1 Closure under the operation, $+$: If a and b are elements, $a + b$ is an element.

F_2 Associativity under the operation, $+$: $(a + b) + c = a + (b + c)$.

F_3 Identity element under $+$: There exists an element called *zero* such that $a + 0 = 0 + a = a$.

F_5 Commutativity under $+$: $a + b = b + a$.

F_6 Closure under the operation, $\times$: If a and b are elements, then $a \times b$ is an element.

F_7 Associativity under the operation, $\times$: $(a \times b) \times c = a \times (b \times c)$.

F_8 Identity element under $\times$: There exists an element called *one*, such that $a \times 1 = 1 \times a = a$.

F_{10} Commutativity under $\times$: $a \times b = b \times a$.

F_{11} Distributive property: $a \times (b + c) = (a \times b) + (a \times c)$.

The natural numbers and zero possess all of these properties.

Note that we skipped F_4 and F_9. This was deliberate. We should like to create a new kind of number out of the natural numbers such that subtraction and division are always possible and the above properties continue to hold. The two missing properties would then be:

F_4 Every element has an additive inverse, or subtraction is always possible: $a + (-a) = (-a) + a = 0$.

F_9 Every element except zero has a multiplicative inverse, or division other than division by zero is always possible:

$$a \times \frac{1}{a} = \frac{1}{a} \times a = 1, \quad \text{where} \quad a \neq 0$$

As we have seen, Section 5.6, the existence of an additive inverse of an element guarantees that the element can be subtracted. If each element has an additive inverse the set of elements is closed with respect to subtraction. Similarly, the existence of a multiplicative inverse guarantees that we may divide by the element. We shall extend our numbers to include first the integers, then the rational numbers, in order that we may have a field. We will then have closure under the four fundamental operations of arithmetic, division by zero excepted.

The set of natural numbers and zero has still another property aside from the nine properties of the eleven properties of a field listed above. The natural numbers are *ordered*. In terms of the counting of sets, a "comes before" b if we must count on after counting set a in order to reach b. Stated more elegantly:

$a < b$ if and only if there exists a natural number c such that $a + c = b$

We shall postpone the definition of an ordered field until we have constructed the rational field. However, one of the properties of an ordered field is given by

$$(a < b) \rightarrow (a + c) < (b + c)$$

If, in the modulo 5 field, $2 < 3$, then $(2 + 1) < (3 + 1)$ or $3 < 4$. But this implies $(3 + 1) < (4 + 1)$ or $4 < 0$. Continuing in this manner,

$$2 < 3 < 4 < 0 < 1 < 2 \text{ or } 2 < 2$$

We conclude that the modulo 5 field is not an ordered field.

The notion of a field is important, because any theorem which can be established by using only these eleven field properties will be valid in all fields. For example, we prove the "right distributive law" for natural numbers,

$$(a + b)c = ac + bc$$

by using only properties which are among those of a field.   Consequently, we know the right distributive law will hold for any set which has the properties of a field.

THE EXTENSION OF NUMBER

5.8   Throughout our discussion of natural numbers in Chapters III and IV, a great deal of emphasis was placed on the concrete interpretation of number.   We accept on intuition the natural numbers as well as the rules for operating with them.   We accept these rules because they are in keeping with our experience with number.   But now we shall adopt a different point of view.   New kinds of numbers will be examined from the standpoint of their usefulness and their application to concrete situations, but we shall also examine them from the logical standpoint.

The natural numbers were undefined; we accepted without proof the laws under which they operate.   As we create new numbers we shall define them in terms of the numbers we already have.   We shall also define the operations of addition and multiplication in terms of the numbers and operations already at our disposal.   We should like the new numbers to behave as the old ones did, that is, obey the associative, commutative, and distributive laws.   The fact that we should like to preserve these properties is no assurance that we shall. It is up to us to *prove* that we have so chosen our definitions that the new creatures will have to conform to these rules.

This point is very significant.   Just a little more than a century ago, mathematicians came to realize for the first time that their axioms were not "self-evident" truths but were mere noncontradictory assumptions.   In the early part of the nineteenth century, it occurred to an English mathematician named Hamilton that a "number," a thing defined in terms of number, did not of necessity *have* to obey the commutative law.   Coincidentally, the same notion of denying time-honored postulates occurred to several men in the field of geometry at about this same time.   It was an important milestone in the history of human thought.   Without this changed conception of the nature of knowledge as obtained from deduction, the atomic age would never have been born.

From the standpoint of logic it is not at all necessary that our new numbers have any practical usefulness.   From the historical standpoint, both logic and utility have been responsible for the extensions of number.   New kinds of number have been invented because of a logical need for completeness, it being long after their invention before man found a practical use for them.   The rational numbers, common fractions, came into existence because man needed such numbers in his daily pursuits, but negative numbers were accepted as "absurd," "fictitious," meaningless symbols long before they were given a meaningful physical interpretation.

THE INTEGERS

5.9   As we have seen, the natural numbers are not closed with respect to subtraction; $a - b$ does not always equal a number if we mean by *number* the natural numbers and zero.   We invent the integers in order that $a - b$, where a, b are natural numbers or zero, shall always equal a number.   Algebraically, we wish to have a solution to the equation

$$x + a = 0, \text{ where } a \text{ is a natural number}$$

The natural numbers are closed under addition.   If a and b are natural numbers, then $a + b = n$ is a natural number.   Our first reaction is that we have combined a and b and obtained a new number n.   But let us center our attention on the $a + b$; we may quite properly think of $a + b$ as being just another way of writing the number n. For example, if we wish we can write $2 + 3$ instead of 5.   We may consider $a + b$ as the sum of two numbers but we may also consider it *a number*.   In the same fashion we may represent 5 as $20 - 15$ or $92 - 87$ or $44 - 39$.   In fact, there are infinitely many pairs of natural numbers we may subtract to get 5.   Just as the natural number 5 is used to identify all sets that may be put in one-to-one correspondence with the fingers of one hand (the ordered set of names one, two, three, four, five, if you insist), we shall now invent a number $+5$ to identify the set of all ordered natural number pairs whose difference is the natural number 5.   In conformity with this idea we shall define the integer.

If a, b are natural numbers or zero it is always possible to subtract one of them from the other and get either a natural number or zero. For example, if $a = 5$ and $b = 2$ we can find $a - b$, a natural number. But if $a = 5$ and $b = 7$ we can then find $b - a$, a natural number. Finally, if $a = b$ we can find either $a - b$ or $b - a$, zero in either case.

D_1 If a, b, and n are natural numbers or zero and if $a - b = n$, the ordered pair (a, b) is the positive integer, $+n$. If $b - a = n$, the ordered pair (a, b) is the negative integer, $-n$.

When we refer to an *ordered* pair we merely mean that it makes a difference which number is first: (3, 4) and (4, 3) are the same pair of numbers but they are different *ordered* pairs. The ordered pair in the definition is merely an implied subtraction. Thus we can say that an integer is obtained by subtracting two natural numbers or zero.

D_2 Two integers are equal, $(a, b) = (c, d)$, if and only if $a + d = b + c$.

D_3 The integer $(a, b) < (c, d)$ if and only if $(a + d) < (b + c)$.

D_4 Addition of integers is defined by $(a, b) + (c, d) = [(a + c), (b + d)]$.

D_5 Multiplication of integers is defined by $(a, b) \cdot (c, d) = [(ac + bd), (bc + ad)]$.

Notice that the integers $+n$ and $-n$ were both defined in terms of the natural numbers and zero and the operation of subtraction, in other words, in terms of what we have already admitted into the system. Note further that $+n$ and $-n$ are integers, neither of which is the natural number n. The relationships $=$ and $<$ are defined in terms of the natural numbers and zero. We see from D_4 and D_5 that the integers are closed under addition and multiplication since the natural numbers are, and further, the operations are defined in terms of addition and multiplication of the natural numbers and zero. That is, the sum (or product) of two integers is an ordered pair of natural numbers or zero.

The first question to confront us in our new set of integers is: Where have the natural numbers gone? Have they, amoebalike, reproduced two new numbers each and lost their identity in the process? This is not quite the case. Although technically the natural numbers are not part of the integers, we can identify a part of the newer, larger set with the natural numbers. We can establish a one-to-one correspondence between the natural numbers and a subset of the integers which will be preserved under addition and multiplication as well as equality and order. For example, if we identify the natural numbers a and b with the integers (c, d) and (e, f) respectively, the same means of identification will pair $a + b$ with $(c, d) + (e, f)$, and $a \cdot b$ with $(c, d) \cdot (e, f)$. That is, the set of natural numbers is isomorphic to a subset of the integers.

Consider the integer $(a, 0)$. From D_1, since $a - 0 = a$, the natural number pair $(a, 0)$ is the integer $+a$. Then any natural number a corresponds to the positive integer $+a$.

From D_2, we have $(a, 0) = (c, 0)$ if and only if $a + 0 = 0 + c$ or $a = c$. We are saying that the integer $(a, 0)$ will equal the integer $(c, 0)$ if and only if the natural number a equals the natural number c.

D_3 requires that $(a, 0) < (c, 0)$ if and only if $a + 0 < 0 + c$ or $a < c$.

From D_4, we have $(a, 0) + (c, 0) = [(a + c), (0 + 0)]$.

In other words, the sum $(a + c)$ of the natural numbers a and c when written as an integer is $[(a + c), (0)]$, which is identically the sum of the integers that correspond to a, c, namely $(a, 0)$ and $(c, 0)$.

Similarly for multiplication: $(a, 0) \cdot (c, 0) = [(ac + 0), (0 + 0)] = (ac, 0) = ac$.

Then for all practical purposes we still have the natural numbers in the guise of positive integers. For this reason we usually write $+n$ simply as n.

Referring once more to D_1, we see that we have created negative integers as well as positive integers. The ordered pair (a, b) defines the negative integer $-n$ if $b - a = n$. Note that the pair (a, b) cannot define both a positive and a negative integer because, if $a - b = n$ where a, b, n are natural numbers, then $b - a$ cannot equal a natural number. Similarly, if $b - a = n$, then $a - b$ is meaningless in the set of natural numbers.

We have shown that the positive integers $(a, 0)$ are isomorphic to the natural numbers. What about the integers $(0, a)$? Do they also "act just like" the natural numbers? The integer $(0, a)$ cannot be a positive integer for, if it were, $0 - a$ would be a natural number. If a is not zero, we conclude that $(0, a)$ is a negative integer. Furthermore, by definition it is the negative integer $-a$, since $a - 0 = a$. There is a negative integer $(0, a)$ corresponding to each natural number a.

D_2 tells us that $(0, b) = (0, d)$ if and only if $0 + d = b + 0$. The condition that two negative integers be equal is precisely the condition that the natural numbers we have associated with them be equal also.

According to D_3, $(0, b) < (0, d)$ if and only if $0 + d < b + 0$; and here the isomorphism breaks down because the larger of two natural numbers is associated with the smaller of the two corresponding negative integers.

But let us continue and see whether the negative integers act like natural numbers with respect to addition and multiplication. By D_4, we have $(0, b) + (0, d) = [(0 + 0), (b + d)]$. And the sum $[(0 + 0), (b + d)]$ is in turn associated with the natural number $(b + d)$. But they do not "behave" under multiplication: $(0, b) \cdot (0, d) = [(0 + bd), (0 + 0)] = (bd, 0)$. If the isomorphism existed we would have to get the result $(0, bd)$. Another way of getting at the idea is to observe that (1) the natural numbers are closed under multiplication, (2) the positive integers are closed under multiplication, but (3) the negative integers are not closed under multiplication.

We have observed that a one-to-one correspondence exists between the natural numbers and the positive integers which are of the form $(a, 0)$. But what about the positive integers (a, b) where $b \neq 0$? Is there a one-to-one correspondence between all the positive integers and the natural numbers? The question reduces itself to whether or not any positive integer is expressible in the form $(a, 0)$ and therefore $+a$. For example, $(20, 15)$ and $(17, 12)$ and $(5, 0)$ are all by definition the integer $+5$. The definition of equal integers provides an affirmative answer to our question. If a, b, c are natural numbers, then the integers (a, b) and $(c, 0)$ are equal provided $a = b + c$; but this implies that $a - b = c$. And, by D_1, $a - b$ must equal some natural number c if (a, b) is a positive integer.

Similar considerations will show that every negative integer (a, b) is expressible in the form $(0, d)$. We may conclude that all positive and negative integers are obtainable from the natural numbers by attaching the sign, $+$ or $-$, as was implied in D_1. But what about zero? Is it an integer? If so, is it positive or negative? If, in D_1, $a = b$, then $a - b = b - a = 0$ and we are justified in saying $(a, b) = +0$ and $(a, b) = -0$. This seems to imply that zero is both plus and minus. No logical difficulties would result if we adopted this point of view; in fact we may attach either sign to zero. Any couple (a, a) is equal to the couple $(0, 0)$. From the standpoint of physical interpretation it is better to adopt the point of view that zero is neither positive nor negative. Then we say the integers consist of the positive integers, the negative integers, and zero.

——————— E X E R C I S E S ———————

1. Use the addition definition D_4 to find:
    (a) $(5, 1) + (1, 4)$ (c) $(5, 0) + (4, 1)$
    (b) $(1, 3) + (6, 2)$ (d) $(2, 6) + (3, 5)$

2. Translate the results of Exercise 1 to the usual form by applying D_1.

3. Use D_5 to find:
   (a) $(1, 3) \cdot (2, 2)$ (c) $(2, 4) \cdot (5, 2)$
   (b) $(4, 3) \cdot (2, 5)$ (d) $(2, 1) \cdot (6, 3)$

4. Translate the results of Exercise 3 to the usual form by applying D_1.

5. Use D_3 to determine which of the following pairs of integers is the greater.
   (a) $(20, 23)$ and $(8, 2)$ (c) $(4, 6)$ and $(3, 9)$
   (b) $(24, 6)$ and $(32, 28)$ (d) $(2, 5)$ and $(8, 16)$

6. Translate the results of Exercise 5 into the usual form by applying D_1.

7. Prove that any positive integer is greater than every negative integer. Use D_3.

8. If a, b are natural numbers and $a > b$, prove that $-a < -b$. Use D_3.

9. On page 96 we defined zero as the additive identity $a + 0 = a$. In the context of integers, zero is defined as the natural number couple (a, a). Prove these definitions are equivalent.

10. Prove that zero is greater than any negative integer.

PROPERTIES OF THE INTEGERS

5.10 We set out to enlarge our set of natural numbers so as to satisfy all eleven field postulates given in Section 5.7. Our motive in creating the integers was to satisfy F_4, that is, produce a system that is closed under subtraction. Not only must we be sure our new creature has this property but we must be sure that it does not do violence to the other properties.

D_4 and D_5 guarantee that F_1 and F_6 respectively are satisfied. The integers are closed with respect to both addition and multiplication. F_2 requires that

$$[(a, b) + (c, d)] + (e, f) = (a, b) + [(c, d) + (e, f)]$$

We shall establish this by evaluating each side of the equation separately and arriving at the same result:

$$[(a, b) + (c, d)] + (e, f) = [(a + c), (b + d)] + (e, f)$$
$$= [(a + c + e), (b + d + f)]$$
and $\quad (a, b) + [(c, d) + (e, f)] = (a, b) + [(c + e), (d + f)]$
$$= [(a + c + e), (b + d + f)]$$

Therefore the integers are associative with respect to addition.

Zero still serves as the identity element under addition since by D_4

$$(a, b) + (0, 0) = [(a + 0), (b + 0)] = (a, b)$$

and F_3 is satisfied.

That F_4 is fulfilled is evident if we add

$$(a, b) + (b, a) = [(a + b), (b + a)] = (0, 0)$$

The inverse of the positive integer $(a, b) = +n$ *is the negative integer* $(b, a) = -n$.

F_5 follows from direct application of D_4 to each side of the equation

$$(a, b) + (c, d) = (c, d) + (a, b)$$
$$(a, b) + (c, d) = [(a + c), (b + d)]$$
$$(c, d) + (a, b) = [(c + a), (d + b)]$$

If we remember that a, b, c, d are natural numbers or zero and therefore commutative, it follows that

$$[(a + c), (b + d)] = [(c + a), (d + b)]$$

The integers are commutative with respect to addition.

We may establish F_7 by applying D_5 to each side of the equation

$$[(a, b) \cdot (c, d)] \cdot (e, f) = (a, b) \cdot [(c, d) \cdot (e, f)]$$

$$[(a, b) \cdot (c, d)] \cdot (e, f) = [(ac + bd), (bc + ad)] \cdot (e, f)$$
$$= \{[(ac + bd)e + (bc + ad)f], [(bc + ad)e + (ac + bd)f]\}$$
$$= [(ace + bde + bcf + adf), (bce + ade + acf + bdf)]$$

and

$$(a, b) \cdot [(c, d) \cdot (e, f)] = (a, b) \cdot [(ce + df), (de + cf)]$$
$$= \{[a(ce + df) + b(de + cf)], [b(ce + df) + a(de + cf)]\}$$
$$= [(ace + adf + bde + bcf), (bce + bdf + ade + acf)]$$

The integers are associative with respect to multiplication.

F_8 holds since

$$(a, b) \cdot (1, 0) = [(a \cdot 1 + b \cdot 0), (b \cdot 1 + a \cdot 0)] = (a, b)$$

The multiplication identity is $(1, 0) = +1$.

F_{10} readily follows from applying D_5 to both sides of the equation

$$(a, b) \cdot (c, d) = (c, d) \cdot (a, b)$$
$$(a, b) \cdot (c, d) = [(ac + bd), (bc + ad)]$$

and

$$(c, d) \cdot (a, b) = [(ca + db), (da + cb)]$$

but

$$(ac + bd) = (ca + db) \text{ and } (bc + ad) = (da + cb)$$

The integers are commutative with respect to multiplication.

In similar fashion F_{11} may be established by evaluating both sides of the equation

$$(a, b) \cdot (c, d + e, f) = (a, b) \cdot (c, d) + (a, b) \cdot (e, f)$$
$$(a, b) \cdot (c, d + e, f) = (a, b) \cdot [(c + e), (d + f)]$$
$$= \{[a(c + e) + b(d + f)], [b(c + e) + a(d + f)]\}$$
$$= [(ac + ae + bd + bf), (bc + be + ad + af)]$$

and $(a, b) \cdot (c, d) + (a, b) \cdot (e, f)$
$$= [(ac + bd), (bc + ad)] + [(ae + bf), (be + af)]$$
$$= [(ac + bd + ae + bf), (bc + ad + be + af)]$$

The integers obey the distributive property.

We have now verified that all the field postulates except F_9 are satisfied by the integers.

To show that F_9 is not satisfied, let us assume that it is. We have already verified on page 138 that the product of two positive integers is a positive integer. Therefore, if the positive integer $(a, 0)$ has a multiplicative inverse (x, y) it must be positive, since the multiplication identity is positive. Our assumption is that there exists a positive integer (x, y) such that

$$(a, 0) \cdot (x, y) = (1, 0)$$

But if we multiply on the left we get

$$[(ax + 0), (0 + ay)] = (1, 0)$$

Applying D_2, this implies that

$$ax + 0 + 0 = 0 + ay + 1$$

which implies that

$$ax - ay = 1 \text{ or } a(x - y) = 1$$

Since (x, y) is positive, $x - y$ is a natural number, and the last equation asserts that the natural number a has a multiplicative inverse; this is false. Thus our assumption that (x, y) exists is false.

If in the set of field properties we replace F_9 by the cancellation property

$$\text{if } a \cdot b = a \cdot c \text{ and } a \neq 0, \text{ then } b = c$$

the resulting system is an *integral domain*. In effect, the cancellation property asserts that we can always perform a division which undoes a prior nonzero multiplication. If a natural number a has been multiplied by 4 we can surely divide the product by 4 and get a as quotient. Both the set of natural numbers and the set of integers obey the cancellation principle.   If a, b, c are either natural numbers or integers and if $a \neq 0$:

$$a \cdot b = a \cdot c$$

implies $\qquad\qquad\qquad b \cdot a = c \cdot a$

and dividing by $a \qquad b \cdot a \div a = c \cdot a \div a$

and by the definition of division

$$b = c$$

INVERSE OPERATIONS

5.11   We define subtraction and division with integers in precisely the same way as was done with the natural numbers.   We *define subtraction as the inverse of addition*, but in doing so we shall take advantage of the fact that F_4 is satisfied.   By definition,

$$(a\,,b) - (c, d) = [(a + d), (b + c)]$$

In effect we are saying that, by definition, subtraction of (c, d) is equivalent to the addition of the additive inverse (d, c).   Since $[(a + d), (b + c)]$ is always an integer, subtraction is always possible.

As with natural numbers, we define *division* by the equations

$$(a, b) \div (c, d) = (e, f) \text{ if and only if } (e, f) \cdot (c, d) = (a, b)$$

Since F_9 is not satisfied we may conclude that there is not always an (e, f) which will satisfy this condition.

Example   If $(5, 3) \div (4, 1) = (x, y)$, then $(x, y) \cdot (4, 1) = (5, 3)$.

But $(x, y) \cdot (4, 1) = [(4x + y), (4y + x)]$.

The assertion that $\quad [(4x + y), (4y + x)] \quad = 5, 3$

implies that $\qquad\qquad (4x + y) - (4y + x) = 5 - 3$

$$3x - 3y = 2$$
$$3(x - y) = 2$$

From this result we know that if the integer (x, y) exists then $(x - y)$ must be a natural number.   But there is no natural number which multiplied by 3 gives 2.   We conclude that the assumption — that an (x, y) exists which satisfies the original equation — is false.

Division by the integer $(0, 0)$ is undefined.   Consider $(a, b) \div (0, 0)$. From the definition of division,

$$(a, b) \div (0, 0) = (x, y) \text{ if and only if } (x, y) \cdot (0, 0) = (a, b)$$

But $\quad (x, y) \cdot (0, 0) = [(x \cdot 0 + y \cdot 0), (y \cdot 0 + x \cdot 0)] = (0, 0)$

This result means that we can divide by $(0, 0)$ only if $(a, b) = (0, 0)$. However, if $(a, b) = (0, 0)$ then the equation

$$(x, y) \cdot (0, 0) = (a, b)$$

is satisfied regardless of the value of (x, y). This is precisely the conclusion we reached in Section 4.11 regarding zero as a divisor in the set of natural numbers.

———————— E   X   E   R   C   I   S   E   S ————————

1. Apply the definitions D_2 and D_4 to show that the following equalities hold.
   (a) $[(4, 3) + (2, 6)] + (5, 2) = (4, 3) + [(2, 6) + (5, 2)]$
   (b) $(3, 6) + (5, 7) = (5, 7) + (3, 6)$
   (c) $(4, 6) + (3, 3) = (4, 6)$
   (d) $[(5, 0) + (0, 3)] + (2, 0) = (5, 0) + [(0, 3) + (2, 0)]$

2. Translate the results of Exercise 1 to the usual form by applying D_1.

3. Apply D_2 and D_5 to show that the following equalities hold.
   (a) $[(3, 6) \cdot (8, 2)] \cdot (4, 2) = (3, 6) \cdot [(8, 2) \cdot (4, 2)]$
   (b) $(9, 5) \cdot (6, 2) = (6, 2) \cdot (9, 5)$
   (c) $(8, 3) \cdot (0, 1) = (3, 8)$
   (d) $[(5, 0) \cdot (0, 3)] \cdot (0, 4) = (5, 0) \cdot [(0, 3) \cdot (0, 4)]$

4. Translate the results of Exercise 3 to the usual form by applying D_1.

5. Apply D_2, D_4, and D_5 to show the following.
   (a) $(5, 3) \cdot [(2, 5) + (1, 4)] = (5, 3) \cdot (2, 5) + (5, 3) \cdot (1, 4)$
   (b) $(3, 7) \cdot [(5, 2) + (2, 6)] = (3, 7) \cdot (5, 2) + (3, 7) \cdot (2, 6)$
   (c) $(2, 0) \cdot [(0, 3) + (7, 0)] = (2, 0) \cdot (0, 3) + (2, 0) \cdot (7, 0)$

6. Translate the results of Exercise 5 to the usual form by applying D_1.

7. Use the definition of subtraction, page 143, to find the following.
   (a) $(3, 7) - (8, 6)$ (c) $(9, 5) - (8, 1)$
   (b) $(0, 5) - (8, 0)$ (d) $(0, 7) - (0, 2)$

8. Translate the results of Exercise 7 to the usual form by applying D_1.

9. Determine whether each of the following is possible. Solve those that are possible.
   (a) $(8, 2) \div (0, 3)$ (c) $(10, 0) \div (0, 5)$
   (b) $(2, 6) \div (6, 3)$ (d) $(1, 6) \div (6, 4)$

10. Prove that the set $\{0, 1, 2, 3, 4, 5\}$ with respect to addition and multiplication, modulo 6, is not an integral domain.

11. Is it possible for a system that contains divisors of zero to satisfy the cancellation principle?

RULE OF SIGNS

5.12   An integer is defined as an ordered pair of natural numbers or zero, expressible as a natural number with one of the signs $+$ or $-$ attached, or as zero.   In Section 5.9 we showed that corresponding to each natural number a there is a positive integer $(a, 0)$ which we agree to write as $+a$.   We also showed that corresponding to each natural number a there is a negative integer $(0, a)$ which we agree to write as $-a$.   We showed further that any nonzero integer (c, d) is equivalent to one and only one of the integers of the form $(a, 0)$ or $(0, a)$.   From the foregoing we may conclude that if we attach a plus sign to each natural number, then attach a minus sign to each natural number, the two resulting sets, plus zero, constitute the set of integers. Unless we revert to a natural number pair for emphasis, from now on we shall indicate an integer by a single letter.

Although $+a$ and $-a$ are not the same number, they have more in common than the mere fact that they are both integers.   They are both derived from the natural number a.   When two numbers differ in sign only, they are said to have the same *numerical value*, or the same *absolute value*.   The number a is the absolute value of both $+a$ and $-a$.   This is symbolized as $a = |+a| = |-a|$.   Since the positive integers are isomorphic to the natural numbers, it would make little difference whether we thought of a as a positive integer or as a natural number.   But for the sake of simplicity when further extensions are made we shall consider it positive.

Let us now reëxamine the definition of addition of integers:

$$(a, b) + (c, d) = [(a + c), (b + d)]$$

If both of the integers to be added are positive we may rewrite the definition as

$$(a, 0) + (c, 0) = [(a + c), (0 + 0)]$$

or $\qquad (+a) + (+c) = +(a + c)$

If both integers are negative we get

$$(0, b) + (0, d) = [(0 + 0), (b + d)]$$

or $\qquad (-b) + (-d) = -(b + d)$

This gives rise to the familiar rule of signs: *When adding like-signed numbers, add the absolute values and attach the common signs.*

If we add a positive integer $(a, 0)$ and a negative integer $(0, b)$ we get

$$(a, 0) + (0, b) = [(a + 0), (0 + b)] = (a, b)$$

Reference to D_1 tells us that (a, b) is the positive number $a - b$ if $a > b$, and is the negative of $b - a$ if $a < b$. This gives rise to the other half of the rule of signs in addition: *When adding unlike-signed numbers, subtract the smaller absolute value from the larger and attach the sign of the larger in absolute value.*

The definition of multiplication

$$(a, b) \cdot (c, d) = [(ac + bd), (bc + ad)]$$

may be written as follows when both factors are positive:

$$(a, 0) \cdot (c, 0) = [(ac + 0), (0 + 0)] = (ac, 0)$$

or $\qquad (+a) \cdot (+c) = +ac$

If both factors are negative, we get

$$(0, b) \cdot (0, d) = [(0 + bd), (0 + 0)] = (bd, 0) = +bd$$

or $\qquad (-b) \cdot (-d) = +bd$

These two results are summarized in the familiar rule: *The product of two like-signed numbers is the positive product of their absolute values.*

If (a, b) is positive and (c, d) is negative, we get

$$(a, 0) \cdot (0, d) = [(0 + 0), (0 + ad)] = (0, ad) = -ad$$

or $\qquad (+a) \cdot (-d) = -ad$

which is equivalent to the rule: *The product of two unlike-signed numbers is minus the product of their absolute values.*

We have *not* proved these rules. We merely emphasize the fact that they are inherent in our definitions.

It is unnecessary to consider (a, b) as negative and (c, d) as positive in the above derivations since we have already shown both addition and multiplication to be commutative.

In Section 5.10 we showed the additive properties of zero to be unchanged; that is, $a + 0 = 0 + a = a$, where a is any integer. We must show that for multiplication

$$a \cdot 0 = 0 \cdot a = 0$$

Since we have already shown multiplication to be commutative, it is sufficient to show $a \cdot 0 = 0$. Using the multiplication definition we get

$$(a, b) \cdot (0, 0) = [(a \cdot 0 + b \cdot 0), (b \cdot 0 + a \cdot 0)] = (0, 0) = 0$$

and we may still say that a product is zero if at least one factor is zero.

The rule, *to subtract signed numbers change the sign of the subtrahend and add,* is justified when we observe that (1) subtraction was defined as the inverse of addition and (2) we obtain the additive inverse of an integer by changing its sign. In view of the rule, we may interpret a minus sign either as an indication that a number is negative or as the indicated operation subtraction.

Remember that we agree, since the positive integers are isomorphic to the natural numbers, that the omission of the plus sign in front of a positive number can cause no ambiguity. The symbol $-a$ may then be thought of as meaning either $0 + (-a)$ or $0 - (+a)$.

The rule of signs for division is identical with that of multiplication: *When dividing like-signed numbers the quotient is plus; when dividing unlike-signed numbers the quotient is minus.* This rule is justified when we recall that division was defined as the inverse of multiplication. If a, b, c are natural numbers such that $a \div b = c$, which implies that $c \cdot b = a$, we have four cases to consider:

(1) $(+a) \div (+b) = (+c)$, because $(+c) \cdot (+b) = (+a)$

(2) $(+a) \div (-b) = (-c)$, because $(-c) \cdot (-b) = (+a)$

(3) $(-a) \div (+b) = (-c)$, because $(-c) \cdot (+b) = (-a)$

(4) $(-a) \div (-b) = (+c)$, because $(+c) \cdot (-b) = (-a)$

———————— E X E R C I S E S ————————

1. Compute the following.
   (a) $(-3) + (-5) + 7 + (-5)$ (e) $(-9) \div 3$
   (b) $(-5)(-9)$ (f) $(-27) \div (-3)$
   (c) $(-3)(-4)(-5)$ (g) $(-5)(-7) - (-8)$
   (d) $(-7) - (-8)$ (h) $4[8 + (-5)]$

2. Simplify the following, $a, b, c, \ldots$ integers.
   (a) $(-a)(-b)(-c)$ (d) $(-a)(-a)$
   (b) $(-a)(b + c)$ (e) $12b \div (-4)$
   (c) $-(-a)$ (f) $-a + (-b) - c$

3. Under what condition is $(-b)$ a positive integer?

4. If a product is negative, what can we infer with regard to the number of positive factors? Negative factors?

5. If a product is positive, what can we infer with regard to the number of positive factors? Negative factors?

6. What can we infer with regard to a if a^2 is negative?

7. Assign values to a, b, c, d such that
   (a) $a > b, c > d$, and $a \cdot c > b \cdot d$
   (b) $a > b, c > d$, and $a \cdot c < b \cdot d$
   (c) $a > b, c > d$, and $a + c > b + d$

8.   Which of the following are possible?
     (a) $a > b$, $c = d$, and $a - c > b - d$
     (b) $a > b$, $c > d$, and $c - a > d - b$
     (c) $a > b$, $c = d$, and $a + c < b + d$

9.   Prove that, if a, b are integers, $a > b$ if and only if $a - b$ is a positive integer. Consider three cases: (1) a, b positive, (2) one positive, one negative, and (3) a, b negative. Use D_3 and the order relation of natural numbers given in Section 5.7, page 134.

10. Rewrite D_2 through D_5, replacing the commas in the ordered pair notation with minus signs. If we interpret a, b, c, d as integers, are the resulting statements correct?

PHYSICAL INTERPRETATION OF SIGNED INTEGERS

5.13   We have given a formal, abstract development of the integers. But what practical application do they have? What physical interpretation can they be given? Our former concept of addition is now inadequate. You may have an empty basket and say the basket contains zero eggs, but how could a basket have minus five eggs in it? Less than nothing is truly impossible. This accounts for the fact that the ancients, although they manipulated negative numbers and even discovered the correct rules of operation with them, rejected them as meaningless and fictitious. The difficulty lies in the fact that we are attempting to give negative numbers a physical interpretation like our interpretation of natural numbers. If this were possible we should have no need of negative numbers. No, a basket cannot contain minus five eggs, but neither can you jump out a window $\frac{3}{4}$ of a time. That does not mean (-5) and $\frac{3}{4}$ are not perfectly good numbers; it does mean that they are not natural numbers and we should not expect them to perform in a way in which they are not intended to. Nobody expects to type a letter with a washing machine.

One of the earliest attempts at interpreting negative numbers was that of Fibonacci, an Italian of the thirteenth century. He decided that, in determining profit, a negative result implied a loss. Here we have the basic idea underlying this extension of number; that is, *direction*. You have played games in which it is possible to "go in the hole." The thermometer sometimes goes below zero. Debits and credits are in opposite directions in that one is for and the other against. We think of numerous situations in which our concern is with not merely how much or how many but in what direction. Is it for or against, profit or loss, up or down, to the left or right?   When our concern is with magnitudes which may be applied in either of two diametrically opposite directions we have a need for *directed numbers.* Just as we thought of addition of natural numbers as counting sets, we can now think of the addition of signed numbers as *directed* counting.   Consider a line extending endlessly in both directions.   Mark an arbitrarily chosen point as zero; then mark, in each direction, points a convenient unit apart.   We name the points in one direction $+1$, $+2$, $+3$, and so on, and in the opposite direction -1, -2, -3, and so on.   It is mere conformance to tradition that requires us to consider positive a direction that is up or to the right, and negative one that is down or to the left.

Zero now takes on a new role as a number.   It is unique in being neither positive nor negative.   But it is on an equal footing with other numbers in that it is a point on a scale that has no first or last number.   Zero is merely the point from which we orient ourselves. The concept of zero as the number of elements in an empty set, a symbol to represent the absence of quantity, is now inadequate.   If in the evening following a hot day in August the thermometer suddenly dropped to zero, that certainly would not be nothing; it would be something indeed.   Zero on the Fahrenheit or centigrade scale does not mean the same thing; we have used two different points of reference.   But in neither case are we to infer that a zero reading means the absence of heat.   Scientists use still another temperature scale, the absolute scale.   On this scale, zero is supposed to mean the complete absence of heat, but that point has never been reached.

To return to our number scale, we can explain the addition of signed numbers in terms of counting.   Keep in mind the fact that we are not defining anything.   That has already been done.   We shall interpret the addition sign as meaning "move to the right" and the subtraction sign as "move to the left" (they are inverse operations). Now if a and b are signed numbers, $a + b$ means start at a and move to the right b units.   This interpretation is meaningful whether it conforms with our definition or not, as long as b is positive or zero. But if b is negative we are being asked to move minus b times, which is meaningless.   Then we shall further agree that when required to move a minus number of steps this is to be interpreted as to move in the direction opposite that implied by the sign of operation.   We interpret $(a) + (b)$ to mean, start at $(+a)$ and move to the right $(+b)$ steps; $(-a) + (-b)$ to mean, start at $(-a)$ and move to the right $(-b)$ steps but, since we cannot move $(-b)$ steps, we move to the *left* $(+b)$ steps. On the other hand, $(-a) - (-b)$ shall mean to start at $(-a)$ and move to the right $(+b)$ steps since it is impossible to move to the left $(-b)$ steps.

We can easily verify the fact that this physical interpretation is consistent with our abstract definition of addition. Let us use numerical examples:

$$(+4) + (+5) = (+5) + (+4) = +(4 + 5) = 9$$

The first member of the equality, $(+4) + (+5)$, means to start at $(+4)$ and move to the right five steps. The second member means start at $(+5)$ and move to the right four steps. In each case we end up $4 + 5 = 9$ units to the right of zero.

$$(-4) + (-5) = (-5) + (-4) = -(4 + 5) = -9$$

In this example we start at (-4) and move to the left five steps, or, in the second member, start at (-5) and move to the left four steps. In either case we end up 9 units to the left of zero.

$$(-4) + (+5) = (+5) + (-4) = +(5 - 4) = +1$$

In the first instance we start at (-4) and move to the right five steps. In the second we start at $(+5)$ and move to the left four steps. In either case we end up one unit to the right of zero.

$$(-5) + (+4) = (+4) + (-5) = -(5 - 4) = -1$$

In the first operation we start at (-5) and move to the right four steps, and in the second we start at $(+4)$ and move to the left five steps. In both instances we end up one unit to the left of zero.

In accordance with our definition of subtraction we may think of using the inverse operation with the inverse element; then $(+4) - (+5) = (+4) + (-5)$ which again gives (-1). We could have interpreted subtraction on the line as follows: $(+4) - (+5)$ equals whatever must be added to $(+5)$ to get $(+4)$ and we obviously must add (-1). All these considerations indicate that our on-the-line interpretation of subtraction should mean that we end up at (-1). According to this interpretation, $(+4) - (+5)$ means, start at $(+4)$ and move to the left five steps, which puts us at (-1).

By the definition of subtraction, $(-4) - (-5) = (-4) + (+5) = +1$. If we start at (-4) and move to the *right* five steps, we end up

at $(+1)$. The consistency of the line interpretation of subtraction
with the definition can be verified easily for the other cases.

We can interpret the multiplication on the directed line, of $(+a)$
times $(+b)$, in a manner analogous to the interpretation of the multiplication of natural numbers; namely, we add $(+b) + (+b) + (+b)$
... for a terms. Thus, $(+a)(+b)$ may be interpreted as meaning
to start at zero and step b units to the right, then b more units
to the right and continue until the operation has been performed
a times.

Similarly, $(+a)(-b)$ may be interpreted to mean $(-b) + (-b) +$
... for a terms, or to start at zero and move to the left b units, then
move to the left b more units, and continue until the operation has
been performed a times.

How shall we interpret $(-a)(+b)$? We can hardly say that it
means $(+b) + (+b) + (+b) \ldots$ for minus a terms. Recall the interpretation of $(+a) + (-b)$ wherein we agree that $(-b)$ does not
mean minus b steps but, rather, take b steps in the other direction.
In a similar manner we may interpret $(-a)(+b)$ to mean $0 - (+b) -$
$(+b) \ldots$ until we have moved to the *left* of zero b units a times.
But this is equivalent to the interpretation given $(+a)(-b)$, which
is in keeping with the fact that our abstract definition preserved
commutativity.

Finally, we seek to give meaning to $(-a)(-b) = +ab$. We could
take the position that it should equal $-ab$ in order that negative
numbers when combined with each other might act as the natural
numbers do. If we tried to paraphrase the multiplication of natural
numbers, we could say that $(-a)(-b)$ means $(-b) + (-b) + (-b)$
... for minus a times. But since we cannot perform the operation
minus a times we can agree as before that this shall mean: perform
the inverse operation a times. Then $(-a)(-b)$ may be interpreted
to mean $0 - (-b) - (-b) - (-b) \ldots$ which we have already agreed
means $0 + (+b) + (+b) \ldots$ for a terms. This leads us to the acceptance of the definition $(-a)(-b) = +ab$. There are, however, more
compelling reasons.

Observe that $3 \cdot 3 = 9$; $3 \cdot 2 = 6$; $3 \cdot 1 = 3$; $3 \cdot 0 = 0$; $3(-1) =$
-3; $3(-2) = -6$; and $3(-3) = -9$. As the multiplier is decreased
by 1, the product is decreased by 3 without exception. Observe further
that $(-3)3 = -9$; $(-3)2 = -6$; $(-3)1 = -3$; and $(-3)0 = 0$.
In this sequence the product increases by 3 each time. If we wish
this pattern to continue, we must get $(-3)(-1) = +3$ as the next

step.   Once again we are led to the desirability of defining the product of two negative numbers as positive.

Perhaps the strongest motive for the acceptance of our definition of multiplication lies in the fact that the distributive law would otherwise not hold.   Consider the following:

$$(+a)(+b) + (+a)(-b) + (-a)(-b)$$
$$= (+a)(+b) + (-b)(+a) + (-b)(-a)$$

since multiplication is commutative.   Applying the associative law to both sides, we get

$$[(+a)(+b) + (+a)(-b)] + (-a)(-b)$$
$$= (+a)(+b) + [(-b)(+a) + (-b)(-a)]$$

But when we apply the distributive law, this reduces to

$$+a[(+b) + (-b)] + (-a)(-b)$$
$$= (+a)(+b) + (-b)[(+a) + (-a)]$$

or $$\qquad (-a)(-b) = +ab$$

This does not prove that minus times minus gives plus.   That is an aspect of the definition of multiplication.   We proved that the distributive law held under this definition.   If we attempt to prove minus times minus equals plus and the distributive law, each in terms of the other, we shall be reasoning in a circle.

———————   E   X   E   R   C   I   S   E   S   ———————

1.   Find the following on the directed line.
(a) $(-5) + (-4)$ (c) $(-3) + (+8)$ (e) $(+2) + (-7)$
(b) $(+3) + (+7)$ (d) $(+9) + (-7)$ (f) $(-3) + (+6)$

2.   Show that the definition of addition of oppositely signed integers is consistent with the interpretation of addition on the directed line.

3.   Interpret the meaning of the following on the directed line.
(a) $(+b) - (+b)$ (c) $(+b) + (-b)$
(b) $(-b) + (+b)$ (d) $(-b) - (-b)$

4.   If $(-a)(-b) = -ab$ and $(-a)(+b) = -ab$, the cancellation principle would force us to what conclusion?

5.   Verify that the definition of subtraction and its interpretation on a directed line are equivalent for the following cases.
(a) $(-5) - (-4)$ (c) $(-4) - (+5)$
(b) $(+5) - (-5)$ (d) $(+5) - (-4)$

6. Concrete should never be poured in freezing weather. If the first number represents the centigrade temperature an hour ago and the second represents the change in temperature during the past hour, how are the two situations $15 - 8$ and $-8 + 15$ the same? How do they differ? Which will be the safer if you wish to begin pouring your concrete?

7. Thales of Miletus, the first Greek geometer, was born 640 B.C. and died 546 B.C. Diophantus of Alexandria, one of the last Greek mathematicians, died about 325 A.D. According to these dates, how long did the Greek Era last?

8. If Diophantus was born 250 A.D., he was 21 years old how long after Thales' death?

9. Archimedes was born 287 B.C. and died 212 B.C. In terms of dates of birth, did Archimedes live nearer in time to Thales or Diophantus? How much nearer?

10. According to the dates given, how long did each live?

11. The Great Pyramid was built about 2900 B.C. How old was it when Columbus discovered America? How old is it now?

12. The Ahmes Papyrus was written 1650 B.C. Which is the older and how much: the Papyrus or the Great Pyramid?

13. If it is 17° colder at the top of a mountain than it is at the foot, determine what temperature each of the following implies: 10° at the top of the mountain; -5° at the foot of the mountain; -10° at the top; -10° at the foot; 20° at the top; -20° at the top; 20° at the foot; -20° at the foot.

14. The following table indicates the fluctuation in the prices of certain common stocks. Determine the final quotation of each stock.

Stock	Initial quotation	Change first day	Change second day
A	$128\frac{3}{4}$	$-2\frac{7}{8}$	$+5\frac{1}{4}$
B	23	$-\frac{7}{8}$	$-3\frac{1}{2}$
C	$47\frac{1}{2}$	$+\frac{3}{4}$	$+1\frac{7}{8}$
D	$146\frac{1}{4}$	$+1\frac{3}{8}$	$-2\frac{1}{2}$
E	$18\frac{3}{4}$	$-2\frac{1}{4}$	$-\frac{7}{8}$

15. In running levels, the surveyor takes a "back sight" on a point whose elevation is known, then takes a forward sight on the point whose elevation is to be determined. His first back sight is taken on a "bench mark" whose elevation we shall take as zero. He reads 4.8 feet on the level rod on his first back sight. The forward reading on point A is 10.4 feet.

B.M. elev. zero

10.4 ft.

A

He then moves his level and back sights on point A; the reading is 5.9 feet. From this position he takes a forward reading on point B and gets a reading of 3.7 feet. He again moves his level and back sights on B, reading 11.6 feet. Find the elevation of points A and B. If the work is accurately done, what reading should he get on the bench mark from this position?

16. Evaluate each side of the following equation separately and show that $[(-5) + (-3)] - (-4) = (-5) + [(-3) - (-4)]$.

17. Show that $-6[3 + (-5)] = (-6)(3) + (-6)(-5)$.

18. What does $(-6) - (-3)$ mean on the directed line? What does $-(6 - 3)$ mean on the directed line? In what sense are the two expressions the same?

THE RATIONAL NUMBER SYSTEM

5.14 The integers make it possible always to add, subtract, or multiply. But even with the restriction that we do not divide by zero, division is not always possible. We have followed what seems to be the more natural logical order in discussing signed numbers before rational numbers. Historically, the other order was followed, just as it is in schoolwork today. Man found a need for rational numbers long before he found any need for negative numbers. We have observed that the signed numbers came into being long before their practical usefulness was discovered. Just the reverse is true of fractions. Man needed fractions long before he invented rational numbers. Various schemes were devised to avoid the use of general fractions. Some of them seem rather weird to us.

The Egyptians were quite fond of unit fractions; a unit fraction is one whose numerator is one. The Ahmes Papyrus, written about 1650 B.C., contained extensive tables of unit fractions. Rather than use the fraction $\frac{2}{43}$ they used $\frac{1}{42} + \frac{1}{86} + \frac{1}{229} + \frac{1}{301}$. Why the most obvious unit fractions $\frac{1}{43} + \frac{1}{43}$ were disregarded remains a mystery. One exception to the exclusive use of unit fractions was the fact that they used the fraction $\frac{2}{3}$.

Another effort at avoiding fractions, popular with the Greeks and Romans, was the invention of submultiples. Rather than use $\frac{7}{12}$ of some unit of measure, a new unit $\frac{1}{12}$ as large was invented and 7 of these were used. Another favorite submultiple was $\frac{1}{16}$. Our English system of weights and measures is eloquent evidence of this practice.

Still another effort at simplifying work with fractions consisted in using powers of a single number as denominator.   The Babylonians used sexagesimal fractions.   The only denominators used were 60, 60^2, 60^3, and so on.   This idea, when combined with the base of the system of numeration, has tremendous advantages.   In fact, this is precisely the idea behind the use of decimal fractions.   A decimal fraction is simply one in which the denominator, though not written down, is some integral power of 10.

RATIONAL NUMBERS DEFINED

5.15   We defined an integer as an ordered pair of natural numbers. We shall define rational numbers as ordered pairs of integers.   If a and b are two integers, and $b \neq 0$, then in the equation $bx = a$, the integer x is equal to the integer $a \div b$ if a is divisible by b.   But in such cases as $5x = 2$ there is no integer which when multiplied by 5 gives 2.   We shall then create a new kind of number, the rational number.

> D_6 We define the rational number x as a number which satisfies the
> equation $bx = a$, where a, b are integers and $b \neq 0$.   We shall agree to
> write the number $x = (a, b)$.

The rational number is thus defined as an *ordered pair of integers*.   In our rational number system the number x which satisfies the equation $4x = 12$ is not 3 but $(12, 4)$.

The rational number (a, b) is an implied division of the two integers a and b.   The invention of rational numbers makes it possible always to add, subtract, multiply, and divide the integers, division by zero excepted.   But the integers are still not closed under division; we are merely sure that we will get a rational number when performing these operations with integers.   We shall see that the rational numbers are, except for division by zero, closed with respect to all four operations.

In order that the rational number system may be of service to us, we wish to define addition and multiplication in such a way that the usual associative, commutative, and distributive laws still hold.   Furthermore, we wish to be able to identify the integers and consequently the natural numbers as a part of this new system.   Finally, the new system must have a practical usefulness.

We may tentatively identify the integers among the rational numbers in the following way.   Since the rational number (a, b) is an implied division $(a \div b)$, the rational number $(a, 1)$ is an implied division $(a \div 1)$. But this is equal to the integer a. Then we may identify the integers as rational numbers whose second component is 1, provided the definitions of addition, subtraction, multiplication, and division of rational numbers yield results consistent with this identification. In other words, we wish to show the integers isomorphic to the subset $(a, 1)$ of rational numbers.

We shall define equal rational numbers as follows:

D_7 $(a, b) = (c, d)$ if and only if $ad = bc$.

Next let us order the rational numbers:

D_8 $(a, b) > (c, d)$ if and only if $abd^2 > b^2cd$.

MULTIPLICATION AND ADDITION OF RATIONAL NUMBERS

5.16   We shall define the product of two rational numbers as the rational number whose first component is the product of the first components of the factors and whose second component is the product of the second components of the factors.

D_9 $(a, b)(c, d) = (ac, bd)$.

We are now able to prove the following important theorem:

Theorem   If each component of a rational number is multiplied by the same integer the resulting rational number is equal to the original.

$$(a, b) = (ka, kb)$$

Proof: By definition of equal rational numbers, $(a, b) = ka, kb$ if and only if $akb = bka$. But since a, b and k are integers they obey the commutative law for multiplication, and $akb = bka$.

We shall now define addition:

D_{10} $(a, b) + (c, b) = [(a + c), b]$.

This defines the addition of rational numbers when the two numbers have the same second component. If we employ the relationship which was proved just above, we may always change two rational numbers so that they will have the same second component. Our definition does not permit the addition of $(a, b) + (c, d)$, but if we multiply both components of (a, b) by d and both components of (c, d) by b we get $(a, b) + (c, d) = (da, db) + (bc, db) = [(da + bc), db]$. We could, if we chose, state this result as a general definition of addition: $(a, b) + (c, d) = [(da + bc), db]$, but it is actually a result of our simpler definition and our theorem.

These considerations and D_9 are sufficient to show that the field properties F_1 and F_6 are satisfied.

Addition is commutative, since

$$(a, b) + (c, d) = [(da + bc), db]$$

and $$(c, d) + (a, b) = [(bc + da), bd]$$

Applying D_7, these two results are the same if

$$(da + bc)bd = db(bc + da)$$

which is seen to be true if we apply the commutative laws of addition and multiplication for integers.   Therefore F_5 is satisfied.

If addition is associative, we must show that

$$[(a, b) + (c, d)] + (e, f) = (a, b) + [(c, d) + (e, f)]$$

Performing the addition inside the brackets, we get

$$[(da + bc), db] + (e, f) = (a, b) + [(fc + de), fd]$$

Applying the theorem at the beginning of this section, this may be expressed as

$$[(fda + fbc), fdb] + (dbe, dbf)$$
$$= (fda, fdb) + [(fcb + deb), fdb]$$

and adding the rational numbers on each side of the equation:

$$[(fda + fbc + dbe), dbf] = [(fda + fcb + deb), fdb]$$

But these two rational numbers can be made identical by applying the fact that integers are commutative under multiplication.   Therefore the two members of the original equation are equal and addition of rational numbers is associative. F_2 is satisfied.

Multiplication is commutative, since

$$(a, b)(c, d) = (ac, bd)$$

and $$(c, d)(a, b) = (ca, db)$$

But the two results are equal rational numbers because $acdb = bdca$. Thus F_{10} is satisfied.

Multiplication is also associative:

$$[(a, b)(c, d)](e, f) = (ac, bd)(e, f) = (ace, bdf)$$

and $$(a, b)[(c, d)(e, f)] = (a, b)(ce, df) = (ace, bdf)$$

Thus F_7 is satisfied.

The distributive law holds for rational numbers. The distributive law requires that $(a, b)[(c, d) + (e, f)] = (ac, bd) + (ae, bf)$. We shall first evaluate the left member of this equation.

$$(a, b)[(c, d) + (e, f)] = (a, b)[(fc, fd) + (de, df)]$$
$$= (a, b)[(fc + de), df] = \{[a(fc + de)], bdf\}$$
$$= [(afc + ade), bdf]$$

But if we add the two rational numbers in the right member, we get

$$(ac, bd) + (ae, bf) = (fac, fdb) + (dae, dbf)$$
$$= [(fac + dae), (fdb)] = [(afc + ade), bdf]$$

and the distributive law is established. This establishes F_{11}.

Returning to the definition of rational numbers, D_6 in Section 5.15, we see that the equation which defined the rational number x involved the multiplication of an integer by a rational number — an operation which has itself never been defined. Let us refine the definition. If a, b are integers and $b \neq 0$, then there always exists the rational number (x, y) where x and y are integers, such that

$$(b, 1)(x, y) = (a, 1)$$

Note that all numbers in the equation are *pairs of integers*, that is, rational numbers. By our definition of multiplication of rational numbers we may verify the fact that the number (x, y) above is (a, b):

$$(b, 1)(a, b) = (ab, b)$$

The number $(ab, b) = (a, 1)$ since we may multiply each component of $(a, 1)$ by b without changing its value.

If we multiply, we have $(a, 1)(b, 1) = (ab, 1) = ab$; and if we add, we have $(a, 1) + (b, 1) = [(a + b), 1] = a + b$.

Then under the interpretation of an integer as a rational number whose second component is 1, both the multiplication and addition of the integers a and b, treated as rational numbers, yield correct results.

Accordingly, we should expect the addition and multiplication identities to be $(0, 1)$ and $(1, 1)$ respectively. Since $(0, 1) = (0, b)$, where b is any integer not 0,

$$(a, b) + (0, b) = [(a + 0), b] = (a, b)$$

Therefore F_3 is satisfied.

To show that $(1, 1) = (c, c)$, where c is any integer not 0, is the multiplication identity, we note:

$$(a, b)(c, c) = (ac, bc) = (a, b)$$

Therefore F_8 is satisfied.

─────────── E   X   E   R   C   I   S   E   S ───────────

Interpret all ordered pairs as pairs of integers.

1.   If $(3, 4) = (b, 12)$, find b.

2.   Express $191/455$ as the sum of unit fractions.

3.   Determine which of the following is the greater.
   (a) $(3, 5)$ or $(2, -6)$
   (b) $(-7, a)$ or $(-9, a)$, where a any integer $\neq 0$.
   (c) $(-4, -6)$ or $(10, -2)$
   (d) $(-3, -3)$ or $(-15, -25)$

4.   Verify the following.
   (a) $([4, 7) + (2, 1)] + (3, 5) = (4, 7) + [(2, 1) + (3, 5)]$
   (b) $[(3, 1) \cdot (-2, 5)] \cdot (6, 4) = (3, 1) \cdot [(-2, 5) \cdot (6, 4)]$

5.   Verify the following.
   (a) $(3, 5) + (5, 3) = (5, 3) + (3, 5)$
   (b) $(6, a) \cdot (2a, 4) = (2a, 4) \cdot (6, a)$
   (c) $(3, 2) \cdot [(2, 4) + (1, 3)] = [(3, 2) \cdot (2, 4)] + [(3, 2) \cdot (1, 3)]$

6.   Verify the following.
   (a) $(a, b) \cdot (-4, -4) = (a, b)$ (d) $(2, -3) + (2, 3) = (0, 1)$
   (b) $(0, 5) + (7, 7) = (3, 3)$ (e) $(4, 6) + (-4, 6) = (0, 1)$
   (c) $(3, 7) \cdot (7, 3) = (1, 1)$

SUBTRACTION AND DIVISION OF RATIONAL NUMBERS

5.17   We shall define subtraction in a manner analogous to that of defining addition.
$$(a, b) - (c, b) = [(a - c), b]$$

As was true of addition, this definition does not permit the subtraction of rational numbers whose second components are different. However, we may again utilize the theorem of Section 5.16, page 156, to change any two rational numbers to this form:
$$(a, b) - (c, d) = (ad, bd) - (cb, db)$$

and the definition of subtraction now applies:
$$(ad, bd) - (cb, db) = [(ad - cb), bd]$$

Under this definition, is subtraction the inverse of addition? It is, if and only if
$$[(ad - cb), bd] + (cb, db) = (ad, bd)$$

Performing the addition on the left, we get

$$[(ad - cb), bd] + (cb, db) = [(ad - cb + cb), db] = (ad, bd)$$

Every rational number (a, b) has an additive inverse $(-a, b)$:

$$(a, b) + (-a, b) = \{[a + (-a)], b\} = (0, b)$$

This establishes F_4 for the rational numbers.

Let us proceed with care in selecting the definition of division. We created rational numbers in order that we might divide integers. Furthermore, we have defined the addition, subtraction, and multiplication of two rational numbers as a rational number in each case. We wish to define the division of two rational numbers as a rational number.

The equation $bx = a$ defined x in Section 5.15, page 155, as the rational number (a, b). Then $bx = a$ and $x = (a, b)$ and $x = a \div b$ are all equivalent statements. The last two of these statements imply that $a \div b = (a, b)$, but if we write a as $(a, 1)$ and b as $(b, 1)$ we get $(a, 1) \div (b, 1) = (a, b)$. However, if we multiply $(1, b)$ by $(a, 1)$,

$$(a, 1) \cdot (1, b) = (a, b)$$

This suggests the following *definition* of division of rational numbers:

$$(a, b) \div (d, c) = (ac, bd), d \neq 0$$

If we compare this with $(a, b) \cdot (c, d) = (ac, bd)$ it suggests that the multiplication inverse of any rational number (a, b), where $a \neq 0$, is (b, a).

$$(a, b)(b, a) = (ab, ba) = (1, 1)$$

Thus F_9 is satisfied, and the rational numbers are a field.

Does this definition make division the inverse of multiplication? If so, we must have $(d, c) \cdot (ac, bd) = (a, b)$. But $(d, c) \cdot (ac, bd) = (dac, cbd) = (acd, bcd)$. The last member is equal to (a, b) since we can multiply both components of (a, b) by cd and obtain (acd, bcd).

Our identification of the integers as rational numbers whose second component is 1 is consistent with both subtraction and division:

$$(a, 1) - (b, 1) = [(a - b), 1] = a - b$$
$$(a, 1) \div (b, 1) = [(a \cdot 1), (1 \cdot b)] = (a, b) = a \div b$$

In the above definition of division, $d = 0$ was excluded; otherwise, we would be dividing by zero. Of course, $b = 0$ and $c = 0$ were automatically excluded by virtue of the definition of rational numbers. If we require the identity $(0, b)$ to have a multiplication inverse $(b, 0)$ we get a result which is not a rational number.

———————————   E X E R C I S E S   ———————————

Ordered pairs are pairs of integers unless otherwise stated.

1.   Verify the following.
      (a) $(4, 5) - (3, 6) = (4, 5) + (-3, 6)$
      (b) $(2a, c) - (b, 1) = (2a, c) + (-b, 1)$
      (c) $(3, 4) \div (5, 6) = (3, 4) \cdot (6, 5)$
      (d) $(2a, 3b) \div (a, b) = (2a, 3b) \cdot (b, a) = (2, 3)$

2.   Apply the definition of division of rational numbers and show that $(a, b) \div (0, c)$ cannot equal a rational number.

3.   Prove that if $(a, b) \cdot (c, d) = (0, x)$ and $a \neq 0$, then $c = 0$.

4.   If we do not know what kind of numbers $a, b, c,$ and d are, is there any way of telling what $(a, b) \cdot (c, d)$ is equal to?

5.   An integer is an implied subtraction, a rational number is an implied division. Replace the addition signs with multiplication signs in D_2 through D_5. Compare the results with D_7 through D_9.

PROPERTIES OF THE RATIONAL SYSTEM

5.18   We have shown that the rational number system obeys the commutative, associative, and distributive laws. We now have a system such that we may perform any of the four fundamental operations, division by zero excepted, and always get a number of the system. We have succeeded in identifying the earlier numbers — integers and, consequently, natural numbers — as special cases of rational numbers. In other words, the rational numbers satisfy the requirements of a field, one in which we have established an isomorphism between the integers and the rational numbers $(a, 1)$.

Inverse elements under addition and subtraction are as they were formerly, namely, oppositely signed rational numbers. Rather than add (or subtract) (a, b) we may subtract (or add) $-(a, b)$. The definition of division indicates that (c, d) and (d, c) are inverse elements under multiplication and division since

$$(a, b) \div (c, d) = (ad, bc) = (a, b)(d, c)$$

Then we can always reduce subtraction to addition by adding the inverse element, and we can reduce division to multiplication by multiplying by the inverse element. Every rational number except $(0, a)$ has an inverse under multiplication and division.

One other property should be mentioned. We may consider a number couple whose components are rational numbers (as opposed to integers) as a rational number,

$$[(a, b), (c, d)] = (a, b) \div (c, d) = (ad, bc)$$

as long as we interpret the number couple as an implied division.

In Section 5.15 the assertion was made that, in the equation $4x = 12$, x is not 3 but $(12, 4)$. Let us examine this more critically. We know now that the integer 3 is equivalent to the rational number $(3, 1)$. If we apply the theorem of Section 5.16, we get

$$(3, 1) = (3 \cdot 4, 1 \cdot 4) = (12, 4)$$

Then, by the definition of rational numbers, x does equal $(12, 4)$; nevertheless 3 is still the solution to the equation $4x = 12$.

ORDERED FIELDS

5.19   The natural numbers are ordered. The integers are ordered. The rational numbers are also ordered; but for the first time we are dealing with a field. The rational numbers are an *ordered field*. An ordered field is a field which satisfies two additional axioms.

F_{12} Of every element a of a field, one and only one of the following is true: a is a positive element; $a = 0$; or the additive inverse of a is positive.

F_{13} For every two positive elements a, b of a field, $a + b$ is a positive element and ab is a positive element.

Consider, as an example of a field that violates both of these axioms, the field of integers 0, 1, 2, 3, 4, modulo 5, discussed in Section 5.5. This field does not satisfy F_{12} because 3 is a positive element and its additive inverse 2 is also positive; yet F_{12} states that only one of these conditions can exist. F_{13} is also violated because once again 3 (a positive element) + 2 (a positive element) = 0 (a nonpositive element).

The field of real numbers, our next extension, is ordered; but our final extension, complex numbers, is not ordered.

INTERPRETATION OF RATIONAL NUMBERS

5.20   We have now built the rational numbers more or less abstractly. They are, of course, nothing more than our familiar common fractions They are called rational because they are the ratios of integers. The notation (a, b) was not used in the place of the more familiar a/b as an aid to the printer. It was used to help the reader concentrate his attention on the logical development of the system and divorce his attention from preconceived notions about fractions.

The multiplication of fractions is accomplished by multiplying the numerators to obtain the numerator of the product and multiplying the denominators to obtain the denominator of the product. Suppose we had defined the addition of fractions in a similar manner, namely

$$\frac{a}{b} + \frac{c}{d} = \frac{a + c}{b + d}$$

It is easy to verify the fact that the commutative, associative, and distributive laws would all hold if addition were defined in this way. All too frequently some persons try to use this method for adding fractions. Why not, in deference to them, choose this as our definition? In the first place, we could no longer identify the integers among the rational numbers. Since $5 + 4 = 9$, we get inconsistent results when we add $\frac{5}{1} + \frac{4}{1} = \frac{9}{2}$.

There is another equally important reason for our choice of definition. Under the definition in the preceding paragraph, rational numbers could not be used for doing what we want them to do. However, we could find meaningful interpretations for that kind of addition. You will find in the study of probability that the probability of an event's taking place is the ratio of the number of ways it can occur to the number of ways it can occur and fail to occur. For example, the probability of drawing a spade from a deck of cards is $\frac{13}{52}$ since there are 13 spades in a deck of 52 cards. Empirical probability is that which is obtained by actual trial or observation. Suppose that of a group of 100 men, aged 34, 3 died within a year; in another group of 250 men, 5 died; and in a third group of 1,050 men, 12 died. The probability of dying at age 34 could be estimated from these samples as $\frac{3}{100} + \frac{5}{250} + \frac{12}{1050} = \frac{20}{1400}$. A strange way of adding fractions? Yes indeed, but we have exhibited a meaningful interpretation of addition if it were defined as

$$\frac{a}{b} + \frac{c}{d} = \frac{a + c}{b + d}$$

We chose our definition as we did because we *want* a/b to mean a pieces, which are obtained by dividing the whole into b equal parts. Thus $\frac{5}{12}$ of an apple means we have 5 pieces, each piece being $\frac{1}{12}$ of the apple. We certainly can add 5 pieces to 3 pieces, obtaining 8 pieces, but unless the pieces are the same size we do not know what quantity the 8 pieces represent.   That accounts for the insistence in the definition that fractions cannot be added unless the denominators are the same.   Recall that *by definition* $a/b + c/d$ is given no meaning.   It is only after we apply the property, that numerator and denominator of a fraction can be multiplied by the same number without changing its value, that we are able to apply the definition of addition to the above fractions.

Is there any difference in meaning between $\frac{5}{12}$ and $\frac{1}{12} \cdot 5$?   We interpret $\frac{5}{12}$ of an apple to mean 5 pieces, each piece $\frac{1}{12}$ of an apple. On the other hand, $\frac{1}{12} \cdot 5$ means we have $\frac{1}{12}$ of 5 apples, which is something quite different unless we are making fruit salad.   But the *number* $\frac{5}{12}$ and the *product* of the numbers $\frac{1}{12}$ and 5 are quantitatively the same since $5 = \frac{5}{1}$, and we may employ the definition of multiplication of rational numbers to $\frac{1}{12} \cdot \frac{5}{1} = \frac{5}{12}$.

The rational number a/b may be interpreted in a variety of ways. First, it is an implied division: $a/b = a \div b$.   The division $a \div b$ and, consequently, the rational number a/b may be interpreted in either of two ways: (1) we are splitting a units up into b equal sets and a/b indicates how many units there are in each of the b sets, or (2) we are splitting the a units into sets, each one of which is to contain b units, and a/b tells how many such sets we get.   Thus $\frac{20}{4}$ may be interpreted as the number we get in each set if we divide 20 into 4 equal sets, or it may be interpreted as the number of sets we get when we divide 20 into sets of 4.   We may also interpret a/b as a comparison of a with b; a is so many times as large as b.

Although fractions in some form have been in use from early times, it would be erroneous to assume that man encountered no difficulties in interpreting these numbers similar to the difficulties encountered with negative numbers.   For example, the writers of the Middle Ages were quite at a loss to explain why multiplication does not always increase the quantity.   How can you multiply and get something less than what you start with?   We could interpret $5 \times \frac{1}{2}$ as $\frac{1}{2} + \frac{1}{2} + \frac{1}{2} + \frac{1}{2} + \frac{1}{2}$, but what of $\frac{1}{2} \times 5$?   We are forced to extend our concept of counting sets to include counting *part of a set;* here we count half of a set of 5.   Similarly, with $\frac{1}{2} \times \frac{1}{3}$, we can think of our sets as containing $\frac{1}{3}$ of a unit each, and we are finding a part, namely half, of such a set.

If we write D_8, the definition of order of the rational numbers, in the more familiar notation,

$$\frac{a}{b} > \frac{c}{d} \text{ if and only if } abd^2 > b^2cd$$

we can see its motivation more easily. If we write the inequality as

$$\frac{ab}{b^2} > \frac{cd}{d^2}$$

this guarantees that the denominators are positive. If we now write the inequality with a common denominator,

$$\frac{abd^2}{b^2d^2} > \frac{b^2cd}{b^2d^2}$$

we see that the necessary and sufficient condition merely requires that the greater fraction have the greater numerator.

―――――――   E X E R C I S E S   ―――――――

1. Prove that $\dfrac{(a/b) + c}{d - e}$ is, in general, a rational number if all letters represent nonzero integers.

2. What is the exception to Exercise 1?

3. Prove that, if addition of rational numbers were defined as $a/b + c/d = (a + c)/(b + d)$, the distributive law would still hold. *Hint:* Evaluate $e/f(a/b + c/d)$ by adding the numbers in the parentheses, then multiply by e/f. Apply the distributive law, then add.

4. Prove $-\dfrac{a}{b} = \dfrac{-a}{b} = \dfrac{a}{-b}$ where $b \neq 0$. *Hint:* Let $x = -(a/b)$, then $-x = a/b$.

5. Prove that, for no integers a and b, can $1/a + 1/b = 2/(a + b)$.

6. What are the inverses of the following?
   (a) -5, under multiplication   (c) zero, under addition
   (b) $\frac{1}{3}$, under subtraction   (d) $-\frac{1}{4}$, under division

7. Prove that, if a, b, c, d are positive integers, $\dfrac{a}{b} > \dfrac{c}{d}$ if and only if $ad > bc$.

8. Prove that if two fractions have the same positive numerator the one which has the larger denominator is the smaller.

9. Reduce the following fractions to a common numerator and arrange from smallest to largest: $\frac{5}{15}, \frac{2}{3}, \frac{3}{13}, \frac{6}{31}, \frac{1}{4}$.

10. Repeat Exercise 9, but reduce to a common denominator. Which is the easier exercise?

11.   A $6\frac{1}{4}$ oz. box of cereal costs 18¢; a $10\frac{1}{2}$ oz. box of the same cereal costs 26¢. Determine which is the better buy without finding the cost per ounce or how many ounces a cent will buy.

12.   Find a rational number between $\frac{5}{13}$ and $\frac{7}{18}$.

13.* Prove that between any rational number a/b and any other rational number c/d there exists another rational number.

14.   In dividing fractions we may divide the numerators to get the numerator of the answer and divide denominators to get the denominator of the answer. Prove that this rule is equivalent to the definition in Section 5.17, p. 160.

15.* What is the difference in meaning between the two expressions $a(1/b)$ and (a/b)? Prove that they are equal.

16.* Are the integers a group under addition? Are the negative integers? Justify your answer.

17.* Are the nonzero integers a group under multiplication? Justify your answer.

18.* Are the positive rational numbers a group under addition? Multiplication? Why?

19.   Replace addition signs with multiplication signs in D_2 and compare the result with D_7.

20.   Replace addition signs with multiplication signs in D_3 and compare the result with Exercise 7.

21.   Replace addition signs with multiplication signs in D_4 and compare the result with D_9.

22.   How are the results in Exercises 19 to 21 related to the definitions of integers and rational numbers? Why can a similar relationship not be shown between D_5 and the generalization of D_{10}?

23.   Rewrite D_7 through D_{10}, replacing the comma in the ordered pair notation with a division sign. If we interpret a, b, c, d as rational numbers, are the resulting statements correct?

THE RATIONAL NUMBERS AS EXPONENTS

5.21   Our definition of exponents in Chapter III includes only positive integers and zero. If we attempt to use negative numbers or fractions as exponents, the symbols are meaningless unless we define them. The question is: Can we extend the concept of exponents to include the new numbers in a meaningful, useful way? If they are to be of any value we should select such definitions as preserve the old rules for combining exponents.

Suppose we divide a^3 by a^5. According to the formal rules established in Chapter III, $a^3 \div a^5 = a^{3-5} = a^{-2}$, which is a meaningless symbol. But we know that

$$a^3 \div a^5 = \frac{a \cdot a \cdot a}{a \cdot a \cdot a \cdot a \cdot a} = \frac{1}{a \cdot a} = \frac{1}{a^2}$$

Since the formal rule produces a^{-2} and we know the quotient is $1/a^2$ our definition of negative exponents is suggested:

Definition $a^{-n} = 1/a^n$, where n is any integer.

This definition permits n to be positive, negative, or zero. It gives rise to the rule: *A factor may be moved from denominator to numerator, or from numerator to denominator, by changing the sign of its exponent.*

If our rules for combining exponents are to extend to fractions, $a^{\frac{1}{2}} \cdot a^{\frac{1}{2}} = a^{\frac{1}{2}+\frac{1}{2}} = a^1 = a$, and $a^{\frac{1}{3}} \cdot a^{\frac{1}{3}} \cdot a^{\frac{1}{3}} = a^{\frac{1}{3}+\frac{1}{3}+\frac{1}{3}} = a^1 = a$. But by definition of square root and cube root, $\sqrt{a} \cdot \sqrt{a} = a$, and $\sqrt[3]{a} \cdot \sqrt[3]{a} \cdot \sqrt[3]{a} = a$. These considerations suggest the following:

Definition $a^{1/n} = \sqrt[n]{a}$, where n is an integer.

However, we must exercise care in interpreting both $a^{1/n}$ and $\sqrt[n]{a}$. We know that 2 is a square root of 4 because $2 \times 2 = 4$, but -2 is also a square root of 4 since $-2 \times -2 = 4$. On the other hand, we do not as yet have a number which is the square root of -4. We agree that if n is even and a is positive, $a^{1/n}$ and $\sqrt[n]{a}$ both mean the positive nth root of a. The cubic root of 27 is 3 because $3 \times 3 \times 3 = 27$. The cube root of -27 is -3 because $-3 \times -3 \times -3 = -27$. Since any odd number of negative factors gives a negative product we agree that, if n is odd, $a^{1/n}$ and $\sqrt[n]{a}$ both mean an nth root of a which agrees with a in sign. We can as yet assign no meaning to $a^{1/n}$ or $\sqrt[n]{a}$, if n should be even and a negative.

If we recall that $m/n = m(1/n) = (1/n)m$, and that $-(m/n) = 1/n(-m) = -m(1/n)$, our definitions cover all rational numbers as exponents, within the limitations stated above.

Example 1 $a^{\frac{3}{5}} = a^{\frac{1}{5} \cdot 3} = (\sqrt[5]{a})^3$

also $a^{\frac{3}{5}} = a^{3(\frac{1}{5})} = \sqrt[5]{a^3}$

therefore $(\sqrt[5]{a})^3 = \sqrt[5]{a^3}$

and in general $a^{m/n} = \sqrt[n]{a^m} = (\sqrt[n]{a})^m$

Example 2 $X^{-\frac{2}{3}} = X^{\frac{1}{3}(-2)} = \dfrac{1}{X^{\frac{1}{3}(2)}} = \dfrac{1}{\sqrt[3]{X^2}}$

Example 3 $$8^{-\frac{2}{3}} = \frac{1}{8^{\frac{2}{3}}} = \frac{1}{\sqrt[3]{8^2}} = \frac{1}{4}$$

otherwise $$8^{-\frac{2}{3}} = 8^{\frac{1}{3}(-2)} = (\sqrt[3]{8})^{-2} = 2^{-2} = \frac{1}{2^2} = \frac{1}{4}$$

"BASIMAL FRACTIONS"

*5.22 Negative exponents make it possible to extend the general notation for a base 10 number to include numbers as small as we please in addition to numbers as large as we please. The general base 10 representation of a number is

$$a_0 10^n + a_1 10^{n-1} + \ldots + a_n 10^0 + a_{n+1} 10^{-1} + a_{n+2} 10^{-2} + \ldots$$

where a_i is some digit 0 through 9, n is an integer, and $a_0 \neq 0$.

Since the scheme is now capable of extension in both directions, we need some means of indicating the starting point, some means of separating the number into parts greater than one and less than one. This is accomplished by means of the decimal point. If we move the decimal point, the value for which each digit stands is changed. If we shift it one place to the right, the power of 10 by which each digit is multiplied is increased by one, and is similarly decreased if we shift to the left.

The basic idea may be carried over to bases other than 10. For example, if we write 76.12_8 we have represented $7 \times 8^1 + 6 \times 8^0 + 1 \times 8^{-1} + 2 \times 8^{-2} = 56 + 6 + \frac{1}{8} + \frac{2}{64} = 62\frac{5}{32}$. We might call $.12_8$ an octonal fraction since 8 is the base. But with complete generality we may call such fractions basimal fractions regardless of what the particular base may be. If we shift the basimal point, we multiply the number by the corresponding power of the base. If we shift the basimal point in 76.12_8 two places to the right and get $7612._8$ the value of each digit has been multiplied by $8^2 = 64$.

In Chapter III we learned that we could convert a number from any base to any other base by dividing the number and succeeding quotients by the desired base. The digits in the new notation are the successive remainders. It is obvious why the method works when we consider the number as already written in the desired base and then consider the effect of shifting the basimal point to the left one digit at a time.

Following this same scheme, we can convert a number less than 1 from any base to any other base by multiplying the fractions, less than 1, by the desired base. The integer in the result gives the first digit in the new notation. We repeat the process — each time multiplying the fraction, less than 1, by the desired base. We know that in base 10 some fractions terminate ($\frac{1}{4}$ = .25) and some do not ($\frac{1}{3}$ = .333 . . .). The same is true of other bases. If we have a terminating basimal fraction in one base, it may or may not terminate in another base. The examples which follow are chosen because they terminate in both bases.

Example   Convert $.5343_6$ to base 8.   All computation is in base 6.

$$
\begin{array}{ll}
.5343 & \qquad .3 \\
\underline{12} & \qquad \underline{12} \\
15130 & \qquad 4.0 \\
\underline{5343} & \\
11.3000 & \\
11_6 = 7_8 & \qquad \therefore \quad .5343_6 = .74_8
\end{array}
$$

We may check the above by converting each fraction to base 10 as follows:

$$.5343_6 = 5 \times 6^{-1} + 3 \times 6^{-2} + 4 \times 6^{-3} + 3 \times 6^{-4}$$
$$= \tfrac{5}{6} + \tfrac{3}{36} + \tfrac{4}{216} + \tfrac{3}{1296} = \tfrac{5}{6} + \tfrac{1}{12} + \tfrac{1}{54} + \tfrac{1}{432}$$
$$= \tfrac{405}{432} = \tfrac{15}{16}$$
$$.74_8 = 7 \times 8^{-1} + 4 \times 8^{-2} = \tfrac{7}{8} + \tfrac{4}{64} = \tfrac{15}{16}$$

Example   Convert 123.53_8 to base 4. When we have a mixed number we may convert the integral part by division and the fractional part by multiplication.   All computation is in base 8.

$$
\begin{array}{ll}
\underline{24}\;\;\text{remainder 3} & \qquad \underline{5}\;\;\text{remainder 0} \\
4)123 & \qquad 4)24 \\
\underline{10} & \qquad \underline{24} \\
23 & \\
\underline{20} & \\
3 &
\end{array}
$$

$$
\begin{array}{lll}
\underline{1}\;\;\text{remainder 1} & \quad \underline{0}\;\;\text{remainder 1} & \qquad \therefore \quad 123_8 = 1103_4 \\
4)5 & \quad 4)1 & \\
\underline{4} & & \\
1 & &
\end{array}
$$

$$
\begin{array}{llll}
.53 & \quad .54 & \quad .60 & \qquad \therefore \quad .53_8 = .223_4 \\
\underline{4} & \quad \underline{4} & \quad \underline{4} & \\
2.54 & \quad 2.60 & \quad 3.00 &
\end{array}
$$

and $123.53_8 = 1103.223_4$

We check this by expressing each in base 10:

$$123.53_8 = 1 \times 8^2 + 2 \times 8^1 + 3 \times 8^0 + 5 \times 8^{-1} + 3 \times 8^{-2}$$
$$= 64 + 16 + 3 + \tfrac{5}{8} + \tfrac{3}{64}$$
$$= 83\tfrac{43}{64}$$

$$1103.223_4 = 1 \times 4^3 + 1 \times 4^2 + 0 \times 4^1 + 3 \times 4^0 + 2 \times 4^{-1} +$$
$$2 \times 4^{-2} + 3 \times 4^{-3}$$
$$= 64 + 16 + 3 + \tfrac{2}{4} + \tfrac{2}{16} + \tfrac{3}{64}$$
$$= 83\tfrac{43}{64}$$

―――――――   E X E R C I S E S   ―――――――

1. Evaluate the following.
   (a) $5^0(3)^{-2}$ (d) $-8^{\frac{1}{3}}$ (g) $10^3 \cdot 10^{-3}$
   (b) $(3 \cdot 4)^2$ (e) $32^{\frac{3}{5}}$ (h) $x^{\frac{1}{2}} \cdot x^{\frac{2}{3}}$
   (c) $3^2 + 4^2$ (f) $4^{-2} \cdot 4^{-\frac{1}{2}}$ (i) $a^{\frac{1}{2}} \div b^{\frac{1}{2}}$

2. Express the following without using negative or fractional exponents.
   (a) $(a + b)^2 y^{-4}$ (e) $x^{-\frac{1}{3}} - y^{-\frac{2}{3}}$
   (b) $\dfrac{x^{-3} \cdot y^2}{x \cdot y^{-4}}$ (f) $(m^2 \cdot n^2)^{-\frac{1}{2}}$
   (c) $a^{\frac{1}{2}} b^{-\frac{1}{2}}$ (g) $\dfrac{a^{-5} b^{-3}}{c^{-\frac{1}{2}} d}$
   (d) $a^{\frac{1}{2}} + b^{\frac{1}{2}}$

3. Demonstrate that $(\sqrt[n]{a})^m = \sqrt[n]{a^m}$ where $a = 64$, $n = 3$, $m = 2$.

4. Apply the laws of exponents in simplifying the following.
   (a) $\dfrac{m^2 n^3}{mn} \cdot \dfrac{m^{-2} n}{mn^4}$ (d) $s^2 \div s^5$
   (b) $a^{\frac{1}{3}} \cdot a^{\frac{2}{3}}$ (e) $\dfrac{r^2 \cdot r^{-\frac{1}{2}}}{r^{\frac{3}{2}}}$
   (c) $b^2 \cdot b^{-\frac{1}{2}}$

5. Convert $.346_8$ to base 12.

6. Convert $.375_8$ to base 2.

7. Convert each digit of $.375_8$ to base 2. Compare your result with the answer to Exercise 6. Explain.

8. Convert 413.12_6 to base 9.

9. Prove that the fraction a/b (a, b have no common factor) will terminate when expressed as a decimal if and only if the only prime factors of b are 2 and 5.

10.* Devise a rule for determining how many steps in the division process will be necessary if the fraction terminates.

11.* State the conditions under which a basimal fraction will terminate in each of two different bases.

THE ALGEBRA OF RATIONAL NUMBERS

5.23   The rules of elementary algebra either are applications of the properties of an ordered field or may be derived therefrom.

An expression of the form

$$a_0 x^n + a_1 x^{n-1} + a_2 x^{n-2} + \ldots + a_n \quad (a_i \text{ members of a field, } a_0 \neq 0)$$

is known as a polynomial of degree n in x.

The polynomial equated to zero

$$a_0 x^n + a_1 x^{n-1} + a_2 x^{n-2} + \ldots + a_n = 0$$

is known as a polynomial equation of degree n.

If $n = 1$ we have a linear, or first degree, equation of the following form.

Equation 1 $\qquad\qquad ax + b = 0$

If a, b are rational, Equation 1 always has a unique rational solution, $-b/a$.

That it has the solution $-b/a$ is evident if we replace x with $-b/a$. Otherwise, we may subtract b from both sides, getting $ax = -b$, then divide by a, getting $x = -b/a$.   To show the solution unique, assume that there are two solutions, c_1 and c_2.   Then

$$ac_1 + b = 0 = ac_2 + b$$

Subtracting b $\qquad\qquad ac_1 = ac_2$

Dividing by a $\qquad\qquad c_1 = c_2$

Any equation in one unknown consisting of terms of degree not more than 1 is reducible to the form

$$ax + b = 0$$

by application of the field postulates and the equality axioms.

Example   Solve $4 - 2x = x + 5 - 4x$.

$$4 - 2x = x - 4x + 5 \text{ (addition commutative)}$$
$$4 - 2x = -3x + 5 \quad \text{(distributive property)}$$
$$4 + x = 5 \qquad\qquad \text{(addition axiom — add } 3x)$$
$$x - 1 = 0 \qquad\qquad \text{(subtraction axiom — subtract 5)}$$

This is in the form $ax + b = 0$ and has the solution $- \dfrac{-1}{1} = 1.$

An equation of the form

$$a_1 x + b_1 y = c_1$$

is known as a *linear equation in two unknowns*.   It is *indeterminate*:

there are infinitely many pairs of values of x and y which will satisfy it. We may solve for x in terms of y:

$$x = \frac{c_1 - b_1 y}{a_1}$$

Then for each value we assign to y an x is determined.

Two such equations

Equations 2
$$a_1 x + b_1 y = c_1$$
$$a_2 x + b_2 y = c_2$$

are known as *simultaneous linear equations* — in two unknowns. If we solve the first of these for x in terms of y, then substitute the obtained value of x in the second, we will then have a linear equation in y of the Equation 1 type:

$$a_2 \frac{c_1 - b_1 y}{a_1} + b_2 y = c_2$$

If we apply the distributive law to the first term, then multiply both sides by a_1, we get

$$a_2 c_1 - a_2 b_1 y + a_1 b_2 y = a_1 c_2$$

If we subtract $a_2 c_1$ from both sides, we get

$$-a_2 b_1 y + a_1 b_2 y = a_1 c_2 - a_2 c_1$$

Applying the distributive law,

$$(-a_2 b_1 + a_1 b_2) y = a_1 c_2 - a_2 c_1$$

and dividing by the coefficient of y,

$$y = \frac{a_1 c_2 - a_2 c_1}{a_1 b_2 - a_2 b_1}$$

This value of y substituted in either equation yields

$$x = \frac{c_1 b_2 - c_2 b_1}{a_1 b_2 - a_2 b_1}$$

Then the system of Equations 2 always has a unique solution if $a_1 b_2 \neq a_2 b_1$.

The solution of Equation 1 or system of Equations 2 is always in the same field as are the coefficients, since they are obtained by applying the field postulates to the coefficients.

We have proved, page 130, that in any field

$$a \cdot 0 = 0, \ a \text{ any element of the field}$$

It follows that any polynomial equation which can be expressed as the product of *linear factors* equal to zero can be solved by equating each factor to zero.

Example $(3x - 2)(x + 5)(2x - 9) = 0$

One of the factors must be zero since the product is.   However, if any one of the three is zero, the equation is satisfied.   Then the solution of the equation is equivalent to solving the three equations

$$3x - 2 = 0 \quad \text{and} \quad x + 5 = 0 \quad \text{and} \quad 2x - 9 = 0$$

Not all polynomials with rational coefficients can be factored into linear factors with rational coefficients.   The second degree or higher equation with rational coefficients does not always have a rational solution.   For example, $x^2 - 2 = 0$ cannot be factored into linear factors and therefore has no rational solution.

––––––––––   E   X   E   R   C   I   S   E   S   ––––––––––

1.   Solve the following.
   (a) $3 - x = 3x + 6$
   (b) $\frac{1}{2}x - 6 = 2x + 4$
   (c) $4 - 3x + 2 = x - 5 + 7x$
   (d) $y + 5 = 2y - 3$

2.   Check to determine whether the system of equations has a solution. If it does, solve:
   (a) $2x + y = 7$
         $3x + 4y = 18$
   (b) $x - 3y = 10$
         $y = -5$
   (c) $3x + 2y = 5$
         $2x + 4y = 7 - 4x$
   (d) $3x = y - 6$
         $2y = 6x + 12$

3.   Solve the following.
   (a) $(2x - 3)(x + 4) = 0$
   (b) $\dfrac{x - 3}{x^2} = 0$
   (c) $3x^2 + 4x = 0$ (use the distributive law)
   (d) $(x - 1)(x + 3) = -4$

4.   The polynomial, page 171,
$$a_0 x^n + a_1 x^{n-1} + a_2 x^{n-2} + \ldots + a_n$$
   is the representation of an integer if the a's are restricted to integers 0 through 9 and if $x = 10$.   Find integral solutions to the following polynomial equations.
   (a) $2x^3 + 4x^2 + 2x + 4 = 364$ (b) $2x^3 + 4 = 436$

5.   Find integral coefficients which will satisfy the following polynomial equations.
   (a) $a_0(7)^3 + a_1(7)^2 + a_2(7)^1 + a_3 = 831$
   (b) $a_0(6)^4 + a_1(6)^3 + a_2(6)^2 + a_3(6)^1 + a_4 = 2149$

EQUATIONS: CONDITIONAL, IDENTICAL, INCONSISTENT

5.24 When we solve an equation we find the value or values of the unknown which make a true statement out of the proposition posed by the equation. We may think of the equation as posing a question: Under what condition will the right member of the equation equal the left member? Three kinds of answer are possible; we may find that only a limited number of values, possibly just one, of the unknown will make both sides of the equation take the same value; we may find that the two members of the equation have the same value for all values of the unknown; and, finally, we may find that the two members can never be equal, regardless of the value of the unknown.

If the first of these situations exists, the equation is called a *conditional equation*. For example, when we solve the equation

$$4x - 3 - x + 5 = 2 - 3x$$

we find that just one value of x makes $4x - 3 - x + 5$ and $2 - 3x$ have the same value, namely $x = 0$.

If the second possibility is present, the equation is called an *identical equation* or simply an *identity*. For example, when we solve

$$4x - 3 - x + 5 = 2 + 3x$$

the first step is the collection of terms, which yields

$$3x + 2 = 2 + 3x$$

But this is obviously true regardless of the value of x.

We usually refer to two or more equations as being *inconsistent* but, if the last of our three possibilities exists, the two conditions placed on the unknown by the two sides of the equation are inconsistent. In any event, the solution of the equation consists of reaching a condition that can never be met. For example, if we solve

$$4x - 3 - x + 5 = 5 + 3x$$

we get
$$3x + 2 = 5 + 3x$$

and then
$$2 = 5$$

and we conclude that the original equation is satisfied if $2 = 5$; in other words, it can never be satisfied.

In Section 5.23 the assertion was proved, that the equation $ax + b = 0$ where $a \neq 0$ always has a unique solution. It was further stated that any equation in one unknown consisting of terms of degree not more than 1 is reducible to the form $ax + b = 0$. But the **proviso**

$a \neq 0$ was not attached. We call attention to this fact lest one see a contradiction between the unique solution statement and what has been said about "identical" and "inconsistent" situations.

A similar situation exists regarding simultaneous linear equations. The system

$$a_1x + b_1y = c_1$$
$$a_2x + b_2y = c_2$$

has a unique solution if $a_1b_2 \neq a_2b_1$. How do we interpret the situation if $a_1b_2 = a_2b_1$? Recall that the x value of the solution is

$$x = \frac{c_1b_2 - c_2b_1}{a_1b_2 - a_2b_1}$$

We have two possibilities. If $a_1b_2 = a_2b_1$ but $c_1b_2 \neq c_2b_1$ we have an impossible situation since we are attempting to divide a quantity that is not 0, by zero. When this situation exists the system of equations is called an *inconsistent* system. The conditions of the two equations are inconsistent and cannot be satisfied by the same pair of values for the unknowns.

Example   Equation 1: $2x - 3y = 5$
            Equation 2: $4x - 6y = 7$

If we divide Equation 2 by 2 we get $2x - 3y = \frac{7}{2}$, and it is required that $2x - 3y$ equal 5 in Equation 1 and equal $\frac{7}{2}$ in Equation 2.

The other possibility occurs when $a_1b_2 = a_2b_1$ and $c_1b_2 = c_2b_1$. Here we are trying to find x by dividing zero by 0, and this can mean anything. Equations satisfying these two conditions are called *dependent;* they are really stating the same relationship twice.

Example   Equation 1: $2x - 3y = 5$
            Equation 2: $4x - 6y = 10$

If we multiply both sides of Equation 1 by 2 we get, identically, Equation 2.

We have solved an equation or system of equations when, by applying the properties of a field and the equality axioms, we reach a relationship which we can identify on inspection. For instance, there is no doubt what condition must be placed on the unknown if $x = 0$ must be satisfied. Furthermore, there is no doubt what the situation is if, for the original equation to be satisfied, 2 must equal 2. And there is no question where we stand if 2 must equal 5 for the original equation to be satisfied.

——————— E X E R C I S E S ———————

1. If the following equation is conditional, solve; otherwise, determine whether it is an identity or impossible.
   (a) $2y - 3 = 4(y - \frac{1}{2}) - y$
   (b) $3(x + 5) = 4x - (6 + x)$
   (c) $(x - 4)^2 + 2(x - 8) = x^2 - 6x$
   (d) $5(p - 6) + 3p = 2(p - 3)$
   (e) $x(x + 4) - 12 = x^2 + 4(x - 3)$

2. Solve the following systems or show why there is no solution.

   (a) $\begin{cases} x - 3y = 6 \\ 2x + 6y = 5 \end{cases}$

   (b) $\begin{cases} 3x - y = 8 \\ 5y = 15 \end{cases}$

   (c) $\begin{cases} 2x + 3y = 10 \\ 4(x - y) = 2x - 7y \end{cases}$

   (d) $\begin{cases} x - y = 1 \\ 2x - 3y = 5 \end{cases}$

   (e) $\begin{cases} 7x + 3y = 2(2x - y - 4) \\ 3x + y = -4y - 8 \end{cases}$

3.* Since the integers 0, 1, 2, 3, 4, modulo 5, are a field, the same procedures used in the solution of equations with rational coefficients may be used in solving equations in this field. Solve the following modulo 5 problems.
   (a) $4x \equiv 3$
   (b) $x - 3 \equiv 4x + 1$
   (c) $x + y \equiv 1$
   $ x - y \equiv 3$
   (d) $x \equiv y + 3$
   $ y \equiv 2x - 4$
   (e) $2x + 3y \equiv 1$
   $ 4x + y \equiv 3$
   (f) $3x \equiv y + 4$
   $ x + 3 \equiv 2y$

4. The game of "sevens" is played as follows: The first player selects any integer from 1 through 7. The second player adds any integer from 1 through 7 to the first player's number. They continue in this manner alternately. The player who reaches 43 wins the game. Does the first player or the second player have the advantage?

5. Write a congruence equation in x, showing the values of x which each player should try to reach in the course of the game described in exercise 4.

6. A puzzle problem which leads to an indeterminate equation requiring a positive integral solution is called a Diophantine problem. Find all positive integral solutions for the equation
   $$17x + 24y = 243$$
   Hint: $17x \equiv 243$, modulo 4.

7. Find all positive integral solutions for the system of equations
   $$2x - 5y + z = -12$$
   $$13x + 10y - 12z = 5$$
   Hint: Eliminate one variable, then proceed as in Exercise 6.

8.   A speculator bought 100 one-dollar tickets to the big game.   Business wasn't too good, he sold some tickets for five dollars each, and some more for three dollars each.   In order to break even he had to unload the remaining tickets for 50¢ a piece.   How many of each did he sell?

9.   Tom needs 30 pieces of fruit for his party.   He has one dollar to spend on the fruit.   Apples are 3 for 10¢, bananas 5¢ each, and peaches 2 for 5¢.   He spent the entire dollar and purchased exactly 30 pieces.   How many of each did he buy?

DO YOU KNOW

What the assertion that two quantities are functionally related means?

How functional relationships may be expressed?

The difference between a variable and a constant?

That a variable may be a constant?

The difference between a continuous variable and a discrete variable?

The difference between the dependent variable and the independent variable?

When a bar graph should be used?

The difference between a formula, a graph, and a table relative to the kind of information each gives concerning a functional relationship?

CHAPTER VI

FUNCTIONAL RELATIONSHIPS

Cause and effect relationships abound all about us. This year's rainfall affects the size of next year's wheat crop which will, in turn, affect the price of wheat. The price of wheat will affect the cost of living index which, in its turn, affects the wages paid automobile workers. Automobile workers' wages affect the price of automobiles. The price of automobiles affects the number of automobiles on the road. The number of automobiles on the road affects the number of automobile accidents. The number of automobile accidents affects the cost of automobile insurance. The cost of my automobile insurance affects the amount of money I have to spend on football games. So, the amount of rain this fall has some relationship to the number of football games I will see next fall. Of course, it would be rather difficult to state exactly what is the relationship between rainfall and football games attended. Many relationships are not of a quantitative nature, and many of those that are quantitative are such that it would be very difficult, if not impossible, to discover exactly what the relationship is. We are concerned here with quantitative relationships which can be precisely determined. The simplest sort of relationship is one that exists between two variable quantities. However, most situations involve more than two variables. The cost of sending first-class mail anywhere in the continental United States is a function of its weight, but the cost of parcel post is a function of its weight and the distance it has to travel.

According to the Behaviorist school of psychology, everything that has ever happened affects what is now happening, which will, in turn, affect everything that ever will happen. However, cause and effect have no bearing on mathematical functions. Whether or not cause and effect are present is entirely irrelevant. Although there may be a cause and effect relationship between the variables, our primary concern is with the correspondence of values. We are concerned more with how they correspond than with why they correspond. Other factors, possibly unknown, may well be causing the change. For example, suppose you have a temperature chart of a hospital patient. This will picture the relationship between the variables, time and temperature. The mathematician can study this relationship and draw many conclusions. But the passage of time alone did not *cause* the changes in temperature. The causes of fluctuations are the concern of the attending physician. The temperature depends on the time in the sense that, corresponding to a known value of the latter, there exists a value for the former.

FUNCTION, VARIABLE, CONSTANT

6.1   We have had occasion to study quite a few sets of numbers — the set of natural numbers, the set of integers, the set of rational numbers, the set of numbers of a field, the set of numbers of a group; we now wish to consider the relationships of sets of pairs of numbers.

As explained in Section 5.1, we use a letter to indicate any one of a set of numbers. The letter is called a *variable*. If the set contains just one number we call the letter a *constant*. For example, in the equation

$$5x - \pi = 0$$

π is a constant since it represents the only element in the set whose elements are the ratios of circumference to diameter of circles. If we consider the set of numbers which will make a true statement out of the assertion that $5x - \pi = 0$, we see that x is also a constant since there is just one number in this set. On the other hand, if we do not require $5x - \pi$ to equal zero or any other specified number and if x is any rational number, then x is a variable. In this case, $5x - \pi$, to which we can give the name y, is also a variable. It will be different for different values of x but it will always be a real number. Real numbers will be defined in Chapter VII.

Consider the two variables x and y, each of which may take any integral value. Suppose that for each x we select a corresponding y by means of the rule $y = 2x^2 - 8$. Since x is an integer, so is $2x^2 - 8$ because the integers are closed under multiplication and subtraction.

Then for any x, a y is always determined. If $x = -4$ then $y = 2(-4)(-4) - 8 = 24$; if $x = 10$ then $y = 2(10)(10) - 8 = 192$; and so on. We define the set of ordered (x, y) pairs as a *function*. The pair is ordered in that x appears first, then y. Notice that by definition the function is a set. The elements of this set are pairs, pairs of elements from two other sets. In the above function, the pairs $(-4, 24)$ and $(10, 192)$ are elements. But -4 and 10 are elements of the set X of values of x, and 24 and 192 are elements of the set Y of values of y.

Although we are usually concerned with functions whose elements are pairs of numbers, this does not have to be the case. If we have two sets, regardless of what their elements may be, such that there is a rule for assigning to each member of the first a unique member of the second, then the set of pairs of elements thus determined is a function. Let X represent the set of states in the United States and Y represent the set of governors. Then to each state (x) there corresponds a governor (y), and the set of (*state, governor*) or (x, y) pairs is a function.

The (*state, governor*) function could just as well be thought of as a (*governor, state*) function. We could let X represent the set of state governors and Y the set of states. Then to each governor (x) there corresponds a state (y).

On the other hand, consider again the function whose (x, y) pairs are obtained by the rule $y = 2x^2 - 8$. It is true that for any x we get a unique y. But it is not true that each y is obtained from a unique x. If $x = 2$, then $y = 2 \cdot 2 \cdot 2 - 8 = 0$ and if $x = -2$, then $y = 2(-2)(-2) - 8 = 0$. We cannot interchange the roles of the variables in the function as we could in the (*state, governor*) function. We make the further stipulation in our definition of a function that no two of its elements have the same first part, that is, the same x if it is an (x, y) function.

We now state formally the following definition of a function:

Definition If, corresponding to each value a variable x may assume, a definite rule associates a unique value of another variable y, then the set of all (x, y) pairs is the function $f: (x, y)$.

This definition does not permit the same value of x to be paired with more than one value of y. We could not have $x = 2$, $y = 3$ as one pair and $x = 2$, $y = 6$ as another, since paired with $x = 2$ there must be one and only one y. But the definition does not prevent a given value of y from being paired with more than one value of x.

For that matter, the same y may be paired with each value of x. In such a case y is, of course, a constant and the function is known as a *constant function*. Suppose a person whose weight we wish to consider has passed or missed the "middle age spread." Through a period of a year, let us say, his weight does not vary (at least the scales indicate no change). If we consider time as one variable, there is certainly a specific weight to be associated with each point of time. Then the two quantities, time and weight, qualify as having a *functional relationship* between them. Associated with each value we assign to time there corresponds a value for weight.

DEPENDENT AND INDEPENDENT VARIABLES

6.2   The definition of a function given in Section 6.1 seems to imply that x and y are the only two letters we can use in expressing a function. This is misleading since any two letters may be used. For that matter, we may interchange the roles of x and y if we wish. The important point is that one of the variables, the first named in the definition, must have different values for each pair in the function. This variable is called the *independent variable*. The other variable is the *dependent variable*. The terminology here is not very fortunate. The behavior of the independent variable does not cause the dependent variable to act as it does. The second variable is dependent in the sense that its value, which corresponds to an assigned value of the first variable, is fixed by the rule which describes the function. For example, consider f, the function (x, y), whose values are given by $y = 2x - 1$. If we assign values to x, the corresponding values of y will depend on what we assign to x. Is 13 one of the elements of the set Y? This depends on whether 7 is one of the elements of the set X. The elements in the set of values which the dependent variable may take depend on the rule of formation of the function as well as on the values which the independent variable may take.

If the correspondence of elements in sets X and Y is one-to-one — a unique x paired with each y as well as a unique y paired with each x — either variable may be considered the independent variable. There is a functional relationship between the amount of money spent for gasoline and the amount of gasoline purchased. Now which is the dependent variable and which is the independent variable? If I am going to charge the gasoline, I will probably have the tank filled and the cost will depend on the amount purchased. But if it is a cash sale, the amount purchased will depend on how much money I have. In this case, the designation of dependent and independent variable is a matter of convenience.

6.3   In the preceding section a function was described as "$f: (x, y)$ the function whose values are given by $y = 2x - 1$." Although correct, this would become tedious if consistently employed. A much more common usage is:

$$y = f(x) = 2x - 1 \text{ or simply } f(x) = 2x - 1$$

Here $f(x)$ stands for the function and is read "*f* of *x*." This symbolism serves a dual role. It may be used to indicate the value of the dependent variable or, what is the same thing, *the value of the function at x*. Used in this sense the symbol $f(x)$ should be read "*f* at *x*." The dual usage of the symbol is rarely confusing and we shall not hesitate to use it in both senses.

Example If $f(x) = 3x - 5$, find $f(3)$. It does not matter whether we interpret $f(x)$ as standing for the function or the value of the function at x; under either interpretation we find $f(3)$ by replacing x with 3 in $3x - 5$: $f(3) = 3 \cdot 3 - 5 = 4$.

If we wish to talk of other functions in the same discussion, we may use letters other than f to designate them, such as $g(x)$, $h(x)$, and so on.

6.4   The set of values which the independent variable may take is known as the *domain of definition* or, simply, *domain* of the function. Within certain limits it is possible to select as domain of definition any set one cares to use.

Example   Consider $f(x) = 3x^2 - x + 5$, where x an integer > 0. Here the function is defined for positive integral values of x, but is undefined and therefore has no meaning if $x = \frac{1}{2}$ or $x = -3$, or for any x other than a positive integer. However, we could have chosen any set of numbers we liked as the domain of x just so that corresponding to each x a y can exist.

The domain of the function

$$g(x) = \frac{x^3 + 7}{x - 3}$$

may be anything we like except that it cannot include $+3$, for if we tried to include it $g(3)$ would equal $\frac{34}{0}$ which is undefined.

Frequently a function is given without stating the domain of definition, in which case it is usually implied that the domain is the real number system (yet to be defined) or a subset of it. The set of values which the dependent variable may take is called the *range* of the function f.

Example   If $f(x) = 2x - 8$, where x a nonnegative integer, the range of f is the set of even integers equal to or greater than -8.

A *variable* may be *continuous* or *discrete*. If it is continuous its domain is an interval of the real number system, possibly all the real numbers. This does not mean much since we have not yet said what real numbers are. Intuitively, it means there are no breaks or gaps in the set of values of the function. If there is a smallest and a largest value, all possible values in between are included in the domain of definition. A discrete variable is defined only for isolated values. For instance, if a function is defined for integers but not for rational numbers, the variable is discrete. First-class postage rates illustrate the idea. The two variables are weight and cost. The weight of a letter is a continuous variable. It may weigh any fractional part of an ounce. The cost of mailing a letter is a discrete variable. The cost may be 4¢, 8¢, 12¢, and so on, but not 5¢ or 3.1829¢, or any amount except some integral multiple of 4¢.

RELATIONS

6.5   The definition of a function given in Section 6.1 precludes the possibility that more than one value of the dependent variable will be associated with a given value of the independent variable. If we remove this restriction we have a *relation*.

Definition   If a definite rule associates the elements of a set x with elements of the set y, the resulting set of (x, y) pairs is a relation.

Thus we see that a function is a special kind of relation.

Two sets, x and y, frequently are so related that there are two or more values of Y which are associated with each value of X. For example, $y = x^2$ is a function of x, since corresponding to each x there is a single y but, in the relation $x = y^2$, for any (x, y) pair which satisfies the relation another pair $(x, -y)$ will also; $x = y^2$ implies that $y = \pm\sqrt{x}$.

The expression $x^2 + y^2 = 25$ describes a relation. The range of values for each variable is the set of real numbers equal to or greater than -5 and equal to or less than $+5$. This is written $-5 \leq x \leq +5$, $-5 \leq y \leq +5$. In this relation, corresponding to each x in its range there are two y's, and corresponding to each y there are two x's. For example, $(2, 3)$, $(2, -3)$, $(3, 2)$, and $(-3, 2)$ are elements of this relation.

A relation is sometimes referred to as a "multiple-valued function." As an example of a nonnumerical, two-valued function, let X represent the set of states of the United States and Y the set of United States senators.

The concept of number congruences explained in Section 4.14 illustrates a relation in which infinitely many values of the dependent variable correspond to each value of the independent variable. If we let X be the set of integers from 1 to n, and Y the set of all positive integers, then corresponding to each value of x there are infinitely many values for y, namely, all those values of y which have a remainder x when divided by n.

In a later chapter we shall study inverse trigonometric functions, which are multiple-valued unless we properly restrict the domain of definition.

————————   E   X   E   R   C   I   S   E   S   ————————

1. If the function $y = f(x)$ is defined by the expression $y = 2x^2 - x + 3$, find the following.

    (a) $f(1)$ (d) $f(a)$

    (b) $f(0)$ (e) $f(x)$

    (c) $f(-1)$ (f) $f(-x)$

2. If f is a function such that $f(x) = \dfrac{x + 5}{x - 1}$, what value of x must be excluded from the domain of definition? Find the following.

    (a) $f(0)$ (b) $f(-5)$ (c) $f[f(-1)]$

3.   Given: X is the set of even positive integers ≤ 10. Y is the set of odd integers obtained by dividing each x by 2 or dividing by 2 and subtract- ing 1, as the case may require. Write out the complete function (a function is a set of ordered pairs).

4.   The following table completely defines a function. Which is the inde- pendent variable? What is the domain? The range?

m	1	-1	0	2	-2
n	1	1	0	4	4

5.   If the domain of the function f defined by $f(x) = 12$ is the rational number system, write down five of its elements.

6.   Assume that you have read a thermometer on the hour for each hour of the day. Construct a table showing this assumed information. Will this table be a function? Why?

7.   Construct a table showing the assumed populations of the United States, France, Great Britain, and Russia. Is this table a function? If so, what is its domain? What is its range?

8.   "Garbage collection is a function of the Department of Health of the city government." "The city tax rate is a function of the services rendered." In which, if either, of the above statements is the word *function* used in the mathematical sense? Explain.

9.   Since the integers are defined as ordered pairs of natural numbers, is the set of integers a function? Is it a relation? Explain.

10.   Is the set of ordered pairs which define $+5$ a function? If so, what is the domain? The range?

11.   The function $y = x + 6$ — domain, natural numbers ≥ 6, and range, natural numbers and zero — defines what integer?

12.   If $f(x) = x^2 - x + 3$ and $g(x) = 2x + 1$, find $f[g(x)]$; find $g[f(x)]$.

WAYS OF EXPRESSING FUNCTIONAL RELATIONSHIPS

6.6   The definition of a function requires that there be some rule for, some means of, establishing the correspondence of values of the independent and dependent variables. This can be done in a variety of ways.

First, the relationship can be expressed by a verbal statement. For example, the number of feet a freely falling body falls is 16 times the square of the number of seconds it falls. A second method of indicating the relationship is by means of a formula or algebraic expression. The expression $d = f(t)$ merely asserts that *some* relationship exists between distance (*d*) and time (*t*).   But $d = 16t^2$ states what *the* relationship is.   Functional relationships may also be expressed by means of graphs.   Figure 6.1 pictures this same relationship

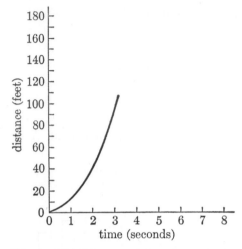

Figure 6.1   Distance fallen by a freely falling body in *t* seconds.

between distance fallen and time of fall.   Finally, functional relationship may be expressed by means of a table (see Table 6.1).

Table 6.1   Distance fallen by a freely falling body in *t* seconds.

Time, seconds	0	1	2	3	4	5	6	7	8	9	10
Distance, feet	0	16	64	144	256	400	576	784	1024	1296	1600

Each of these four methods has its special characteristics and advantages.   Of the four, the verbal statement is perhaps the clearest for purposes of defining the relationship.   We shall examine each of the three remaining methods in detail.   Each one may be used to define the function or to convey information about one that has already been defined.

GRAPHS

6.7   The most commonly used types of graphs are (1) the bar graph, (2) the circle graph or pie chart, (3) the pictograph, (4) the broken-line graph, and (5) the continuous-curved-line graph.   The graph is the best means of exhibiting a functional relationship when the purpose is to give a visual representation of the general nature of the relationship.

Of the illustrations in Section 6.6 the graph shows the general nature of the relationship much more forcefully than do the other methods. We can immediately see not only that distance increases as time increases but also that distance increases much more rapidly than does time. The best type of graph to use will depend upon what aspect of the relationship we wish to emphasize. If we wish to compare several measures with each other, the bar graph is advisable. As a rule, the independent variable is discrete. For instance, Figure 6.2 shows the mean monthly temperature at Ashland City for the

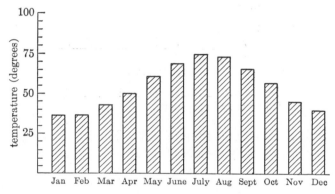

Figure 6.2   Mean monthly temperature at Ashland City for 1942.

year 1942. Since there is a mean temperature associated with each month, a functional relationship exists between the two. We may consider the month as the independent variable and the temperature the dependent variable. We see both vertical and horizontal bars used, but in either case the length of the bar indicates the value of the dependent variable.

The bar graph also is used to compare magnitudes that occur simultaneously but are classified by geographic location or some other nonquantitative characteristic. For instance, we might have a graph comparing the number of automobiles in operation, classified by make or color or body style. Figure 6.3 shows mean temperatures for the year 1946 at selected geographic locations. In Figure 6.3, the independent variable is not a continuous magnitude nor is it a discrete magnitude. It isn't a magnitude at all, but a place. Yet there is a value for the dependent variable (mean temperature) to correspond to each value (place) we assign to the independent variable (mean temperature). Figure 6.3 actually is a representation of two distinct

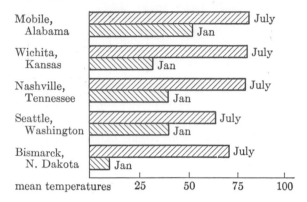

Figure 6.3 Mean temperatures for 1946 at selected locations.

functions. The mean temperature for July is pictured as a function of the location and the mean temperature for January is an entirely different dependent variable, associated with the same set of values of the independent variable, the places. The combining of the two graphs into one picture is frequently done. The combined chart reveals more information more readily than would two separate charts. For example, the combined graph in Figure 6.3 shows at a glance which location has the most variable weather.

Figure 6.4 Annual precipitation for Nashville by seasons. Total 46.5 inches.

The pie chart is of value when we wish not only to compare a group of magnitudes with each other but also to compare each magnitude with the total. The pie chart, Figure 6.4, shows the annual rainfall in Nashville, Tennessee, by seasons. The complete circle represents the total annual rainfall, and each sector may be compared visually with each other as well as with the total.

The pictograph is used for the same type of situation in which bar graphs are appropriate. Any advantage they may possess is not mathematical. If well done, they are dramatic and catch the eye. It is not advisable to use different-sized pictures to make comparisons. All the pictures should be the same size, the comparison being obtained from the number of pictures used.

Figure 6.5 is a pictograph showing the number of cattle on United States farms by years.

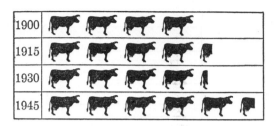

Figure 6.5   Cattle population in the United States.   Each cow represents 15,000,000 head.

BROKEN-LINE GRAPHS

6.8   The broken-line graph is used to better advantage than the bar graph when the primary concern is with rates of change and trends rather than with a comparison of individual magnitudes.   A broken-line graph would not be at all appropriate for the situation pictured in Figure 6.3.   Here we are showing mean temperatures for particular localities.   The data do not justify any assumption relative to the mean temperature at points between successive values of the independent variable.   For example, we have no justification for assuming that the mean July temperature for St. Louis is between 79° and 80° simply because the city is between Nashville and Wichita. The geographic location of the values of the independent variable has no bearing on the function.   The independent variable is not continuous in the geographic or any other sense.

On the other hand, the data on which Figure 6.2 is based could have been pictured with a broken-line graph.   The rise and fall of the line would picture the rise and fall of the average temperature through the year.   However, we still could not make any assumption regarding the mean monthly temperature midway between April and May.   The independent variable, month, is a discrete variable.

Many times, although both the dependent and the independent variables are continuous, only isolated, discrete pairs of values are available.   In such situations the broken-line graph is quite appropriate.   Suppose we had data showing the family income of families in the United States, grouped in $1,000 income brackets.   (Family income is not a continuous variable.   But its discrete values are so close together, one cent apart, compared with a thousand-dollar interval, that it serves quite well to illustrate the idea.)   All those families whose income ranged from $3,500 to $4,500 would be counted in the $4,000 bracket, those with over $4,500 and not over $5,500 would be in the $5,000 bracket, and so on.   When this information is pictured in a broken-line graph, we not only have a picture of the number of families in each group but can get some idea of the distribution of families within an interval from the rise or fall of the line.

A temperature chart is a very good illustration of this idea.   Suppose a patient's temperature is read every fifteen minutes.   The passage of time is continuous, and the patient has a temperature at every instant of that time.   We actually know nothing about his temperature between readings.   But, if we assume that the readings are sufficiently frequent to show any marked fluctuations, then we can infer how the temperature is behaving between readings.

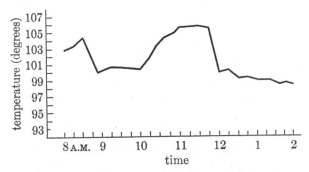

Figure 6.6   A temperature chart; readings at 15-minute intervals.

In Figure 6.6, the patient appears to have had his highest fever between 11:00 and 11:45 A.M.   We cannot be certain of this, however, because there was a rise between 8:15 and 8:30 and a drop between 8:30 and 8:45.   We cannot be sure there was not a continued rise after 8:30 before the drop began.   It is quite possible that 105° was reached between 8:30 and 8:45.   The foregoing is quite plausible.   It is hardly plausible that the patient's temperature was 107° at 1:37 P.M. but we cannot be certain in view of the chart.

The broken-line graph gives the appearance of a continuous variable. Furthermore, it conveys the impression that the dependent variable is changing at a constant rate between the points that are plotted. It should be used only when it is desirable to convey this impression.

CONTINUOUS-CURVED-LINE GRAPHS

6.9   The weather bureau has thermometers which record, in contrast with the above chart, continuous temperature readings on a revolving drum.   The drum revolves at a constant rate.   A thermostat, which moves up and down as the temperature rises and falls, is equipped with a pen which makes contact with the paper on the drum. This automatically and continuously graphs the temperature.

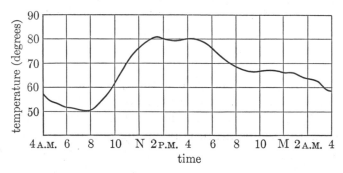

Figure 6.7   Continuously recorded temperature for a 24-hour interval.

The graphs shown in Figure 6.3, Figure 6.6, and Figure 6.7 have fundamental differences in so far as the information we may obtain from them is concerned.   Figure 6.3 gives the mean January temperature for Wichita, Kansas, as 32° and the mean January temperature for Nashville, Tennessee, as 40°.   We cannot infer that midway between those locations the mean January temperature was 36°.   In fact, we have no right to infer anything about the mean January temperature at any intermediate point between the two locations. We may properly consider geographic location as a continuous variable since there is a continuously changing "place" between the two locations.   However, the isolated observations are too far apart for us to make any assumptions concerning the way in which the mean temperature varies with the continuous place changes between Nashville and Wichita.   By contrast, Figure 6.6, we know the patient's temperature at 8:15 A.M. was approximately 103.1° and at 8:30 A.M., 104.5°.   In this case we may infer with a reasonable degree of safety that at 8:22$\frac{1}{2}$ A.M. the patient had a temperature of approximately 103.8°.   As was true in Figure 6.3, we have only isolated pairs of values for our variables, time and temperature in this case.   But the variables are continuous and the isolated pairs of values are close enough together for us to assume that the rate of change is nearly constant between con-

secutive readings.   On the other hand, in Figure 6.7 we actually have
a picture of *continuous* change which takes place in the two variables.
The only limitation in determining the temperature at 2:30 A.M. (or
any other time) is the degree of accuracy with which we can read the
graph.   The temperature at 2:30 A.M. is approximately 52°.

———————— E   X   E   R   C   I   S   E   S ————————

1.   Decide what type of graph is the most appropriate for picturing each of
the following sets of information; then construct a graph.

(a)   A proposed family budget for a family of four with $5,000 income
(after taxes) is as follows:
Food ————; clothing ————; housing ————; char-
ity ————; savings and insurance ————; transportation ————; entertainment ————; miscellaneous ————.
(You supply the amounts for each item.)

(b)   The information from Table 6.3 (Section 6.11).

(c)   The following table gives the average price of eggs paid the farmer
at a local market in 1952.   Price is given in cents per dozen.

Jan.	21.4	July	17.6
Feb.	19.6	Aug.	19.7
Mar.	16.3	Sept.	24.9
Apr.	16.0	Oct.	31.6
May	15.8	Nov.	35.2
June	15.3	Dec.	34.4

(d)   Food market construction, 1955.   Number of stores completed
and total square feet of floor space built are shown.

	Number of stores completed	Square feet of floor space
United Markets	185	499,011
H and W	33	122,100
French, Inc.	10	42,880
Slo Way	78	226,350
Hi-Lo	71	186,500
Mammoth	1	22,900
Oriental	177	145,900
Roadside	23	25,700
Nuway	14	32,607

(e)   Common stock dividends paid by Utilities Unlimited.

Year	Dividend per $100 share	Year	Dividend per $100 share	Year	Dividend per $100 share
1927	$ 9.32	1933	$2.15	1939	$11.00
1928	7.52	1934	1.00	1940	24.00
1929	17.00	1935	7.20	1941	25.00
1930	9.00	1936	4.05	1942	30.00
1931	4.50	1937	1.80	1943	33.00
1932	.21	1938	5.60	1944	12.05

2   Criticize the following graphs.

(a)

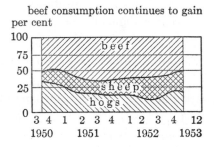

(b)

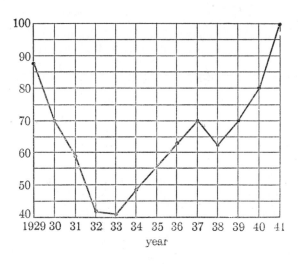

(c)

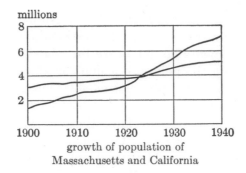

growth of population of
Massachusetts and California

3.   From Figure 6.6 obtain the patient's temperature at 15 minute intervals
and arrange the information in tabular form.

4.   From Figure 6.7 estimate the temperature at 11 A.M.   At what time of
day did the maximum temperature occur?   What were the minimum
and maximum temperatures?

RECTANGULAR COORDINATES

6.10   The functions pictured in Figures 6.1 and 6.7 have both independent and dependent variables which are continuous.   We need a
number scale for each.   Functions of this sort, particularly those defined by a mathematical formula, are best shown by means of rectangular coordinates.

There is a geometric postulate known as Archimedes' Postulate of
Continuity.

Archimedes' Postulate   Let A_1 be any point between two arbitrary
points A and B of a straight line.   Let points A_2, A_3, A_4, ... be so chosen
that A_2 lies between A_1 and A_3, and A_3 between A_2 and A_4, etc. and, further, let segments AA_1, A_1A_2, A_2A_3, ... be equal.   Then there is a point
A_n such that B lies between A and A_n.

This assumption has to do with the measurement of line segments.
It states in effect: There is an integral multiple (the n in A_n) of any
segment no matter how small (AA_1) which is greater than any other
segment no matter how large (AB).   This is the geometric equivalent
of the assumption that the rational number system exists.

Archimedes' Postulate enables us to find a point on our directed
line (see Section 5.13) to correspond to each rational number.   Between any two points of the line there is a point.   Between any two

rational numbers there is a rational number (Exercise 13, Section 5.20). Beyond any point on a directed line there is a point. There is a rational number greater than any chosen (in advance) rational number. The points on the line are ordered. The rational numbers are ordered. These pairs of statements do not prove but they strongly suggest an isomorphism between the points of a line (or at least some of them) and the rational numbers. Whether or not there are other points on a line is up to you. It depends on what other assumptions you make regarding points and lines. In fact, there is another assumption, accepted by most mathematicians, the consequence of which gives the line many more points. But that need not concern us here; we shall return to it when we consider real numbers.

If we draw two perpendicular lines in a plane, they may serve as lines of reference for any point of the plane. Any point is a unique distance above or below the horizontal line in Figure 6.8, and it is a unique distance to the right or left of the vertical line.

We call the intersection 0 of the perpendicular lines the *origin*. The horizontal line we call the *x-axis* and the vertical line the *y-axis*. This divides the plane into four parts or *quadrants*. The quadrants are numbered as indicated in Figure 6.8. We select a convenient unit and lay off a scale on each axis. By tradition, the right is considered positive, the left negative; up is positive and down negative. There is a unique point in the plane corresponding to each ordered pair of rational numbers. The numbers of the pair are called the *coordinates* of the point. The first number is called the *x*-distance or *abscissa*. The second number is called the *y*-distance or *ordinate*. The perpendicular axes provide a system of *rectangular coordinates*.

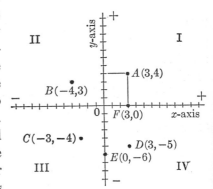

Figure 6.8   Rectangular coordinates.

To locate the point corresponding to a number pair, we move out the *x*-axis the number of units corresponding to the *x*-distance and erect a perpendicular to the *x*-axis at this point; we move out the *y*-axis the *y*-distance and erect a perpendicular to the *y*-axis at this point. The required point is the intersection of these two perpendiculars.

In Figure 6.8, the point $A = (3, 4)$ is found by moving to the right 3 units and up 4 units, then finding the intersection of the perpendiculars to the axis at these points. Verify the correctness of the location of the other points: $B = (-4, 3)$, $C = (-3, -4)$, $D = (3, -5)$, $E = (0, -6)$, $F = (3, 0)$.

Quadrant I contains points whose corresponding number pairs are both positive. The points of Quadrant II have negative abscissas and positive ordinates. In Quadrant III both coordinates are negative, and in Quadrant IV the abscissa is positive and the ordinate negative.

The idea of a coordinate system for locating positions in a plane is an ancient one. It has been used by engineers and cartographers in the same way that we use circles of latitude and longitude to locate positions on the earth. Its real importance in mathematics is due to the correspondence between points in the plane and ordered number *pairs*. This idea dates back to the seventeenth century and René Descartes' work in analytic geometry. The coordinate system is sometimes referred to as *Cartesian coordinates*, in his honor.

This scheme is ideally suited to graphing a function. Each point is defined by an ordered pair of numbers. Each element of the function, being an ordered pair of numbers, may be pictured by the point whose defining ordered pair of numbers is the same. For example, if one of the elements of the function is the ordered pair $(3, 4)$, the point $(3, 4)$ on the graph is the picture of this element of the function. Then the graph of the function is simply the totality of points which correspond to elements of the function.

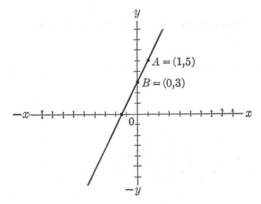

Figure 6.9 Graph of the function $f(x) = 2x + 3$.

The function $f(x) = 2x + 3$ is a straight line (see Sec. 11.2 and page 400). Thus to draw its graph it is sufficient to find the points corresponding to two elements of the function and then connect them with a straight line.   In Figure 6.9 we find the points $A = (1, 5)$ and $B = (0, 3)$ because $f(1) = 2(1) + 3 = 5$ and $f(0) = 2(0) + 3 = 3$. We cannot picture the total graph because it extends infinitely both to the right and to the left.   But with respect to that part of the graph which is shown, the coordinates of each point on the line are identically some ordered pair of the function.   For example, the point $(-2, -1)$ is on the line and the ordered pair $(-2, -1)$ is an element of the function.

It is not always so simple to find the graph of a function defined by an algebraic expression.   This is true even of the function graphed in Figure 6.10.   But once it is drawn we know that every point on the

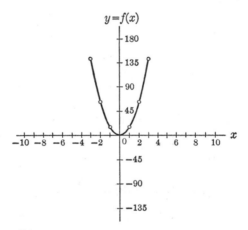

Figure 6.10   Graph of the function defined by $y = 16x^2$.

graph has coordinates that are identical with one of the ordered pairs of the function.   Furthermore, within the physical limitations of the graph every ordered pair of the function determines a point of the graph.   In this connection we should note that it is not essential that the same scale, the same unit distance, be used on both x-axis and y-axis.   The same unit is not used in Figure 6.10.

The domain of the function $d = 16x^2$ pictured in Figure 6.1 is the set of numbers equal to or greater than zero.   Negative values are excluded because, in their physical interpretation, such values are meaningless: a body cannot fall for -5 seconds.   If instead of $d = 16x^2$

we think of $y = 16x^2$, we have *defined y* in terms of x.   We can remove the restriction on the independent variable to nonnegative values. Neither x nor y is assigned any particular physical meaning.   We have merely defined the relationship between the two.   Figure 6.10 gives the graph of this abstract function.

The picture in Figure 6.1 is actually the right-hand half of Figure 6.10.   In Figure 6.1 we have had to restrict, owing to the nature of its definition, the domain of the independent variable x (or t), to positive values.   A graph similar to Figure 6.1 could be obtained by finding experimentally the time required for a body to fall certain specified distances and plotting these pairs of values.   The resulting graph would be like the temperature chart of Figure 6.6.   The fact that such graphs very closely approximate that of Figure 6.1 causes the physicist to believe that the law of falling bodies is expressed by the formula $d = 16t^2$.   The conclusion of the physicist is an inductive conclusion. If we take this inductive conclusion as our hypothesis, then the assertion that a body falls 144 feet in 3 seconds is a deductive conclusion.

——————   E   X   E   R   C   I   S   E   S   ——————

1.   Draw a set of rectangular coordinates and locate the following points.
   (a) $A(4, -5)$ (d) $D(4, 0)$
   (b) $B(0, -3)$ (e) $E(4, 4)$
   (c) $C(-2, -3)$ (f) $F(4, -4)$
2.   Demonstrate Archimedes' Principle with $\frac{1}{100}$ and 150.
3.   What do you know about all number pairs which correspond to points on the y-axis?
4.   Where are those points all of whose corresponding number pairs have abscissas -3?
5.   Describe the locus (place) of all points whose coordinates are equal.
6.   Construct a graph of the weight-cost postage function described on page 184.   Use 0 to 10 ounces as the domain.
7.   Plot the graphs of the following functions on the same axis.
   (a) $y = 2x + 1$ (b) $y = 2x - 3$ (c) $y = 2x$
8.   From Exercise 7 what generalization can be made concerning the coefficient of x?   What generalization can be made concerning the constant term?
9.   From Figure 6.9 estimate the following.
   (a)   The value of x corresponding to $y = 4$
   (b)   The value of x corresponding to $y = 0$
   (c)   The value of y corresponding to $x = 2$

10. Do the ordered pairs obtained in Exercise 9 satisfy the relation $y = 2x + 3$?

11. Complete the following ordered pairs such that they are elements of the function $y = 2x + 3$.

    (a) (____, 3)   (b) (4,____)   (c) (−1, _____)

12. Do the ordered pairs obtained in Exercise 11 define points on the graph in Figure 6.9?

TABLES

6.11   We have seen that the data from which graphs may be constructed may come from three entirely different types of source. We may have obtained the information from actual measurement of the corresponding pairs of values of the variables, as in Figure 6.6, or we may have computed the values from the definition of the variables, as in Figure 6.10. Or, finally, the graph may define the function, as in Figure 6.7. The same is true of tables. According to Boyle's Law, the volume of a given mass of gas is inversely proportional to the pressure if the temperature is kept constant. Stated otherwise, if the temperature is constant the product of volume and pressure is constant. Once this constant is known, the pressure corresponding to any given volume may be computed. Table 6.2 shows the pressure of a given quantity of air corresponding to various volumes.

The data in both Tables 6.1 and 6.2 were obtained by computation based on the stated law of relationship between the variables. Scientists know that, although freely falling bodies may obey exactly the law $d = 16t^2$ when they fall through a vacuum, the bodies actually follow this law only approximately when falling through air. The same is true of Boyle's Law; gases actually only approximately follow this law. Furthermore, the divergence from the predicted behavior is not the same for all gases. Table 6.3 shows the (assumed) behavior of some common gases.

Table 6.2   Pressure of various volumes of a given mass of air.

Volume in cubic centimeters	Pressure in meters of mercury
1000	1
500	2
250	4
125	8
100	10
50	20

Table 6.3   Pressures of certain gases corresponding to various volumes.   Values are assumed.

Volume	Pressure			
	Air	Oxygen	Helium	Carbon dioxide
100	100	100	100	100
50	200	200	200	199
10	993	996	1002	925
5	1970	1980	2025	1670
1	9755	9781	10120	7053

Whether we are concerned with constructing a table or reading one which has already been constructed, we should remember that a table merely shows, in a convenient form, pairs of corresponding values of the dependent and independent variables.   The correspondence of values may be shown by two rows of figures, as in Table 6.1, or by two columns, as in Tables 6.2 and 6.3.   Table 6.3 actually consists of four tables combined into one.   If we consider volume as the independent variable, there are four dependent variables to be paired with it.   There is a functional relationship between volume and pressure for air, another relationship between volume and pressure for oxygen, another for helium, and still another for carbon dioxide.   The same values of the independent variable are used in all cases.   A number of functional relationships are often combined into one table for purposes of comparison, as in Table 6.3, or as a matter of convenience.   Frequently, the independent variable can assume only a finite number of values.   In this case the function can be completely displayed, and thus defined, by means of a table.   A table showing baseball standings is a case in point.   The values of the independent variable are the teams in the league.   Each team's ratio of games won to games played is the corresponding value of the dependent variable. The table of standings defines the function.

Any table or graph should be self-explanatory.   What the two variables are should be clearly indicated.   The way in which the values from a table are to be paired should be evident.   As was true of graphs, a table may show paired values of a discrete variable or selected values for a continuous variable.   In the case of a continuous variable we may estimate intermediate values from a table in much the same manner as is done on a graph.   The process of interpolation, which will be explained in Section 9.15, enables us to find values between two consecutive values in the table.

—————————   E   X   E   R   C   I   S   E   S   —————————

1. Find four ordered pairs not listed in Table 6.2 which are elements of the volume-pressure function.

2. Construct a table showing the temperature at each hour from 4 A.M. to 4 A.M. as determined from Figure 6.7.

3. Write in algebraic form the function completely defined by the following table. What is its domain? Its range?

x	0	1	2	3	4	5	6
$f(x)$	5	8	11	14	17	20	23

4. Given: $f(x) = x^2 - x - 1$; domain, integers such that $-5 \leq x \leq +5$. Construct a table of the function.

5. Draw the graph of the function defined in Exercise 4.

6. If we change the domain of the function in Exercise 4 to the rational numbers between -5 and $+5$, the table becomes a table of selected values. Draw the graph of this function.

7. From the graph of Exercise 6 estimate the following.
    (a) $f(1.5)$ (b) $f(-.5)$ (c) $f(2.5)$ (d) $f(-1.5)$

8. What is the range of the function in Exercise 6?

9. Mr. Jones was 30 years old when his son entered school at the age of 6 and they both died in a plane crash when the father was aged 56. Describe the son's age.

10. Assume that Mr. Jones' son, Exercise 9, progressed normally through high school. Construct a table showing the father's age, to the nearest year, as a function of the son's grade in school.

SUMMARY

6.12 A *functional relationship* exists between two variables if, corresponding to any value of one variable (the independent variable), there exists one value of the other (the dependent variable). The function is the set of all pairs thus generated. We may define the relationship — state the manner in which the pairs of values of the variables may be obtained — by a verbal descriptive statement or by means of a mathematical formula. A graph gives the picture of the paired values of the variables. A table gives the numerical values of pairs of the variables. If the table, or graph, shows all the pairs in the function it may be considered as defining the function.

If we wish to compare specific sets of values of the variables a bar graph is appropriate.   If we wish to compare parts with each other and with the whole the pie chart is desirable.   When dealing with a discrete variable we may use either a bar graph or a broken-line graph.   If the variables are continuous a continuous-curved-line graph is desirable.   The line graphs are useful for showing the general nature of trends and fluctuations in the variation.

What a real number is?

What an imaginary number is?

It is possible to have an algebra that does not deal with numbers at all?

Over 2,000 years elapsed between the discovery that incommensurate quantities exist and the development of a satisfactory theory of irrational numbers?

There are more numbers between zero and one than there are natural numbers?

What a transfinite number is?

CHAPTER VII

MORE ALGEBRA

In this chapter we shall see why the rational number system, which was studied in Chapter V, is not sufficient either to represent magnitudes or to solve simple equations. We shall extend the rational number system to the real and, finally, to the complex system. We shall briefly examine the algebra of the field of real numbers and that of the complex numbers. Finally, we shall construct an algebra of sets and give it a practical interpretation.

INCOMMENSURATE MAGNITUDES

7.1   Since the field of rational numbers is closed with respect to all four fundamental operations, division by zero excluded, one might suppose that there is no need for further extensions of number. The obvious answer to this is that we have no need for further extensions if we never intend to use numbers other than in the four fundamental operations. However, the solution of a very simple equation like $x^2 = 2$ requires a new kind of number. There is no rational number x which when multiplied by itself will give 2. This fact was discovered relatively early. You may recall the Pythagorean Theorem:

> *Theorem*   The square of the hypotenuse of a right triangle is equal to the sum of the squares of the two other sides.

Pythagoras was a Greek who lived about five centuries before Christ. He and his followers made many contributions to arithmetic and geometry. Pythagoras represented a strange admixture of the modern scientific mind and mystic mumbo jumbo. He, or some of his followers, discovered that the hypotenuse of a right triangle with unit sides is incommensurate with the side. This means that we cannot find a common unit which will exactly measure both the side and the hypotenuse. Since the side is 1 and the hypotenuse $\sqrt{2}$, their discovery showed that there are no two integers whose ratio equals the ratio of $\sqrt{2}$ to 1. The Pythagoreans, believing that number was the source of all things, decided that they had found a flaw in God's handiwork. They tried to keep their discovery a secret. The story is told that when one of the society divulged the secret some of his brothers took him out on a lake and drowned him.

Euclid, another famous Greek, some two centuries later proved that there is no rational number whose square is 2. This proof is given in Section 2.9 on page 36. The same method can be adapted to show that the square root of any integer which is not a perfect square is irrational. We shall prove $\sqrt{3}$ irrational. Assume $\sqrt{3} = a/b$ where a, b have no factor in common. (We have assumed what we wish to disprove, namely $\sqrt{3}$ is rational.) Squaring and multiplying by b^2, we get $3b^2 = a^2$.

Since a^2 has the factor 3, so must a. (Every prime factor of a^2 must be present an even number of times.) Then a can be written $3c$, where c is an integer. Substituting,

$$3b^2 = (3c)^2 = 9c^2$$

Dividing by 3 we get

$$b^2 = 3c^2$$

from which it is seen that b^2 and therefore b must have the factor 3. But a and b were to have no factor in common. Therefore we must reject the original assumption that $\sqrt{3}$ is rational.

In Section 6.10 we agreed that there is a point on a line to correspond to every rational number but we left open the question of whether there is a rational number corresponding to every point. This, despite the fact that we proved there was a rational number between any two rational numbers. In case you did not work Exercise 13, Section 5.20, the proof follows. Let $a/b > c/d$ be any two rational numbers. Since the rational numbers are closed under addition and under division other than by zero, $(a/b + c/d)/2$ is a rational number. Simplifying, we may express it as $(ad + bc)/2bd$. If we apply D_8, Section 5.15, we see that $a/b > (ad + bc)/2bd > c/d$. Since there is a rational number between any two rational numbers we know the same thing relative to the points associated with them. One is tempted to surmise that these rational points encompass all the points of the line.

If we construct a square with unit side, Figure 7.1, the diagonal forms with two adjacent sides the triangle which caused the Pythagoreans all the trouble. Since the sides of our triangle are unity, the square of the hypotenuse is $1^2 + 1^2 = 2$ and we designate the hypotenuse $\sqrt{2}$, which we know is not a rational number. If we draw an arc with the origin as center and the diagonal as radius it will cut the x-axis in some point P. This makes us wonder whether there might not be points on a line besides the rational points.

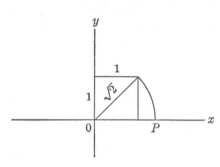

Figure 7.1   P is not a rational point.

But how do we know the arc cuts the x-axis? If we imagine a copper wire so thin that its cross section consists of a single molecule there will be "gaps" between each successive molecule. If we had another wire thin enough, we could pass one through the other without disturbing either. How do we know that a mathematical line does not have such properties? The answer is obvious; we create the mathematical line in such a way that it will not. A mathematical line has whatever properties it does by virtue of the postulates we accept. According to Archimedes' Postulate, there cannot be a last rational point on the right-hand end of the segment OP, nor can there be a first rational point to the right of P. This is one of several reasons why a mathematical line cannot be likened to the theoretical wire above. The points of a line are not discrete elements like the individual beads of a string of beads.

But there is *something* at the extremity of the segment OP. Either there is a gap at P, or P is a point but not a rational point. We resolve the difficulty by *giving* the line other points and at the same time decreeing that the "thing" $\sqrt{2}$ be a number. We give the line points other than rational points by means of an axiom:

Dedekind Axiom of Continuity   If all the points of a straight line are separated into two sets such that every point of the first set is to the left of every point of the second set, then there exists one and only one point which produces this division.

We shall not pursue this further. This is Dedekind's point of departure in developing the real numbers. We shall follow a procedure somewhat closer to that of his contemporary, Cantor. It is of more than passing historical interest that the struggle for a satisfactory theory of the real number system spans a surprisingly large segment of the history of mathematics.   As we have observed, the discovery of incommensurate (irrational) magnitudes was made nearly twenty-six hundred years ago.   Yet a satisfactory foundation for the real number system was finally proposed less than a hundred years ago. It was done independently by two German mathematicians, Richard Dedekind in 1872 and Georg Cantor in 1883.   Leopold Kronecker, who was Cantor's teacher, contended that there was no such thing as an irrational *number* because it could not be expressed exactly with a finite number of natural numbers.   He is credited with saying: "God made the natural numbers, all the rest is man's handiwork."   If the reader is interested in the Dedekind development of the real numbers, a quite readable description is available in *What Is Mathematics?* by Courant and Robbins.*

———————— E   X   E   R   C   I   S   E   S ————————

1.   Figure 7.1 indicates how one may construct a segment $\sqrt{2}$ units long. How can we construct a segment $\sqrt{3}$ units long?

2.   Prove that $\sqrt{5}$ is irrational.

3.   Apply to $\sqrt{4}$ the same argument as that used on page 206 to show $\sqrt{3}$ irrational.   Where does the argument break down?

4.   Prove that $\sqrt[3]{2}$ is irrational.

5.   If the two legs (sides adjacent to the right angle) of a right triangle are 5 feet and 12 feet what is the hypotenuse?

6.   Is it possible for all three sides of a right triangle to be odd integers? Why?

7.   If the diagonal of a square is an integer can the side be a rational number? Why?

8.   The hypotenuse of a right triangle is 100 yards and one of the legs is 56 yards.   Find the other leg.

RATIONAL NUMBERS ARE REPEATING DECIMALS

7.2   Recall that we observed, when considering our system of numeration, that any number may be thought of as extending infinitely to the right of the decimal point if we fill in with zeros beyond the last

* Oxford University Press, 1941.

nonzero digit.   For example, we may think of 14.56 as being
$$14.56000\ldots.$$
Every rational number when converted to decimal form will either
terminate or repeat.   The division algorithm makes this evident.
Consider the conversion of $\frac{4}{17}$ to decimal form:

$$
\begin{array}{r}
.23 \\
17\overline{)4.0000} \\
3.4 \\
\hline
60 \\
51 \\
\hline
9
\end{array}
$$

The first remainder we obtained is 6, the next remainder is 9.   If the
division does not terminate, there are at most 16 different remainders
possible, namely the numbers 1 through 16.   If we can obtain the
remainder 4, we are right where we started and begin picking up the
same sequence of digits in the quotient all over again.   If we ever
get the same remainder a second time, such as the first remainder 6,
from that point on we begin to repeat what we have already done.
Then after not more than 17 steps we must have started a repetition
of the same sequence of digits.   By completing the division, you may
verify the fact that in this case all 16 remainders appear.   On the
other hand, if we reduce $\frac{1}{13}$ we do not get 12 different remainders;
the cycle is completed in only six steps.   The cycle of repeating digits
does not have to begin with the decimal point.   The reasoning is
perfectly general.   In the conversion of the rational number a/b to a
decimal, we can get at most $(b-1)$ different remainders.   Then after
b steps in the division we must have started a repetition of the same
digits.   If we consider those rational numbers which terminate, such
as $\frac{1}{4}$, as having an endless sequence of zeros following the last nonzero
digit, then we may consider them repeating decimals.   Under this
interpretation, every rational number is a repeating decimal.

A REPEATING DECIMAL IS A RATIONAL NUMBER

7.3   The last section tells us that we can always express a rational
number as a repeating decimal.   We now wish to consider the converse: Is every repeating decimal just another representation of
some rational number?

Let us look at a few examples.

Example   Let $N = 13.\overline{127}\ 127\ 127 \ldots$ (We place the bar over 127 to indicate that it is the repeating period.)

Multiplying by 10^3, we get $10^3 N = 13127.\overline{127}\ 127\ 127 \ldots$

If we subtract N from $10^3 N$ we get

$$10^3 N - N = 13127.\overline{127}\ 127\ 127 \ldots - 13.\overline{127}\ 127\ 127 \ldots$$
$$999N = 13114$$
$$N = \frac{13114}{999} \text{ , a rational number}$$

Example

Let $\qquad\qquad\qquad\qquad N = .05\overline{31}3131 \ldots$

Then $\qquad\qquad\qquad 10^4 N = 531.\overline{31}3131 \ldots$

and $\qquad\qquad\qquad\ 10^2 N = 5.\overline{31}3131 \ldots$

Subtracting, $\quad 10^4 N - 10^2 N = 526$

or $\qquad\qquad\qquad 9900N = 526$

$$N = \frac{526}{9900} \text{ , a rational number}$$

Example

Let $\qquad\qquad\qquad\qquad N = .\overline{3}333 \ldots$

Then $\qquad\qquad\qquad\ 10N = 3.\overline{3}333 \ldots$

Subtracting, $\qquad 10N - N = 3$

$$9N = 3$$
$$N = \tfrac{3}{9} = \tfrac{1}{3}, \text{ a rational number}$$

Example

Let $\qquad\qquad\qquad\qquad N = .4\overline{9}99 \ldots$

Then $\qquad\qquad\qquad 10^2 N = 49.\overline{9}99 \ldots$

and $\qquad\qquad\qquad\ 10N = 4.\overline{9}99 \ldots$

Subtracting, $\qquad\quad 90N = 45$

$$N = \tfrac{45}{90} = \tfrac{1}{2}$$

But $\qquad\qquad\qquad\qquad \tfrac{1}{2} = .5\overline{0}00 \ldots$

Therefore $\qquad\quad .5\overline{0}00 \ldots = .4\overline{9}99 \ldots$

The method is completely general. Let the repeating decimal less than 1 be indicated by $N = .a_1 a_2 \ldots a_n \overline{b_1 b_2 \ldots b_m} b_1 b_2 \ldots b_m \ldots$ where a_i are digits not in the period and $b_1 b_2 \ldots b_m$ is the period of the cycle.

$$10^{n+m} N = a_1 a_2 \ldots a_n b_1 b_2 \ldots b_m.\overline{b_1 b_2 \ldots b_m} \ldots$$
$$10^n N = a_1 a_2 \ldots a_n.\overline{b_1 b_2 \ldots b_m} \ldots$$

Subtracting,

$$(10^{n+m} - 10^n)N = a_1 a_2 \ldots a_n b_1 b_2 \ldots b_m - a_1 a_2 \ldots a_n$$
$$N = \frac{a_1 a_2 \ldots a_n b_1 b_2 \ldots b_m - a_1 a_2 \ldots a_n}{10^{n+m} - 10^n},$$

a rational number.

We complete the argument with the observation that any repeating decimal can be expressed as an integral power of ten, times a repeating decimal less than one. In other words, we can always express the number as $10^x N$, x an integer. If N is rational so is $10^x N$.

Example $17.\overline{135}\,135\ldots = 10^2 \times .17\overline{135}\,135\ldots$ Since $.17\overline{135}\,135\ldots$ is rational so is $17.\overline{135}\,135\ldots$

——————   E   X   E   R   C   I   S   E   S   ——————

1. Prove that $3.\overline{25}\ldots$ is equal to $3.2\overline{52}\ldots$

2. Find integers a, b such that

   (a) $\dfrac{a}{b} = .1\overline{47}\ldots$ (b) $\dfrac{a}{b} = 1.2\overline{34}\ldots$ (c) $\dfrac{a}{b} = 1.\overline{234}\ldots$

3. Which is the greater, $.6\overline{75}\ldots$ or $.67\overline{5}\ldots$?

4. Convert $.134_6$ to base 10.

5. Convert $.463_8$ to base 10.

6. Convert $.25_{10}$ to base 7.

7. Prove that $7.\overline{0}\ldots = 6.\overline{9}\ldots$

8. Find a rational number between $.\overline{376}\ldots$ and $.3759\ldots$

9. Which is the greater, $\frac{2}{3}$ or $.67$? How much greater?

10. Which is the greater, $\frac{1}{3}$ or $.333$? How much greater?

11. Reduce $\frac{1}{7}$ to a decimal and carry the division far enough to discover the cycle. Multiply the digits in this period (the part of the decimal up to the point where the repetition begins) by 3 and compare your result with the decimal expansion of $\frac{3}{7}$. Multiply the period of $\frac{1}{7}$ by all integers from 2 through 7. Can you explain the phenomenon?

12. Select a one-digit number and multiply it by 9. Multiply this product by 12,345,679. Explain the result. *Hint:* Find the decimal expansion of $\frac{1}{81}$.

THE REAL NUMBER SYSTEM

7.4   The square root of 2 is not a rational number, as we have proved. The square root algorithm enables one to obtain as close an approximation to $\sqrt{2}$ as may be desired. We can do the same thing by another method which is longer but more meaningful. Since

$1^2 = 1$ is less than 2 and $2^2 = 4$ is more than 2, if there is a number whose square is 2 it must lie between 1 and 2.*   By trial we can find the best approximation to the nearest tenth, for instance $1.3^2 = 1.69$, $1.4^2 = 1.96$, $1.5^2 = 2.25$.   Thus 1.4 is too small and 1.5 is too large, so $1.4^2 < 2 < 1.5^2$.

Thus we have:

$$1^2 = 1 < 2 < 4 = 2^2$$
$$1.4^2 = 1.96 < 2 < 2.25 = 1.5^2$$
$$1.41^2 = 1.9881 < 2 < 2.0164 = 1.42^2$$
$$1.414^2 = 1.999396 < 2 < 2.002225 = 1.415^2$$

This process may be continued for as many digits as we care to compute.   But we know the decimal will never terminate or repeat because we have already proved that $\sqrt{2}$ is not a rational number.   What, then, is this endless nonrepeating succession of digits which continually squeezes $\sqrt{2}$ into ever narrower limits, yet never pins it down?

We might think of 2 as being squeezed into ever narrower limits in much this same way.

$$1 < 2 < 3$$
$$1.9 < 2 < 2.1$$
$$1.99 < 2 < 2.01 \quad \text{and so on}$$

In contrast to Dedekind's approach, Cantor conceived of this "squeezing" process as defining a real number.   Sometimes, as in the foregoing, the squeeze is made on a rational number, as 2, and sometimes it is not, as on $\sqrt{2}$.

A satisfactory development of the theory of real numbers offers difficulties much more formidable than those encountered in developing the integers and the rationals, as well as those to be encountered in developing the complex numbers.   We succeeded in defining an integer as an ordered pair of natural numbers.   In so doing, we utilized the inverse of addition.   We defined the rationals as ordered pairs of integers, utilizing the inverse of multiplication.   The need for reals, from the algebraic standpoint, stems from the extraction of square roots.   In this operation we are concerned with one number, rather than with two numbers as in subtraction or division.   Efforts

* This is equivalent to the assertion that $a < b$ implies $a^2 < b^2$ where $a, b > 0$.   We have used the relations *less than* and *greater than* for the purpose of ordering various sets. These relations obey certain axioms just as does the relation *equal to*, as set forth in Section 4.8.   One of the *less than* axioms states: $a < b$ and $0 < c$ implies $ac < bc$.   This justifies the assertion that $a < b$ implies $a^2 < b^2$ where $a, b > 0$, since $a < b$ implies both $a^2 < ab$ and $ab < b^2$.

at defining real numbers as ordered pairs of rational numbers have not met with success. The difficulties go much deeper. Development of the real number system requires the limit concept, discussed in the next chapter, and advanced mathematics. It is beyond our scope, but it can be shown that endless sequences of digits, repeating or not, fulfill all the requirements of an ordered field under proper definitions. We therefore rely on intuition at this point and state the definition: *Every endless sequence of digits represents a real number.* We have already seen that if it repeats we have a rational number. Here we have a ready-made isomorphism between a subset of the reals and the rationals. By definition: *Every nonrepeating endless sequence of digits represents an irrational number.*

Neither of these definitions requires a one-to-one correspondence. We have already seen that there are two ways to write $\frac{1}{2}$ as a repeating decimal, $.4\overline{9}99\ldots$ or $.5\overline{0}00\ldots$. This suggests the possibility of defining a real number as an ordered pair of *something*. This is the Cantor approach. If you are interested, read the section on nested intervals in *What Is Mathematics?**

In so far as the foregoing discussion is concerned, we have no assurance that there is more than one irrational number, namely $\sqrt{2}$. We cannot look at the succession of digits and tell whether or not the number is rational. The mere fact that the sequence does not repeat after the first hundred or million digits gives us no assurance that the repetition will not begin with the next digit after the last one we find. The method we used for approximating $\sqrt{2}$ is such that we have no assurance that the decimal will not terminate somewhere down the line, notwithstanding the fact that we have proved it cannot happen. And the proof did not require that we find any digits. It may be something of a surprise to realize that nature abounds with irrational quantities. In fact, there are more irrational numbers than there are rational. The square root of every positive integer which is not a perfect square is irrational. So, also, is the cube root of every integer which is not a perfect cube. Similarly for higher roots. This type of irrational number is called *algebraic*. A number is algebraic if it satisfies an equation of the form

$$a_0x^n + a_1x^{n-1} + \ldots + a_n = 0, \text{ where } a_0 \neq 0$$

where a_i is rational and n a positive integer. Since $\sqrt{2}$ satisfies the equation $x^2 = 2$, it is an algebraic irrational. Not all algebraic num-

* Oxford University Press, 1941.

bers are irrational, however. The equation $x^2 = 9$ has roots $+3$ and -3; therefore $+3$ and -3 are algebraic. In fact, all rational numbers are algebraic since by definition the rational number x must satisfy the equation $ax = b$, where a, b are integers.

There are irrational numbers which are not algebraic. They are called *transcendental numbers*. Every real transcendental number is irrational. The most familiar example of a transcendental number is probably the number π, the ratio of the circumference of a circle to its diameter.

Obviously, we cannot identify an irrational number by examining all of its digits so as to guarantee that a repeating cycle does not exist. For that matter, the same is true of rational numbers. We know that .25 is rational because it is assumed that the endless succession of digits is a succession of zeros. We know $3\overline{2.5}$ . . . is rational because it is agreed that the bar over the digits 25 implies an endless succession of this cycle. If we are to exhibit an irrational number there must be some rule of succession of digits which assures that there will not be a repeating cycle. This may be done in many ways. Some, but not all, convergent infinite series (see Section 8.15, page 268) converge to irrational numbers.

However, it is possible to exhibit a succession of digits which continues infinitely that is an irrational number.

Example   101001000 . . . is an irrational number if we continue to adjoin a 1 followed by a set of as many zeros as the total of the previous set, plus 1.

We implied that an algebraic irrational is expressible as a root of some rational number. It is true that irrationals which can be so expressed are algebraic. But there are still other algebraic numbers. This means that numbers exist which satisfy the equation on page 213 but which cannot be expressed in terms of roots of rational numbers. This was discovered in the quest for a solution to the general fifth-degree equation. This discovery was made by the Norwegian, Niels Abel, in 1825, in the course of proving that the general fifth-degree equation cannot be solved by radicals. The existence of transcendental numbers was discovered by the Frenchman, Joseph Liouville, in 1844.

Summarizing, the real numbers constitute an ordered field. The rational numbers are isomorphic to the subset of real numbers which are repeating decimals. Every real number is either rational or irrational. Every real number may also be classified as algebraic or transcendental. All rationals are algebraic. All transcendentals are irrational.

——————— E   X   E   R   C   I   S   E   S ———————

1. If two positive real numbers are written as endless decimals, how can you tell which is the greater?

2. Two commonly used approximations to π are $\frac{22}{7}$ and 3.1416.   Which is the greater?   If a better approximation than either of these is 3.14159, which of the former is closer to π?

3. Use the method on page 212 to find $\sqrt{10}$ to the nearest hundredth.

4. One may find square roots by a method of averaging.   If we wish to find $\sqrt{N}$ we can divide N by any number $d < N$.   If the quotient is q, we then use $\dfrac{d + q}{2}$ as a new divisor.   We continue the process until d and q are equal, to the desired number of digits.   This is then the approximate $\sqrt{N}$.   Use this method to find, to three digits, the following.

   (a) $\sqrt{289}$ (b) $\sqrt{500}$ (c) $\sqrt{1.34}$ (d) $\sqrt{13.4}$

5. Prove that any positive integral root of a positive integer is an algebraic number.

6. Why is it impossible for a transcendental number to be rational?

7. Use the fact that a rational number is a repeating decimal to show that there is always a rational number between any two rational numbers.

8. Show that there is always an irrational number between any two rational numbers.

9. Show that the irrational numbers do not form a field.

10. The equation $\pi x = 1$ has the root $1/\pi$.   Why is $1/\pi$ not an algebraic number?

11.* Do the irrationals and multiplication form a group?   Why?

THE ALGEBRA OF REAL NUMBERS

7.5   All our conclusions in Chapter V relative to the solution of equations with rational coefficients now apply with equal force to equations with real coefficients.

Aside from the fact that the equations may now have real coefficients, is our algebra any more powerful?   In other words, are we now able to solve more extensive types of equations?   We were restricted to those quadratic equations, that is, polynomial equations of degree two, which could be factored into linear factors whose product is zero.

Specifically, we could not solve

$$x^2 - 2 = 0$$

Now we can, since $x^2 - 2 = 0$ implies $x^2 = 2$, and we can take the square root of both sides, getting $x = \pm\sqrt{2}$. Since $\sqrt{2}$ is a symbol indicating a number whose square is 2, the same must be true of the same number with its sign changed, $-\sqrt{2}$, because of the law of signs in multiplication. By convention, if there is no sign preceding the radical, the positive square root is implied.

Consider the general second-degree polynomial equation:

$$ax^2 + bx + c = 0, \text{ where } a, b, c \text{ are real}$$

We can divide by a, getting

$$x^2 + (b/a)x + c/a = 0$$

then subtracting c/a,

$$x^2 + (b/a)x = -c/a$$

Now, if we add $b^2/4a^2$,

$$x^2 + (b/a)x + b^2/4a^2 = b^2/4a^2 - c/a = (b^2 - 4ac)/4a^2$$

The expression $x^2 + (b/a)x + b^2/4a^2$ is a *perfect square*, that is, the square of one term, x, plus the square of another term, $b/2a$, plus twice the product of the two terms, $2 \cdot x \cdot (b/2a)$. An expression such as this is the square of the sum of the terms, $(x + b/2a)^2$. We may verify this by applying the distributive property:

$$(x + b/2a)^2 = (x + b/2a)(x + b/2a) = x^2 + (b/a)x + b^2/4a^2$$

Making the indicated substitution in our equation, we get

$$(x + b/2a)^2 = \frac{b^2 - 4ac}{4a^2}$$

Now taking the square root of both sides, we get

$$x + b/2a = \frac{\pm\sqrt{b^2 - 4ac}}{2a}$$

and finally

$$x = -\frac{b}{2a} + \frac{\pm\sqrt{b^2 - 4ac}}{2a} = \frac{-b \pm \sqrt{b^2 - 4ac}}{2a}$$

You may recognize this as the familiar *quadratic formula*.

In the algebra of reals, the second-degree polynomial equation always has a solution *if $\sqrt{b^2 - 4ac}$ is real.* Suppose $b^2 - 4ac = -4$. There is no real number whose square is -4. Every real number different from zero is either positive or negative. The rule of signs in multiplication tells us that the square of either a positive or negative number is positive. Indeed, the real number system is not closed under the extraction of roots. No negative number has a real square root.

The *radicand,* $b^2 - 4ac$, is called the *discriminant* of the quadratic. It enables one to distinguish the character of the roots without finding what they are. If the coefficients of the equation are rational, a positive discriminant means the roots are real and unequal. If the discriminant is zero, the roots are real, rational, and equal. If the discriminant is a positive square, the roots are real, rational, and unequal. If the discriminant is negative, the equation does not have real roots.

RECTANGULAR COORDINATES

7.6   In Section 6.10 we saw, by virtue of Archimedes' Postulate, that there is a point on the line corresponding to each rational number. The Dedekind Axiom of Continuity leads to the conclusion that there are also points corresponding to irrational numbers. We shall assume this here, since its proof depends upon advanced mathematics. We assume that *there is a one-to-one correspondence between the points on a line and the real numbers.* It follows that there is a one-to-one correspondence between ordered pairs of real numbers and the points on a plane. It is this concept that is the bedrock of the analytic geometry of René Descartes. Any function whose pairs are real numbers is represented on the coordinate plane by a set of points. These points may form a continuous line, depending on the nature of the function. Conversely, any set of points, on a continuous line or not, defines a function, if no two of the points lie on the same vertical line. It is thus possible to study geometric problems by studying their corresponding functions, as it is also possible to study a function by studying the geometric properties of its graph.

In Figure 7.2, every point on the line determines a number pair which is an element of the set of ordered pairs (function) defined by the relation $y = 2x + 5$. Furthermore, every number pair in this function defines a point which is a point of the line.

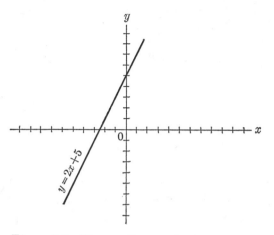

Figure 7.2   The coordinates of every point of the line satisfy $y = 2x + 5$, and every (x, y) pair satisfying $y = 2x + 5$ defines a point on line.

We should note that we are not restricted to rational numbers. For example the pair $(\sqrt{2},\ 2\sqrt{2} + 5)$ is an element of the function and it is a point on the line. We may convince ourselves of the latter statement by locating the point $(1.41, 7.82)$ which is an approximation of the original point.

———————— E   X   E   R   C   I   S   E   S ————————

1. Express the following as the ratio of two integers, thus showing that it is a rational number.

$$\frac{\dfrac{1}{\sqrt{2}}}{\dfrac{\sqrt{2}}{4}}$$

2. All rational numbers may properly be thought of as fractions. May all fractions be thought of as rational numbers? Explain.

3. Prove that the sum of a rational number and an irrational number must be irrational. *Hint:* The sum, difference, product, or quotient of two rational numbers must be rational.

4. Since $-\sqrt{3} + \sqrt{3} = 0$ we know that the sum of two irrational numbers may be rational. Can this be true even though their sum is different from zero?

5. Add to both sides of the following equations the constant necessary to make the left side a perfect square.
   (a) $x^2 + 6x + 5 = 0$ (c) $4x^2 - 4x - 8 = 0$
   (b) $9x^2 - 12x - 5 = 0$ (d) $x^2 + x + 1 = 0$

6. Find the square roots of both sides of the equations obtained in Exercise 5, and solve the resulting linear equations. Why are two linear equations obtained from each quadratic equation?

7. Solve the equations given in Exercise 5 by the quadratic formula.

8. In each of the following equations find the value of k, given that the equation has equal roots.
   (a) $3x^2 + 5x + 4k = 0$ (c) $2x^2 + 4kx + 2k = 0$
   (b) $2x^2 + kx - 6 = 0$

9. In the modulo 5 field, which elements are perfect squares? What are their square roots?

10. Verify: $x = 2$ is a solution to the equation $2x^2 - 3x - 2 \equiv 0$, modulo 5.

11. Verify: $(x - 2)(2x + 1) \equiv 2x^2 - 3x - 2$, modulo 5.

12. Solve:
   (a) $x - 2 \equiv 0$, mod 5   (b) $2x + 1 \equiv 0$, mod 5

13. Find the discriminant, as defined on page 217, of the equation in Exercise 10.

14. Find the discriminant of $x^2 - 2x + 4 \equiv 0$, modulo 5. Is it the square of any element, modulo 5? Determine by substitution whether any of the elements 0, 1, 2, 3, 4 satisfy the equation.

15. Use the discriminant to determine whether the following equations have solutions in the real field. If they do, determine whether the roots are rational or irrational and equal or unequal.
   (a) $5x^2 + 3x - 2 = 0$ (d) $3x^2 + 3x + 1 = 0$
   (b) $x^2 - 5x - 6 = 0$ (e) $x^2 - 4x + 4 = 0$
   (c) $3x^2 + 4x + 1 = 0$

16. Determine whether the following have solutions in the real field. Solve those that do.
   (a) $m^2 + 3m - 4 = 0$ (c) $a^2 - a - 5 = 0$
   (b) $p^2 - 2p + 3 = 0$ (d) $x^2 + 4x - 1 = 0$

17. If the graph of a function is the straight-line segment between $(0, 0)$ and $(3, 2)$, what is its domain of definition? What is its range?

18. If the following table completely defines a function, describe its graph.

x	0	1	2	3
y	0	2	4	6

TRANSFINITE NUMBERS

*7.7   In Chapter IV the notion was advanced that a natural number is a name by which we may identify all finite sets that can be placed in one-to-one correspondence.   Sets are said to be equivalent if they can be put in one-to-one correspondence, and a number name is associated with the set of all such sets.   We extend the idea to infinite sets. Infinite sets are equivalent if they can be placed in one-to-one correspondence.   Such sets have the same *transfinite cardinal number*.   At this point it would be well to reread Section 4.4.

We shall show that the rational numbers are countably infinite; that is, they can be placed in one-to-one correspondence with the natural numbers.   All infinite sets which possess this property are said to have the transfinite cardinal number $\aleph_0$, called *aleph-null*.   The array extended infinitely to the right and down will include every

$$
\begin{array}{ccccccc}
1/1 \rightarrow 1/2 & & 1/3 \rightarrow 1/4 & & 1/5 \rightarrow 1/6 & & \cdots \\
\swarrow & \nearrow & \swarrow & \nearrow & \swarrow & & \\
2/1 & 2/2 & 2/3 & 2/4 & 2/5 & 2/6 & \cdots \\
\downarrow \nearrow & \swarrow & \nearrow & \swarrow & & & \\
3/1 & 3/2 & 3/3 & 3/4 & 3/5 & 3/6 & \cdots \\
\swarrow & \nearrow & \swarrow & & & & \\
4/1 & 4/2 & 4/3 & 4/4 & 4/5 & 4/6 & \cdots \\
\downarrow \nearrow & \swarrow & & & & & \\
5/1 & 5/2 & 5/3 & 5/4 & 5/5 & 5/6 & \cdots \\
\swarrow & & & & & & \\
6/1 & 6/2 & 6/3 & 6/4 & 6/5 & 6/6 & \cdots \\
\cdots & \cdots & \cdots & \cdots & \cdots & \cdots & \cdots
\end{array}
$$

possible ratio of natural numbers.   This being true, it will include every positive rational number.   But this array may be counted, placed in one-to-one correspondence with the natural numbers, by following the arrows.   Continuation of these diagonals "sweeps the array clean" as we go.   A portion of the correspondence follows:

$$
\begin{array}{cccccc}
1 & 2 & 3 & 4 & 5 & 6 \\
\downarrow & \downarrow & \downarrow & \downarrow & \downarrow & \downarrow \\
1/1 & 1/2 & 2/1 & 3/1 & 2/2 & 1/3
\end{array}
$$

Notice that the array has been ordered so that it can be counted.   It was not ordered as to magnitude, however; that is not necessary. Since this array is countable and since it contains each positive rational number infinitely many times, for example, $\frac{1}{2} = \frac{2}{4} = \frac{3}{6} = \ldots$, we certainly may conclude that the positive rational numbers are countable.   Incidentally, we have shown that, in this case at least, $\aleph_0 \times$

$\aleph_0 = \aleph_0$, since each of the countably infinite positive rational numbers appears a countably infinite number of times.

But we set out to show *all* the rational numbers countable. To do this, imagine a mirror image of our array adjoined at the left with a minus sign attached to each ratio. We can count the double array with zero thrown in by associating 1 with 0, then alternately going to the right array, then the left, and moving through each array in precisely the same manner as indicated above. The correspondence begins as follows:

1	2	3	4	5	6	7	8	9	10	11	12	13
↕	↕	↕	↕	↕	↕	↕	↕	↕	↕	↕	↕	↕
0	1/1	−1/1	1/2	−1/2	2/1	−2/1	3/1	−3/1	2/2	−2/2	1/3	−1/3

We have now not only shown the rational numbers to be countable, we have also shown in this case that

$$\aleph_0 + \aleph_0 = \aleph_0$$

But not all infinite sets are countable. We shall show the real numbers not countable by showing those real numbers between zero and one not countable. Consider the array obtained from the array

$$
\begin{array}{cccccc}
A_{11} & A_{12} & A_{13} & A_{14} & A_{15} & A_{16} & \cdots \\
A_{21} & A_{22} & A_{23} & A_{24} & A_{25} & A_{26} & \cdots \\
A_{31} & A_{32} & A_{33} & A_{34} & A_{35} & A_{36} & \cdots \\
A_{41} & A_{42} & A_{43} & A_{44} & A_{45} & A_{46} & \cdots \\
\cdots & \cdots & \cdots & \cdots & \cdots & \cdots & \cdots
\end{array}
$$

of rationals by replacing each ratio x/y with the element A_{xy}. Let each element A represent some digit 0 through 9. With the understanding that a decimal point precedes it, each row is an endless decimal; that is, it is a real number between zero and one. The number of rows is countably infinite; there are the same number of rows as there are rational numbers. If the real numbers are countably infinite, this array contains *all* real numbers. We shall show that this is not true by exhibiting a real number which is not in this array. Consider the diagonal $A_{11}A_{22}A_{33}\ldots$. We replace A_{11} with some digit b_{11} other than A_{11}, 0, or 9. We similarly replace $A_{22}, A_{33}\ldots$ — all elements in the diagonal. We then have an endless decimal, $b_{11}b_{22}b_{33}\ldots$, which is different from each row in the A_{ij} array in at least one digit. We excluded 0 and 9 to be sure that the sequence $b_{11}b_{22}b_{23}\ldots$ is not merely another form of one of the original rows, as, for example, $.49\overline{9}\ldots$ is merely another form of $.50\overline{0}\ldots$ The set of real numbers has the transfinite number C.   It is called the *count of the continuum*.

Whether or not there are other transfinite numbers between $\aleph_0$ and C is a question mathematicians have not as yet answered.   It is known, however, that there are no transfinite numbers smaller than $\aleph_0$ and that there are at least $\aleph_0$ transfinite numbers.

As we have already hinted, the arithmetic of the transfinite is quite different from that of the finite.   A few examples follow, in which n is a finite number.

$$\aleph_0 + n = \aleph_0, \quad \aleph_0 + \aleph_0 = \aleph_0, \quad n\aleph_0 = \aleph_0, \quad \aleph_0{}^n = \aleph_0$$

In fact, we must use $\aleph_0$ as an exponent in order to get to C.

$$\aleph_0{}^{\aleph_0} = C, \quad \aleph_0 + C = C, \quad \aleph_0 C = C$$

────────── E   X   E   R   C   I   S   E   S ──────────

1. Give examples to illustrate the following.
   (a) $\aleph_0 - \aleph_0 = 0$ (b) $\aleph_0 - \aleph_0 = \aleph_0$ (c) $\aleph_0 - \aleph_0 = 100$

2. Which is the greater, the number of real points on a directed line between 0 and 1, or the number of rational points between 0 and 1,000?

3. If on a line a point 0 is selected for origin, can one tell whether another arbitrarily chosen point A is rational or irrational?   Discuss.

4. Prove there are as many positive integers greater than 100 as there are positive integers.

5. Give examples to illustrate the following: If n is a finite number
   (a) $\aleph_0 - n = \aleph_0$ (b) $\aleph_0 + \aleph_0 = \aleph_0$ (c) $C - \aleph_0 = C$

6. Prove there are more irrational numbers than rational.

THE COMPLEX NUMBERS

7.8   Our motivation for this extension of number has been indicated. Negative numbers do not have real square roots.   As simple an equation as $x^2 + 1 = 0$ has no real solution.   In order that these limitations may be removed we create the complex numbers.   We shall define them formally, then discuss their meaning.   We state the following definitions:

C_1 A complex number is an ordered pair of real numbers (a, b).

C_2 The sum of two complex numbers is given by $(a, b) + (c, d) = [(a + c), (b + d)]$.

C_3 The product of two complex numbers is given by $(a, b)(c, d) = [(ac - bd), (ad + bc)]$.

C_4 Two complex numbers (a, b) and (c, d) are equal if and only if $a = c$ and $b = d$.

Compare these definitions with the corresponding ones for the integers and rationals. Note particularly that a complex number can be expressed only in one way. We make no attempt to order the complex numbers. The reason for this will be evident presently.

Subtraction and division are, as usual, defined as the inverse of addition and multiplication respectively. This means in the case of subtraction that $(a, b) - (c, d) = (x, y)$ if and only if $(x, y) + (c, d) = (a, b)$. Adding the left side, we get $[(x + c), (y + d)] = (a, b)$. Applying C_4 to this, we get $x + c = a$ or $x = a - c$, and $y + d = b$ or $y = b - d$. We have shown that subtraction is always possible and we can state the difference:

C_5 $(a, b) - (c, d) = [(a - c), (b - d)]$.

Since division is the inverse of multiplication, $(a, b) \div (c, d) = (x, y)$ if and only if $(c, d) \cdot (x, y) = (a, b)$. Multiplying on the left, we get $[(cx - dy), (cy + dx)] = (a, b)$. If we apply C_4 to this, we get

$$cx - dy = a$$
$$dx + cy = b$$

We know from Section 5.23 that this system has the solution

$$x = \frac{ac + bd}{c^2 + d^2}, \quad y = \frac{bc - ad}{c^2 + d^2}$$

provided $c^2 + d^2 \neq 0$. If $c^2 + d^2 = 0$, we know $c = d = 0$. Then (x, y) exists and division is possible, with the restriction that we do not divide by $(0, 0)$. One would suspect that $(0, 0)$ is made to correspond with the real number 0. As usual, division by zero is not allowed. With this limitation stated, we may define division.

C_6 Division: $(a, b) \div (c, d) = \left(\dfrac{ac + bd}{c^2 + d^2}, \dfrac{bc - ad}{c^2 + d^2} \right)$ if $(c, d) \neq (0, 0)$.

We wish to show that the set of complex numbers is a field. To refresh your memory: the eleven field postulates are listed in Section 5.7.

The closure postulates F_1 and F_6 are satisfied by the definitions of addition and multiplication respectively. The sum of two complex numbers is a complex number according to C_2. The product of two complex numbers is a complex number according to C_3.

F_2, associativity under addition, is satisfied:

$$[(a, b) + (c, d)] + (e, f) = [(a + c), (b + d)] + (e, f)$$
$$= [(a + c + e), (b + d + f)]$$

but

$$(a, b) + [(c, d) + (e, f)] = (a, b) + [(c + e), (d + f)]$$
$$= [(a + c + e), (b + d + f)]$$

F_3, identity under addition, is satisfied by the element $(0, 0)$:

$$(a, b) + (0, 0) = [(a + 0), (b + 0)] = (a, b)$$

As we might infer from C_5, the additive inverse of (a, b) is $(-a, -b)$ since

$$(a, b) + (-a, -b) = (a - a), (b - b) = (0, 0)$$

Therefore F_4 is satisfied.

F_5, addition is commutative, holds:

$$(a, b) + (c, d) = [(a + c), (b + d)] = [(c + a), (d + b)]$$
$$= (c, d) + (a, b)$$

F_7, multiplication is associative:

$$[(a, b)(c, d)](e, f) = [(ac - bd), (ad + bc)](e, f)$$
$$= \{[(ac - bd)e - (ad + bc)f], [(ac - bd)f + (ad + bc)e]\}$$
$$= [(ace - bde - adf - bcf), (acf - bdf + ade + bce)]$$

but we also have

$$(a, b)[(c, d)(e, f)] = (a, b)[(ce - df), (cf + de)]$$
$$= \{[a(ce - df) - b(cf + de)], [a(cf + de) + b(ce - df)]\}$$
$$= [(ace - adf - bcf - bde), (acf + ade + bce - bdf)]$$

F_8 is satisfied by the element $(1, 0)$:

$$(a, b)(1, 0) = [(a - 0), (0 + b)] = (a, b)$$

Since division by nonzero complex numbers is always possible, we expect F_9 to be fulfilled. We may show that it is by finding the product $(a, b) \times \{[a/(a^2 + b^2)], [-b/(a^2 + b^2)]\}$ to be the multiplication identity:

$$(a, b) \times \left(\frac{a}{a^2 + b^2}, \frac{-b}{a^2 + b^2} \right) =$$

$$\left(\frac{a^2}{a^2 + b^2} - \frac{-b^2}{a^2 + b^2} \right), \left(\frac{-ab}{a^2 + b^2} + \frac{ab}{a^2 + b^2} \right) = \left(\frac{a^2 + b^2}{a^2 + b^2}, 0 \right) = 1, 0$$

F_{10} holds:

$(a, b)(c, d) = [(ac - bd), (ad + bc)]$

$(c, d)(a, b) = [(ca - db), (cb + da)] = [(ac - bd), (ad + bc)]$

F_{11}, the distributive property, remains:

$(a, b)[(c, d) + (e, f)] = (a, b)[(c + e), (d + f)]$

$\qquad = \{[(ac + ae) - (bd + bf)], [(ad + af) + (bc + be)]\}$

$\qquad = [(ac + ae - bd - bf), (ad + af + bc + be)]$

but we also have

$(a, b)(c, d) + (a, b)(e, f)$

$\qquad = [(ac - bd), (ad + bc)] + [(ae - bf), (af + be)]$

$\qquad = [(ac - bd + ae - bf), (ad + bc + af + be)]$

We have now shown that all the properties of a field are fulfilled in the set of complex numbers. Hence we may now apply the algebra of rationals, and thus reals, to polynomial equations with complex coefficients.

Is there a subset of the complex numbers isomorphic to the real numbers? We excluded division by $(0, 0)$ which was the identity element under addition. This suggests that the complex number $(0, 0)$ is to correspond to the real number 0. We found that $(1, 0)$ was the identity element under multiplication. This suggests a correspondence between the complex number $(1, 0)$ and the real number 1. Let us examine the possibility that we establish the isomorphism between the subset of complex numbers $(a, 0)$ and the real numbers a. There is an obvious one-to-one correspondence between the two sets of numbers. If we add $(a, 0) + (b, 0) = [(a + b), 0]$ we get a result which corresponds to the real number $a + b$. But this is the same result we get when we add the real numbers a and b. When we multiply, $(a, 0) \cdot (b, 0) = [(ab - 0 \cdot 0), (0 \cdot b + a \cdot 0)] = (ab, 0)$. But this complex number corresponds to the real number ab which is the product of the real numbers that correspond to $(a, 0)$ and $(b, 0)$. This establishes the isomorphism; it is not necessary to examine subtraction and division. However, it is reassuring to demonstrate that our numbers behave under these operations, too. Subtract $(a, 0)$ —

$(b, 0) = [(a - b), (0 - 0)] = [(a - b), 0]$; but this corresponds to the real number $(a - b)$. If we divide $(a, 0) \div (b, 0) = \left(\dfrac{ab + 0}{b^2 + 0}, \dfrac{0 - 0}{b^2 + 0} \right)$ $= (a/b, 0/b^2) = [(a/b), 0]$ which is associated with the real number a/b in our correspondence.

But what of our original motive in creating the complex numbers? Can we now extract the square root of a negative number? Stated otherwise, is there a number whose square equals a negative number? Let us multiply $(0, 1) \cdot (0, 1) = [(0 \cdot 0 - 1 \cdot 1), (0 \cdot 1 + 0 \cdot 1)] = (-1, 0)$ which is the equivalent of the real number -1. Any positive real number has a real square root. Any negative real number may be considered a positive number times -1. Then any negative real number has a complex square root.

Example $\sqrt{-25} = \sqrt{(-1)(25)} = \sqrt{-1} \cdot \sqrt{25} = (0, 1)(5, 0)$
$= [(0 \cdot 5 - 1 \cdot 0), (0 \cdot 0 + 1 \cdot 5)] = (0, 5)$

The rational numbers were created because we could not always divide integers. Strictly speaking, we still cannot divide the integer 5 by the integer 3. What we can do is divide the rational number $\frac{5}{1}$ by the rational number $\frac{3}{1}$, these being elements of the subset of rational numbers which are isomorphic to the integers. But not only can we divide this special kind of rationals, we can divide any two rationals.

We have created the complex numbers in order that a subset of them, isomorphic to the real numbers, may have a square root. But does any complex number have a square root? The answer is in the affirmative but one needs trigonometry to establish the fact. However, we can illustrate the fact with examples. Since $(0, 1)(0, 1) = (-1, 0)$ we can say $(0, 1) = \sqrt{-1, 0}$. But $(0, 1)$ itself has a square root also, as we may demonstrate by multiplying $(\sqrt{\frac{1}{2}}, \sqrt{\frac{1}{2}})$ by itself:

$$(\sqrt{\tfrac{1}{2}}, \sqrt{\tfrac{1}{2}})(\sqrt{\tfrac{1}{2}}, \sqrt{\tfrac{1}{2}}) = [(\tfrac{1}{2} - \tfrac{1}{2}), (\tfrac{1}{2} + \tfrac{1}{2})] = (0, 1)$$

INTERPRETATION OF COMPLEX NUMBERS

7.9   The development of the complex numbers in the preceding section may seem a bit strange. However, if we compare their development with the abstract development of either the integers or rationals, it seems just as straightforward. In each of the three cases the new number was abstractly defined as an ordered pair of more primitive numbers.

In the two earlier cases it is almost impossible to avoid associating the abstract creation with some physical interpretation.   It is frankly much more difficult to give complex numbers a convincing interpretation.   It does not follow that they are mere intellectual toys.   The electrical engineer has as great a need for the complex number $(0, 1)$ (he does not write it this way) as an electrician has for a pair of pliers. The names given the two components of complex numbers attest the struggle which preceded their acceptance as bona fide numbers.   The first member, a, of the ordered pair (a, b) is called the *real* part and the second member, b, is called the *imaginary* part.   To be sure, we cannot count with imaginary numbers, but that does not keep them from being perfectly good numbers.   The imaginary numbers are no more "imaginary" than are the natural numbers.   Kronecker to the contrary, all numbers are the product of man's imagination and have a real existence only as ideas.   The imaginary numbers are just as "real" as the real numbers.

As with integers and rationals, the complex number (a, b) is usually written in a different form, namely $a + bi$.   This form is conducive to ease of computation, particularly multiplication.   The i serves a dual role: it labels the imaginary part, and it prevents confusion with the real sum of the two real numbers $a + b$.

The number whose square gave -1, namely $(0, 1)$, would be written $0 + 1i$ but it is usually shortened to i.   With the understanding that it is merely a short way of writing $0 + 1i$, we may call i a number, such that $i^2 = -1$.

If we translate our definition to the $a + bi$ notation we have

$$(a + bi) + (c + di) = (a + c) + (b + d)i$$

We add real parts and add imaginary parts:

$$(a + bi) - (c + di) = (a - c) + (b - d)i$$

We subtract real parts and subtract imaginary parts:

$$(a + bi)(c + di) = (a + bi)c + (a + bi)di$$
$$= ac + bci + adi + bdi^2 = (ac - bd) + (bc + ad)i$$

We now see multiplication in the same light as any other multiplication of binomials.   If we write division as an indicated quotient we get

$$(a + bi) \div (c + di) = \frac{a + bi}{c + di}$$

Multiply numerator and denominator by $c - di$:

$$\frac{a + bi}{c + di} \cdot \frac{c - di}{c - di} = \frac{(a + bi)(c - di)}{c^2 - d^2 i^2} = \frac{ac - bdi^2 + bci - adi}{c^2 + d^2}$$

$$= \frac{(ac + bd) + (bc - ad)i}{c^2 + d^2} = \frac{ac + bd}{c^2 + d^2} + \frac{bc - ad}{c^2 + d^2}i;$$

Complex numbers did not receive general acceptance until a means was devised for picturing them graphically. This can be done with the aid of rectangular coordinates.

We have seen that there is a one-to-one correspondence between the real numbers and the points on a line. We call the x-axis the real axis and the y-axis the imaginary axis. There is a one-to-one correspondence (see Section 7.6) between the points of the plane and ordered real number pairs. It makes no difference whether these pairs are elements of a set which is a function or are complex numbers. The number pairs may be represented on the coordinate system as points.

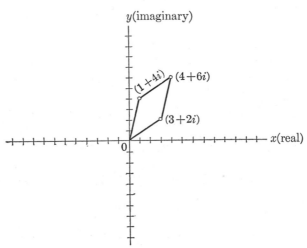

Figure 7.3   Geometric addition of $(3 + 2i) + (1 + 4i)$.

Figure 7.3 shows a geometric interpretation of the addition of complex numbers $(3 + 2i) + (1 + 4i)$. We obtain the sum $(3 + 2i) + (1 + 4i)$ by determining the diagonal of the parallelogram formed by the lines from the origin to the two given points as adjacent sides.

This method of representing complex numbers makes it evident intuitively why we do not try to order them. Which of the following is the greater, $(3 + 4i)$, $(4 + 3i)$, $(3 - 4i)$, or $(-4 + 3i)$? We cannot say that one is greater than another or that they are equal. But they do have something in common. We note that 5 and −5 have the same absolute value, $| 5 | = | −5 | = 5$. Graphically, this means the two points are the same distance from the origin, but in opposite directions. Now, according to the Pythagorean Theorem, each of the points $(3 + 4i)$, $(4 + 3i)$, $(3 − 4i)$, $(−4 + 3i)$, $(−4 − 3i)$ is $\sqrt{4^2 + 3^2}$ = 5 units from the origin also, but they are directed differently. Two complex numbers having the property of being represented by points the same distance from the origin are said to be equal in absolute value. The absolute value of a complex number $a + bi$ is given by

$$| a + bi | = \sqrt{a^2 + b^2}$$

The creation of the integers out of the natural numbers gave number the property of direction. We think of $−a$ as being obtained by moving from the origin (zero) in a direction directly opposite that obtained by moving to $+a$. However, the same effect may be obtained by rotating the point $(+a, 0)$ about the origin through 180°. We may think of the rotation of a point about the origin through 180° as the geometric equivalent of multiplying the number which corresponds to the point by −1. Since $i^2 = −1$, we should expect multiplication by i to be equivalent to a rotation of 90°. Four successive multiplications by i should bring the number back to its original value.

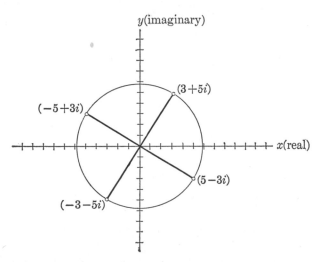

Figure 7.4 Multiplication by i rotates the point 90°.

Figure 7.4 shows $(3 + 5i)$ and successive values obtained by multiplying by i.   In general

$$(a + bi)i = ai + bi^2 = -b + ai$$
$$(-b + ai)i = -bi + ai^2 = -a - bi$$
$$(-a - bi)i = -ai - bi^2 = b - ai$$
$$(b - ai)i = bi - ai^2 = a + bi$$

The elements $(a + bi)$ of the number system are called *real* numbers if $b = 0$.   They are called *imaginary* numbers if $b \neq 0$.   Under this convention, is zero real, imaginary, both, or neither?   If $a = 0$ in an imaginary number, it is called a *pure imaginary*.

The complex number system is said to be complete in that it is closed under the four fundamental operations of arithmetic and the extraction of square roots.   However, it would be a mistake to assume that this is the end of the line as far as number is concerned.   The further use of number pairs, that is, an ordered pair of complex numbers, may not be fruitful.   But there is nothing to prevent the use of number triples, or for that matter n-tuples, instead of pairs.   In fact, there are still higher systems of which the complex system is a part, just as the real number system is a part of the complex.   However, these super systems fail to obey some of the laws we have required of our numbers.

All this is indeed a far cry from the counting of the prehistoric shepherd.   It is an everlasting monument to man's curiosity, tenacity, ingenuity, and intellect.   Its importance in man's quest for the truth and in the spectacular miracles of science cannot be overestimated.   Mathematics is truly the "queen of the sciences," and number is the thread that runs the length and breadth of mathematics.

———————— E X E R C I S E S ————————

1.   There are two subsets of the complex numbers which are ordered, the reals and the pure imaginaries.   Multiply $2i$ by $3i$ and prove the complex numbers do not satisfy F_{13} (Section 5.19).

2.   Of the complex numbers $a = 3 + 2i$ and $b = 4 - i$, which is the greater, $|a|$ or $|b|$?

3.   Let $a = 4 + 2i$ and $b = 3 + i$.   Find $c = a + b$.   Plot in coordinate axes a, b, and c.   Compare $|a| + |b|$ with $|c|$.

4.*   Do the numbers 1, -1, i, $-i$, and multiplication form a group?   Justify your answer.

5. Do the numbers 1, -1, i, $-i$ form a field?   Why?

6. State the inverse of the given element with respect to the given operation.
    (a) $3 + 5i$, multiplication
    (b) $\frac{1}{3}$, subtraction
    (c) $-5i$, addition
    (d) $5 - 4i$, addition
    (e) $-\frac{1}{16}$, division
    (f) 1, multiplication
    (g) 0, multiplication

7. Plot $3 - 2i$ on rectangular coordinates.   Multiply by i and plot the result.   Repeat the process three times.

8. Add $(3 + 2i) + (5 + i)$ both algebraically and geometrically.

9. If a number located on one of the axes is multiplied by some power of i, where will the result be located?

10. Solve each of the following and plot the numbers and their sums.
    (a) $(2 + 4i) + (-1 + i)$
    (b) $(3 - 2i) + (4 - 5i)$
    (c) $(-2 + 3i) - (-3 - 2i)$

11. Express each of the following in the form $a + bi$ where a, b are real.
    (a) $\dfrac{1}{3 + 5i}$
    (b) $(1 + i) \cdot (1 - i)$
    (c) -4
    (d) $(2 + 3i)/(3 - 4i)$
    (e) $5i$
    (f) $\frac{1}{2}$

12.* Prove that i has the same inverse element under addition and multiplication.

13. Solve the following.
    (a) $x^2 - 3x + 5 = 0$
    (b) $x^2 + 16 = 0$
    (c) $2ix - 5 = x + 5i$
    (d) $ix^2 - x + 4i = 0$

CLASSIFICATION OF NUMBERS

7.10 We began with the natural numbers and have, through a sequence of steps, constructed the complex number system.   The chart on the next page reverses the procedure.   It begins with the complex numbers and shows the relationships of the simpler types of number to them and to each other.   Notice the right diagonal indicates the isomorphism between the various types of number.

For example, the natural number 2 is equivalent to the integer $(2, 0) = +2$, which is equivalent to the rational number $(+2, 1) = +2$, which is equivalent to the real number $+2.000 \ldots = +2$, which is equivalent to the complex number $+2 + 0 \cdot i = +2$.

We can move up the chart from any position, but we may move down only as the lines indicate.   For example, the irrational number

π is a real number and it is the complex number $\pi + 0 \cdot i$, but it is neither an imaginary number nor an integer.

The chart should be interpreted as follows: Under "integers," we see "negative integers and zero" on the left and "natural numbers" on the right. This means that the integers include, in addition to the subset isomorphic to the natural numbers (the positive integers), the negative integers and zero.

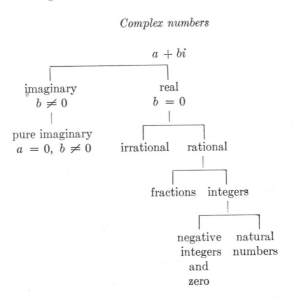

Complex numbers

SETS

*7.11 We have freely used the concept of a set without bothering to say what one is. We have worked with the set of natural numbers, the set of real numbers, finite sets, infinite sets, sets of ordered pairs, and so on. The notion of a set is one of the most basic concepts in mathematics. Remember that we cannot define everything, and we have treated "set" and "element" as undefined terms. Even so, we may talk about what a set is in the hope that we have a sharper, more precise concept. We may think of a set as a collection (assemblage, aggregate — take your pick) of things which for convenience we mentally bundle together in one bunch. The set is not the same as the things we bundle together; they are the elements. The bundle, but not the wrapping, is the set. Suppose we have a dozen apples in a sack. The sack is not the set, it holds the set. The dozen apples is the set.   Each apple is an element of the set.   We cannot say the set is an apple.

Even if the sack contains just one apple the one element and the the set are two different things.   Suppose Sam Jones is the only student who signs up for a given course.   The class is the set of students; it is a set of one element, Sam Jones.   If the Dean decides to eliminate the class this does not mean that Sam is in mortal danger. The point is, the set and its elements are two basically different kinds of things.   This does not prevent the elements of a set from being sets.   For example, a sentence is a set of words, but words are sets of letters.

A set may be infinite or it may have any finite number of elements. In fact, it is convenient to think of an empty sack as holding a set. A set that has no elements is called the *null set* or *empty set*, or the set 0.

The set which contains *all* elements under consideration in a given discussion is called the *universal set*, which we designate as the set U.

Two sets are *equal* if they contain exactly the same elements.   If they have the same number of elements, the elements can be placed in one-to-one correspondence; the sets are *equivalent*.

We say that a set A is a *subset* of set B if every element of A is an element of B.   It is a *proper subset* if B has at least one element not contained in A.

COMBINING OF SETS

*7.12   In arithmetic and the algebra of a field we worked with elements of a set.   Addition and multiplication were relationships between elements.   We add or multiply two elements and produce another element.   We are now concerned, not with the elements of a set, but with sets themselves.   The addition of two sets defines a third set; similarly for multiplication.

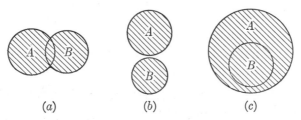

(a) (b) (c)

Figure 7.5   Addition of sets.   The shaded area is the set $(A + B)$.

Definition   Set A + set B = set C, which is composed of all the elements that are in either set A or set B or in both (Figure 7.5).

Example   Set A = integers 1 through 15.   Set B = integers 10 through 20.   Set C = set A + set B = integers 1 through 20.

The operation, addition, is also called *union*.   The symbol for union is ∪ (called "cup").   The symbol for union is used in precisely the same way we have used +.

Definition   Set A × set B = set C, the product, which is composed of all those elements found in both set A and set B (Figure 7.6).

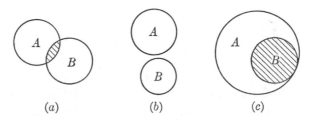

(a)   (b)   (c)

Figure 7.6   Multiplication of sets.   The shaded area is the set $(A \times B)$.

Example   Set A = integers 1 through 15.   Set B = integers 10 through 20.   Set C = set A × set B = integers 10 through 15.

Multiplication of sets is also called *intersection*.   The symbol for intersection is ∩ (called "cap"); it is used exactly as we have used ×.

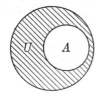

Figure 7.7   The shaded area is the complement of A.

Definition   The set whose elements are elements of U but not of A is called the complement of A and is written A' (Figure 7.7).

Example   If set U is the set of integers 1 through 100 and set A is the set of integers 2 through 98, then A' is the set of integers 1, 99, and 100.

The elements of a set may be indicated in either of two ways: (1) by describing the elements or (2) by listing the elements.   Whether the set is finite or infinite either method may be used.   When method 2 is used the elements are enclosed in braces.

Example   "The set of even integers greater than 10" and {12, 14, . . . $2(n + 5)$, . . .} describe the same set.

"The forty-ninth and fiftieth states of the United States" and {Alaska, Hawaii} are the same set.

───────────── * E   X   E   R   C   I   S   E   S ─────────────

1. If set A is {Tom, Dick, and Harry}, and set B is {Tom, Harry, and Jack}, what set is $A + B$? AB?

2. Write down a set equivalent to the set {5, ÷, #, b, 12}.   Write down a set that is equal to the set {5, ÷, #, b, 12}.

3. Is the set {2, 4, 6, . . . $2n$ . . .} a subset of the rational numbers?   Are they equivalent?

4. Are the positive and negative integers a proper subset of the integers? Why?

5. Are two infinite sets necessarily equivalent?   Illustrate.

6. If A is a finite set, can a proper subset B of A be equivalent to A? What if A is infinite?

7. What does $A \times A'$ equal? $A + A'$?

8. If U is the set of all positive integers under 1,000 and A is the set of positive integers expressible with three digits, describe the set A'.

9. If A is the set of real numbers from 3 through 7 and B is the set of real numbers from 8 through 10, find the set $A + B$.   Find the set $A \cdot B$.

10. If A is the set of real numbers 2 through 8 and B is the set of real numbers 5 through 12, what is $A + B$?   What is $A \cdot B$?

11. Draw a diagram similar to those in Figure 7.5 to represent $(A + B) + C$.

12. Draw a diagram similar to those in Figure 7.6 to represent $A(BC)$ and another to represent $(AB)C$.

13. Prove that $(A')' = A$.

14. Find:
    (a)   The solution set {x} such that $x - 5 = 0$
    (b)   The solution set {x} such that $x^2 + 5x + 6 = 0$
    (c)   The solution set {x} such that $x - 5 = x + 7$

BOOLEAN ALGEBRA POSTULATES

*7.13   Boolean algebra takes its name from its founder, George Boole. It is also called the *algebra of sets* and the *algebra of logic*.   Symbolic logic dates from the work of Boole, approximately 1850.   The alternative names, algebra of sets and algebra of logic, suggest two possible interpretations which this abstract algebra may be given.   Quite recently, Boolean algebra has proven extremely useful for studying the design of electrical switching networks.   First we wish to look at it as a purely abstract system; then we shall attempt to give the system a physical interpretation.

We assume the existence of undefined elements A, B, C, and so forth and the undefined operations, addition and multiplication. (*Caution:* Do not attempt to give meaning to the undefined operations; they have meaning only as the postulates we accept give them meaning.)

We accept the following postulates:

B_1 Closure under addition: If A and B are elements, $A + B$ is an element.

B_2 Addition is commutative: $A + B = B + A$.

B_3 Addition is associative: $A + (B + C) = (A + B) + C$.

B_4 Identity element under addition: There is an element O such that for any element A, $A + O = A$.

B_5 Addition is distributive with respect to multiplication: $A + B \times C = (A + B) \times (A + C)$.

B_6 Corresponding to each element A there is an element A', called the complement of A, such that $A \cdot A' = O$.

B_7 Closure under multiplication: If A and B are elements $A \cdot B$ is an element.

B_8 Multiplication is commutative: $A \cdot B = B \cdot A$.

B_9 Multiplication is associative: $A \cdot (B \cdot C) = (A \cdot B) \cdot C$.

B_{10} Identity element under multiplication: There is an element U called the universal element such that for any element A, $A \cdot U = A$.

B_{11} Multiplication is distributive with respect to addition: $A \cdot (B + C) = A \cdot B + A \cdot C$.

B_{12} The complement A' of A described in B_6 has the added property that $A + A' = U$.

This set of postulates is similar to the postulates of a field, but there are important points of dissimilarity. The Boolean postulate B_5 does not have its counterpart in the field postulates. B_6 and B_{12} present entirely new concepts. We may not say that A' is the additive inverse of A because they combine under multiplication rather than addition to produce the identity element under addition. Nor can we say A' is the multiplicative inverse of A because they combine by addition to produce the identity element under multiplication. You should carefully compare B_6 and B_{12} with F_4 and F_9.

We are now ready to prove theorems in our abstract algebra. Some theorems which are valid in the algebra of a field will still be valid here; others will not.   If a given theorem is valid in both algebras, this is because all the postulates needed to derive the theorem are present in both algebras.

B_{11} requires that $A(B + C) = AB + AC$, the left-hand distributive law.   We wish to prove the right-hand distributive law:

$$(B + C)A = BA + CA$$

Proof:

$$A(B + C) = AB + AC \qquad \text{(by } B_{11})$$
$$AB + AC = BA + CA \qquad \text{(by } B_8)$$

But
$$A(B + C) = (B + C)A \qquad \text{(by } B_8)$$

Therefore
$$(B + C)A = BA + CA \qquad \text{(by substitution)}$$

Examination of the postulates used will show that each is also a field postulate.   Then the right-hand distributive law is valid in both a field algebra and a Boolean algebra.

We know that $a + a = a$ is not correct in a field unless a is the identity element under addition, that is, zero.   We shall prove that $A + A = A$ is valid for any element in a Boolean algebra.

By B_4 we know that

$$A + O = A$$

By B_6 we know

$$A \cdot A' = O$$

Then by substitution

$$A + A \cdot A' = A$$

Applying B_5 on the left,

$$(A + A)(A + A') = A$$

By B_{12} we get

$$(A + A)U = A$$

But from B_{10} we know

$$(A + A)U = A + A$$

Then by substitution we have the result announced at the beginning,

$$A + A = A$$

We use B_5, B_6, and B_{12}, which do not have a counterpart in the field postulates.   This valid theorem in Boolean algebra is not valid in a field algebra.   Why can we not continue from $A + A = A$ to $2A = A$ and then $2 = 1$?

The same property holds with respect to multiplication: $A \cdot A = A$.

Proof:

$$AU = A \qquad \text{(by } B_{10})$$
$$A + A' = U \qquad \text{(by } B_{12})$$
$$A(A + A') = A \qquad \text{(by substitution)}$$
$$AA + AA' = A \qquad \text{(by } B_{11})$$
$$AA + O = A \qquad \text{(by } B_6)$$
$$AA = A \qquad \text{(by } B_4)$$

The property exhibited by these two theorems, $A + A = A$ and $A \cdot A = A$, is known as the *idempotent property*.

7.14   If any one of the axioms B_1 through B_{12} is altered by changing "addition" to "multiplication" and "multiplication" to "addition" and by replacing O by U and U by O, the result will be another one of the axioms.

> *Example*   We indicate the change in B_4, which yields B_{10}, *identity element*
> $\qquad\qquad multiplication \qquad\qquad\qquad\qquad\qquad U$
> *under* ~~addition,~~ *or there is an element* ~~O~~ *such that, for any element* A,
> $\qquad\qquad A \times U$
> $\qquad\qquad A + O = A$

The two theorems which were proved in the last section, $A + A = A$ and $A \times A = A$, are related in the above way.   If we compare the two proofs we find that corresponding statements are also related in this way.   For example, the fifth step is $(A + A) \cdot U = A$ in one case, and $(A \times A) + O = A$ is the corresponding statement in the other.   The justification for the former is B_{12} and for the latter it is B_6, which is related to B_{12} in the above manner.

This addition-multiplication symmetry of the Boolean algebra axioms is the basis for a property known as the *principle of duality*. Corresponding to any statement that can be proved, another statement, called its dual and obtained by interchanging addition and multiplication and O and U, can also be proved.   Furthermore, the proof of one implies the proof of the other because we know the first proof can be dualized.

We prove the theorem
$$(A + B)' = A' \cdot B'$$

By B_{12} we know that $(A + B) + (A + B)' = U$.   Therefore it will be sufficient to show that $(A + B) + A' \cdot B' = U$.

$$
\begin{aligned}
(A + B) + A' \cdot B' &= [(A + B) + A'][(A + B) + B'] & \text{(by } B_5) \\
&= [B + (A + A')][A + (B + B')] & \text{(by } B_2 \text{ and } B_3) \\
&= [B + U][A + U] & \text{(by } B_{12}) \\
&= [B + U]U[A + U]U & \text{(by } B_{10}) \\
&= [B + U][B + B'][A + U][A + A'] & \text{(by } B_{12}) \\
&= [B + UB'][A + UA'] & \text{(by } B_5) \\
&= [B + B'U][A + A'U] & \text{(by } B_8) \\
&= [B + B'][A + A'] & \text{(by } B_{10}) \\
&= UU & \text{(by } B_{12}) \\
&= U & \text{(by } B_{10})
\end{aligned}
$$

One can dualize each step of this argument and have a proof that $(A \cdot B)' = A' + B'$.

ALGEBRA OF SETS

*7.15 One application of Boolean algebra is suggested in Sections 7.11 and 7.12. We may let the undefined elements be sets. The undefined operations of addition and multiplication may be interpreted as addition and multiplication of sets as defined in Section 7.12. A', the complement of A, found in B_6 and B_{12}, may be interpreted in the manner of a complementary set as in Section 7.12. The element O we may associate with the null set. The element U, the *universal set*, is a set whose elements consist of the *universe* under consideration. Stated otherwise, the universal set U has as subsets all elements of our algebra.

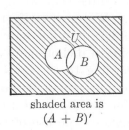

shaded area is
$(A + B)'$

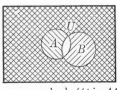

area marked /// is A'
area marked \\\ is B'
cross hatch is $A' \cdot B'$

Figure 7.8 $(A + B)' = A' \cdot B'$.

Diagrams similar to those of Figures 7.5, 7.6, and 7.7 are helpful in verifying that the above interpretation is consistent with the Boolean postulates. For example, Figure 7.8 verifies the theorem we proved in Section 7.14 that $(A + B)' = A' \cdot B'$.

——————— *E X E R C I S E S ———————

1. Show by means of a diagram that $A + A' = U$.

2. State in the language of the algebra of sets what B_4 means.

3. Draw diagrams to illustrate B_5.

4. Prove that $O' = U$.

5. Prove that $(A')' = A$. Illustrate this with diagrams.

6. Prove that $A + A \cdot B = A$.

7. Prove that $(A \cdot B)' = A' + B'$.

8. Prove that $A = A \cdot B + A \cdot B'$.

9. Prove that $U + A = U$.

10. If U is the set of positive real numbers < 100, A is the set of positive even integers < 100, B is the set of positive odd integers < 100, C is the set of positive rational numbers < 100, describe the following.

    (a) $A + B'$ (d) $(A + C')'$

    (b) $(A + B)' \cdot C$ (e) $A(A + B)$

    (c) $A \cdot B$ (f) $A + A \cdot B$

11. Dualize Exercise 6. Illustrate the resulting theorem with a diagram.

12. Dualize Exercise 7. Illustrate the resulting theorem with a diagram.

BOOLEAN ALGEBRA (O, U)

7.16 The set of Boolean postulates requires that we have at least two elements in our algebra, O and U. We may verify that all the postulates can be satisfied by a system containing only these two elements. The resulting algebra is useful in dichotomous, take-it-or-leave-it, situations. For example, according to the laws of logic, a proposition must be either true or false and cannot be both. When we express an integer in binary notation we either do use or do not use each power of 2. This notation suggests the use of the symbols 0, 1. We associate 0 with the undefined element O, the identity element under addition. We associate 1 with the universal element U, the identity element under multiplication.

Let us interpret 1 to mean *true* and 0 to mean *false*, multiplication to mean *and*, addition *or*, A' as *not A*, and $=$ to mean *logically equivalent*. Under this interpretation, the Boolean algebra of (1, 0) becomes the algebra of logic. This is the algebra George Boole invented in the middle of the last century. The theorem $A \times B = (A' + B')'$ would be interpreted thus: The assertion that proposition A and proposition B both are true is logically equivalent to the assertion that it is not true that A is not true or that B is not true.

Nearly a hundred years after Boole's contribution, the same binary (1, 0) algebra was adapted to the study of switching circuits in telephone switchboards and electronic computers. This was first suggested by the young scientist C. E. Shannon in 1938.

We now interpret 1 to mean the presence of a signal on a line and 0 to mean its absence. An OR switch is one that transmits an electric signal from any one of its multiple inputs to its output. A door bell that may be rung from either the front door or the back door is an example of an OR circuit. The output has the value 1 (the bell rings) when either or both of the inputs have the value 1 (one or both buttons are pushed). We continue to associate the OR situation with Boolean addition. An AND switch is one that will transmit the signal only when it is present on all its input lines. Some presses are so equipped that they remain locked unless the release levers on opposite sides are simultaneously pushed. This is a safety device, forcing the operator to have both hands clear when the press is released. It illustrates the AND switch, and is equivalent to Boolean multiplication.

Still another type of switch is the *inverter*. In the inverter the presence of a signal on the input line means its absence on the output, or its absence on the input means its presence on the output. The inverter converts A input to A' output.

Table 7.1 Table of $+$, $\times$, and $'$ combinations in the algebra of (O, U).

A	B	$A \times B$	$A + B$	A'	B'
1	1	1	1	0	0
1	0	0	1	0	1
0	1	0	1	1	0
0	0	0	0	1	1

Since our algebra is two-valued, we may readily write down all possible combinations. We can verify the results in Table 7.1 in terms of switches. We can also prove the results correct by using the Boolean postulates.

The OR, AND, and inverter switching functions are accomplished in a variety of ways. Perhaps the easiest to visualize is the relay. If you know the principle on which an electric bell works, you know the essentials of a relay. The essential parts of a relay are a source of current, a coil, and an armature. Figure 7.9(a) shows the relay with no current in the coil. The spring mechanism of the armature forces the points of contact apart. The circuit is open. In our algebra, this condition of the relay we designate 0. Figure 7.9(b) shows the

(a) Relay not activated, condition 0. Circuit open, condition 0.

(b) Relay activated, condition 1. Circuit closed, condition 1.

(c) Inverter switch. Relay activated, condition 1. Circuit open, condition 0.

Figure 7.9   Relay switches.

relay closed. The flow of current in the coil creates an electromagnet which attracts the armature and closes the circuit. This condition of the relay we designate 1. Thus, the input in condition 1 closes the main line and permits current to flow at the output and we indicate its condition as 1. If the relay is in condition 0 the main line circuit is broken and the output is in condition 0.   An inverter switch is obtained when we align the armature relative to the main line, as indicated in Figure 7.9(c).   When the relay coil is activated, the armature is pulled away from the contact points and the main line circuit is broken.   In this arrangement if the relay is in condition 1 the output is in condition 0.   If the relay coil is not activated (condition 0) the main line is closed and the output is in condition 1.

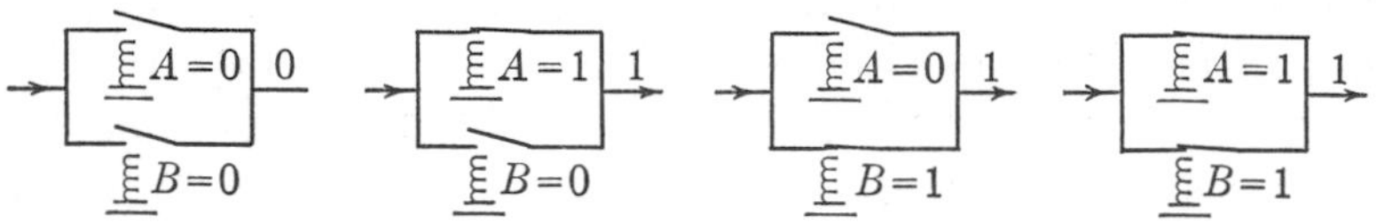

Figure 7.10   An OR switch.

An OR switch is obtained when we have two relays in *parallel*. Figure 7.10 shows all possible states if relays A and B are connected in parallel.   In Figure 7.10(a) A and B are both in condition 0 and the main circuit is broken, leaving the output in condition 0.   Figures 7.10(b) and 7.10(c) show one of the two relays open and the other closed, and 7.10(d) shows both A and B closed.   If either or both of inputs A and B are in condition 1, then the output is in condition 1. Compare these results with the addition facts in Table 7.1.

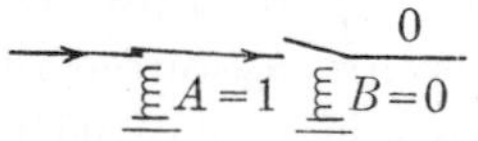

Figure 7.11   An AND switch.

An AND switch consists of relays arranged in *series*, that is, one after the other.   The series arrangement is shown in Figure 7.11.   If either relay is open, the circuit is broken.   The output is in condition 1 only when both relays are in condition 1.

Figure 7.12(a) shows the arrangement $A(B + C)$.   If we call the condition of the output D we obtain the equation $A(B + C) = D$. Remember that the only possible values of the variables A, B, C, D are 0 or 1.   Reference to Table 7.1 will verify that $D = 1$ if and only if $A = 1$ and $B + C = 1$, but $B + C = 1$ if B or C or both $= 1$. We reach the same conclusions by tracing the possible paths of a completed circuit in Figure 7.12(a).

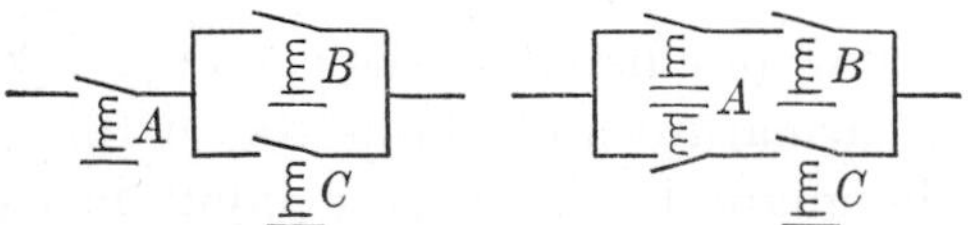

(a) $A(B + C)$ (b) $AB + AC$

Figure 7.12 $A(B + C) = AB + AC$.

According to B_{11}, $A(B + C) = AB + AC$. Figure 7.12(b) indicates the arrangement of $AB + AC = D$.   Either by using Table 7.1 or by tracing out the circuits we can verify that $D = 1$ under precisely the same conditions as before.   Figure 7.13 demonstrates postulate B_5:

$$A + BC = (A + B)(A + C)$$

The value of Boolean algebra in the design of switching networks lies in the fact that equivalent algebraic expressions represent equivalent networks.   In this way simpler networks may be discovered merely by manipulating the algebraic symbols.

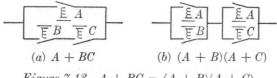

(a) $A + BC$ (b) $(A + B)(A + C)$

Figure 7.13 $A + BC = (A + B)(A + C)$.

——————— * E   X   E   R   C   I   S   E   S ———————

1. Compute the following.
   (a) $a \times (1 + 1)$
   (b) $[1 \times (0 + 1)] + (1 \times 0)$
   (c) $1 + (1 \times 1)$
   (d) $[1 + (0 \times 1)] \times (1 + 0)$
   (e) $[(1 + 1 + 1) \times (0 + 1)] + [(0 + 0) \times (0 + 1)]$

2. Write the dual of
   (a) $A'B + AB'$ (c) $A + BC$
   (b) $(A + B')C'D'$ (d) $A + (A \times B)$

3. Interpret $A'B + AB' = (A + B)(A' + B')$ in the terminology of logic.

4. What does $(A' + B')'$ mean in terms of logic?

5. Write an expression to represent the circuit shown below.

6. Draw a circuit to illustrate each of the following equations.
   (a) $A + (B + C) = D$ (b) $(A + B) + C = D$

7. Draw circuits to illustrate the fact that $A + (A \times B) = A \times (A + B) = A$.

Where our systems of weights and measures came from?

What determines how long a foot is?

There is no such thing as an exact measurement?

A gallon is not the same amount in Great Britain as in the United States?

Sixteen ounces do not necessarily make a pound?

How the furlong got its name?

Where the metric system originated?

Why its use greatly simplifies measurement?

Why mass production would be impossible without standards of measurement?

How many kinds of pounds we use?

How many different kinds of units are used to measure angles?

How do the following compare: kilograms and pounds, meters and yards, liters and quarts, kilometers and miles?

CHAPTER VIII

SYSTEMS OF MEASUREMENTS

Man doubtless began measuring things almost as early as he began counting. Measurement plays an inestimably important role in man's efforts at controlling his environment. Without measurement there would be no automobiles, no highways to drive them on, and no road maps to keep from getting lost on the highways. There would be no television sets and no clocks to tell us when to turn them on, no three-minute eggs and no electric stoves to cook them on. There would be no yardsticks to measure for rugs which could not be made, except possibly by hand, and no money to buy them with anyway. To modern-day man, a world without measurement is truly inconceivable.

In this chapter we shall get a glimpse of how our system of weights and measures evolved and compare it with the metric system. We shall attempt to get a clearer picture of the nature of measurement and to see how certain mensuration formulas were derived.

A MEASUREMENT IS A COMPARISON WITH A STANDARD

8.1 The development of satisfactory standards for comparison offered difficulties quite as formidable as those encountered in developing the number system. Those difficulties were, however, of a different kind. We need no bureau of standards to preserve the value of 100, but the same cannot be said of a pound. Numbers themselves are ideas, but when they are used in measurement they must be applied to concrete things. Every measurement is a comparison with a standard. The standard with which the comparison is made is an arbitrary, man-made something. The history of measurement is, to a large extent, the story of a search for a better standard.

If I measure a plank and find it to be $2\frac{1}{4}$ yards long, my standard is the yardstick.   I have found that the length of plank contains the length of the yardstick two and one-quarter times.   There is an element of counting in measurement in that the number of times the standard is applied must be counted.   But measuring and counting are not the same thing.   Perhaps the most important difference lies in the fact that counting is exact and measurement is approximate. *No measurement is ever exact.*   We will not deny that it is possible to have exactly one pound of sugar in a bag.   The thing that is impossible is the verification that a given bag does contain exactly one pound. Suppose we place a bag on a scale, and the scale reads one pound.   In the first place, how do we decide that it reads exactly one pound?   We all do not see things alike.   If a dozen persons, chosen at random, were to inspect our scale very carefully, about half of them would say we had less than a pound and the other half would say we had more than a pound.   Let us pretend that the scale is so sensitive that the addition of a single grain of sugar makes it obvious that we have too much and, similarly, the removal of a grain makes it obvious that we have too little.   We could then be sure that we have a pound of sugar *to the nearest grain.*   But we still might be able to add or take off a fourth or thousandth of a grain without being able to detect the difference.   Extremely sensitive scales have been built, but perfect sensitivity can never be attained simply because there is no next number to zero.   No matter how small the weight a scale responds to, there is always a smaller one.

For the sake of argument, let us suppose that we do have a scale with perfect sensitivity.   How may we be sure that this weight, which the scale indicates is exactly a pound, actually is a pound?   This raises another important question: Just what is a pound, anyway, and why?

STANDARDS ARE ESTABLISHED BY LAW

8.2   In the United States a pound is whatever it is, because Congress passed a law.   Congress has decreed *the* pound to be .4535924 of the weight of a metal bar housed in the Bureau of Standards.   Furthermore, certain specified atmospheric conditions must prevail for this weight to be a pound.   (Is there any fundamental difference between this law and the one passed by a certain state legislature which decreed the value of π to be 3?)   If an individual wishes to use some other standard, as some ladies seem to do in determining their own weight, that is his affair.   But it is not advisable to buy or sell merchandise under one's private standard.

Our hypothetically perfectly sensitive scale would be measuring *exactly* a pound of sugar only if it exactly measured the standard pound as being a pound.   Every pound weight, every yardstick, every gallon measure, all measuring units that we use are copies, probably third or fourth hand, of *the* standard units which are created by law. These copies are correct up to a certain point; a given yardstick may not differ from a standard yard by more than one thousandth of an inch, but we can never be certain that the copies are exact duplicates of the original standard.   All measurements are approximate because: (1) There is a limit to the sensitivity of the measuring instrument.   A yardstick may have one-inch subdivisions, it may have sixteenths of an inch subdivisions, and even smaller ones, but there is some smallest fraction of a yard which it can measure.   (2) The measuring instrument is itself an approximation of the standard.   (3) The operator of the measuring instrument must exercise judgment in estimating and approximating when he compares his copy of the standard with the object measured.

WHY WE NEED STANDARDS OF MEASUREMENT

8.3   The need for units of measurement is as old as the ownership and exchange of property.   When trade and commerce were restricted to the local community, there was need for standards of measurement only within the community.   When two communities happened to have different standards, no particular inconvenience resulted.   But when commerce expanded as a result of better communication and transportation, the need for uniformity became obvious.   The development of standards of measure followed this pattern.   First, there were local standards, devised by the people themselves.   Later, the state or nation stepped in and decreed which local standard must be the standard for the whole realm.   The enforcement of these standards was sometimes very difficult.   At best, the same old confusion resulted when commerce was carried on between realms.   What was needed was a universal standard, accepted the world over.   Division of labor was an equally compelling reason for developing fixed standards.   If a cabinetmaker wishes to use the width of his hand as a unit of length, it is no great handicap as long as he does all his own measuring.   But when he decides to subcontract the making of drawers for his cabinets, they are not apt to fit unless the subcontractor happens to have the same sized hand.

THE ENGLISH SYSTEM OF MEASURES

8.4   The hodgepodge system that evolved from local custom is best typified by the English system, which is also in vogue with certain variations in the United States. The United States gallon and the British gallon are not the same size. The United States gallon is approximately eight-tenths of a British gallon. There is a slight difference between the British and the United States bushel, the United States bushel being about .97 of a British bushel. Now, the gallon and bushel are both units of volume, but the former is liquid measure and the latter, dry measure. To add to the confusion, both liquid and dry measures contain units called *quarts* and *pints*, and the liquid and dry quart are not the same.

At one time there were five different kinds of pounds in common use in Britain. Even worse, the same kind of pound had different values in different localities. Today there are three kinds of pounds in use both in America and Britain: the avoirdupois, the troy, and the apothecary. The troy system contains the pound, ounce, penny-weight, and grain. The apothecary units are the pound, ounce, dram, scruple, and grain. The units common to both the troy and the apothecary systems are the same size. In the troy system there are 12 ounces per pound, 20 pennyweights per ounce, and 24 grains per pennyweight. In the apothecary system there are 12 ounces per pound, 8 drams per ounce, 3 scruples per dram, and 20 grains per scruple. The avoirdupois system has an even less logical connection with the others. Here there are 16 ounces per pound, 16 drams per ounce, and about $27\frac{1}{3}$ grains per dram. The grain is the same size in all three systems. To further complicate matters, the ounce and the dram are also units of liquid measure.

Linear measure is much less confusing, but here also we have no uniform multiple in moving from unit to unit. There are 320 rods per mile, 5.5 yards per rod, 3 feet per yard, and 12 inches per foot. There are two kinds of mile in common use, the statute mile of 5,280 feet and the nautical mile, which is the length on one minute of arc on the earth's surface and is approximately 6,080 feet.

Not only are the systems of length, capacity, and weight very clumsy but there is no natural connection between the systems.   This is easy to understand when one realizes how they originated.

The grain, the basic unit of weight which is common to all three of our systems, was presumably the weight of a grain of barley.   Henry III of England decreed that the pound should weigh 7,680 grains of wheat.   Grains of wheat or barley have also been used to define units of length.   At one time in England the length of three barleycorns defined an inch.   A more common practice throughout the ancient world was to use the human body in establishing units of length.   The Bible refers to a unit, the cubit, which was the length of the forearm. Lovers of horseflesh still refer to the height of a horse as so many hands.   The palm, span, and fathom are other examples of the use of the human body in establishing units of measure.   It is said that Henry I of England decreed the yard to be the length of his arm. Convenience in terms of the use to which the units were put accounts for some of them.   For instance, the furlong is literally furrow long, or the length of a furrow plowed before resting the horses.

Like Topsy in *Uncle Tom's Cabin*, the system "just growed."   It would seem that man's ingenuity should be great enough to devise a more convenient, more systematic, more scientific set of weights and measures than those in common use today.

———————   E   X   E   R   C   I   S   E   S   ———————

1.   Find the circumference of the earth in nautical miles; in statute miles.

2.   One liquid quart contains 32 ounces.   If a pint of a given liquid weighs one pound, how much does an ounce of the liquid weigh?

3.   If a one-ounce volume of water weighs one ounce, how much does a gallon weigh?

4.   Find the number of inches in 10 rods.

5.   Which is the heavier, an avoirdupois ounce or a troy ounce?

6.   Which is the heavier, 16 pounds troy or 12 pounds avoirdupois?

7.   A penny is one hundredth of a dollar; is a pennyweight one hundredth of a pound?

8.   Which is the greater, a scruple or a pennyweight?

9.   Since the British gallon is used in Canada, would you expect to pay more for a gallon of gasoline in Canada than in the United States?   For a tankful?

THE METRIC SYSTEM

8.5   As a matter of fact, a better system of weights and measures —
the metric system — has been devised.   The world is indebted to the
French for this great contribution.   The system was formulated by a
committee of French scientists near the beginning of the nineteenth
century.   The basic unit is the meter, which was supposed to be one
ten-millionth of the distance from the equator to the North Pole.   The
fact that a mistake in the survey makes the meter differ slightly from
this measurement does not detract from the value of the system.

The international standard meter and kilogram, which are the basic
units of length and weight, are housed in the International Bureau of
Standards, just outside of Paris.   Extremely accurate copies of these
standards have been distributed to the various countries of the world.
Many persons would be surprised to know that the standards for the
United States are not the yard or foot, or the pound.   They are our
copies of the international standard meter and kilogram.   The common units we use are defined by law in terms of these international
units.   The legal avoirdupois pound in the United States is .4535934
kilogram.   The legal yard is .914402 meter.

Our monetary system, unlike that of the British, is based on the
same principle as the metric system.

In the United States, the metric system is used almost exclusively
by scientists.   Some governmental agencies have adopted it.   The
general public is gradually becoming accustomed to calories, cubic
centimeters, grams, kilometers, centigrade thermometer readings, and
so on.   But the full benefits of the metric system will be denied us
until we are willing to discard *in toto* the archaic and unsystematic
feet, pounds, gallons, scruples, barrels, and ounces.   Almost the whole
civilized world, with the exception of English-speaking countries, has
now adopted the metric system in its entirety.

Any universal system would have obvious advantages over many
different systems.   But the metric system has other advantages besides
universality.   Its advantages stem from its decimal nature, plus the
fact that measures of length, area, and volume are all tied together
and are quite simply and conveniently related to units of weight.

The basic unit of length is the meter which, incidentally, is very
nearly the same as a yard.   One meter equals about 1.09 yards.   The
subdivisions of the meter are the decimeter (*deci* = $\frac{1}{10}$), centimeter
(*centi* = $\frac{1}{100}$), and millimeter (*milli* = $\frac{1}{1000}$).   Thus 10 millimeters =
1 centimeter, 10 centimeters = 1 decimeter, 10 decimeters = 1 meter.

Multiples of the meter are the dekameter (*deka* = 10), hectometer (*hecto* = 100), and kilometer (*kilo* = 1,000). Thus 10 meters = 1 dekameter, 10 dekameters = 1 hectometer, and 10 hectometers = 1 kilometer (the kilometer is a little over six tenths of a mile).

Table 8.1   Some common metric units and equivalents.

Length	Volume	Mass	Equivalents (approximate)
1,000 millimeters	1,000 milliliters	1,000 milligrams	1 meter = 1.1 yards
= 100 centimeters	= 100 centiliters	= 100 centigrams	1 kilometer = .62 mile
= 10 decimeters	= 10 deciliters	= 10 decigrams	1 liter = 1.06 liquid quarts
= 1 meter	= 1 liter	= 1 gram	1 liter = .91 dry quart
= .1 dekameter	= .1 dekaliter	= 1 dekagram	
= .01 hectometer	= .01 hectoliter	= .01 hectogram	
= .001 kilometer	= .001 kiloliter	= .001 kilogram	

The same prefixes are used for units of capacity and mass (weight). The basic unit of capacity is the liter, which is slightly more than one liquid quart and slightly less than one dry quart. Subdivisions of the liter are the deciliter ($\frac{1}{10}$ liter), the centiliter ($\frac{1}{10}$ deciliter), and the milliliter ($\frac{1}{10}$ centiliter). Multiples of the liter are the dekaliter (10 liters), the hectoliter (10 dekaliters), and the kiloliter (10 hectoliters). The basic unit of mass or weight is the gram. Other units are the decigram ($\frac{1}{10}$ gram), the centigram ($\frac{1}{10}$ decigram), the milligram ($\frac{1}{10}$ centigram), the dekagram (10 grams), the hectogram (10 dekagrams), and the kilogram (10 hectograms).

The three systems are linked together as follows: One liter is the volume occupied by one kilogram of pure water under certain standard temperature and atmospheric-pressure conditions, and it is also a volume of 1,000 cubic centimeters. Thus one cubic centimeter of pure water weighs one gram.

The centigrade temperature scale is used with the metric system; the English system employs the Fahrenheit scale. The relative convenience of the two scales is typical of the two systems. On the Fahrenheit scale water freezes at 32° and boils at 212°. The more convenient centigrade scale places the freezing point at 0° and the boiling point at 100°. It may seem strange to us to refer to a 35° temperature as a heat wave, but that is merely because we have for so long referred to hot weather as "100 in the shade." If weather reports and clinical thermometers employed the centigrade scale, it would not seem strange for long.

The unit of heat in the metric system, the calorie, is the heat required to raise one gram of water one degree centigrade. The corresponding English unit is the British thermal unit (B.T.U.); it is the heat required to raise one pound of water one degree Fahrenheit.

——————— E X E R C I S E S ———————

1. Convert to meters:
   (a) 2 kilometers   (d) .005 kilometer
   (b) .03 dekameter   (e) .2 hektometer
   (c) 1.25 centimeters   (f) 325 centimeters

2. Convert 1 to:
   (a) centimeters   (c) millimeters
   (b) hektometers   (d) dekameters

3. (a) Find the total weight in kilograms of the following volumes of water under standard conditions: 4 liters, 6 deciliters, 1.6 centiliters.
   (b) Find the weight of the above in grams; in milligrams.

4. How much does a pint of water weigh in:
   (a) grams   (c) pounds
   (b) kilograms   (d) ounces

5. How many calories are required to raise a gallon of water from the freezing point to the boiling point?

6. How many B.T.U. are required to raise a dekaliter of water from the freezing point to the boiling point?

7. If gasoline costs 8¢ per liter, how much would it cost per U.S. gallon? Per British gallon?

THE METRIC SYSTEM SIMPLIFIES COMPUTATION

8.6   Since the metric system is constructed on the same base as our system of numeration, its universal use would all but eliminate the need for common fractions. Simon Steven, the inventor of the decimal fractions, strongly advocated such a system long before it was established. Its decimal nature, together with the convenient relationships between lengths, volumes, and weights, tremendously reduces the amount of computation required in problems involving measurement.

The following two examples well illustrate the advantage of the metric system.

Example 1   Find the amount of heat required to raise one quart of water from the freezing point to the boiling point.

First, we must find the weight of a quart of water. One gallon contains 231 cubic inches.

One cubic foot of water weighs 62.4 pounds. Therefore one quart of water weighs $\frac{231}{4} \times \frac{1}{1728} \times 62.4 = 2.1$ pounds to the nearest tenth of a pound.

If a quart of water is raised from the freezing point (32°) to the boiling point (212°), the temperature has been increased: $212° - 32° = 180°$. Then the B.T.U. required is $180 \times 2.1 = 378$.

Example 2 Now let us find the amount of heat required to raise one liter of water from the freezing point to the boiling point.

One liter contains 1,000 cubic centimeters. One cubic centimeter of water weighs one gram. Therefore one liter of water weighs 1,000 grams.
There are 100 degrees between the freezing point (0°) and the boiling point (100°). Then the number of calories required is $1,000 \times 100 = 100,000$.

If the reader will carry through the computation in these two examples the effort saved in using the metric system will be apparent. Compare the two following examples.

Example 1 We wish to paint a floor that measures 12 feet 4 inches by 16 feet 6 inches. One quart of paint will cover approximately 12 square yards. Find the amount of paint required.

12 feet 4 inches $= \frac{37}{3}$ feet; 16 feet 6 inches $= \frac{33}{2}$ feet; $\frac{37}{3} \cdot \frac{33}{2} = \frac{1221}{6} = \frac{407}{2}$ square feet
Nine square feet equal one square yard; therefore

$$\frac{407}{2} \cdot \frac{1}{9} = \frac{407}{18} \text{ square yards}$$

The paint required is then

$$\frac{407}{18} \div 12 = 1.88 \text{ quarts, approximately}$$

Illustrating the use of the metric system, a similar example which, incidentally, is purposely expressed more awkwardly than necessary, follows.

Example 2 We wish to paint a floor that measures 12 meters 4 decimeters by 16 meters 6 decimeters. One liter of paint will cover approximately .12 square dekameters. Find the amount of paint required.

12 meters 4 decimeters = 12.4 meters
16 meters 6 decimeters = 16.6 meters
$12.4 \times 16.6 = 205.84$ square meters
205.84 square meters = 2.0584 square dekameters
$2.0584 \div .12 = 17.15$ liters, approximately.

—————— E   X   E   R   C   I   S   E   S ——————

1.   (a)   A building lot is 156 feet $7\frac{3}{8}$ inches by 82 feet $5\frac{7}{8}$ inches. What is its area?
       (b)   A building lot is 47 meters 74 centimeters by 25 meters 14 centimeters. What is its area?

2.   (a)   What will a 2-pound 7-ounce steak cost at $89\frac{1}{2}$¢ per pound?

    (b)   What will a 1-kilogram 106-gram steak cost at $1.97 per kilogram?

3.   (a)   Change 173 inches to feet; to yards.

    (b)   Change 173 centimeters to decimeters; to meters.

4.   (a)   If a long ton (2,240 pounds) of coal costs $16.00, what is the cost per pound?   Per ounce?

    (b)   If a metric ton (1,000 kilograms) of coal costs $16.00, what is the cost per kilogram?   Per gram?

5.   If gasoline costs 22.6¢ per gallon in the United States, 28.3¢ per gallon in Canada (where the British gallon is used), and 7.6¢ per liter in Mexico, in which country is it the cheapest?   Assume that one United States gallon is equal to 3.8 liters.

6.   The United States Navy guns are measured in inches while Army artillery guns are measured in millimeters.   The Navy 6-inch gun most nearly approximates which of the following artillery pieces: the 155-millimeter, 105-millimeter, or 75-millimeter?

7.   Which is the better time, 100 yards in 9.4 seconds or 100 meters in 10 seconds?

8.   What is the equivalent of 100 yards in 10 seconds, expressed in miles per hour?

9.   What is the equivalent of 100 meters in 10 seconds, expressed in kilometers per hour?

10.   A tank in the form of a cube measures 4 feet $8\frac{1}{5}$ inches on each edge. Find the weight of water it will hold in pounds, its volume in cubic inches, and its capacity in gallons.

11.   The edge of the tank referred to in Exercise 10 is also 1 meter 43.5 centimeters.   Find the weight of water it will hold in kilograms, its volume in cubic decimeters, and its capacity in liters.

12.   You wish to fence a field whose sides are 252.5 feet, 197.4 feet, 218.3 feet, and 159.1 feet.   If the fencing to be used costs $16.35 per roll and a roll contains 20 rods, how much will the fencing for the field cost?

13.   A field has sides of 252.5 meters, 197.4 meters, 218.3 meters, and 159.1 meters.   If the fencing to be used costs $16.35 per roll and contains 20 dekameters, how much will the fencing for the field cost?

14.   Sixty miles per hour equals how many feet per second?

15.   One hundred kilometers per hour equals how many meters per second?

16.   A 5-foot 9-inch boy weighs 156 pounds.   Express his weight and height in the metric system.

17.   If milk costs 25¢ per quart, at the same rate how much should you expect to pay for a liter of milk?

18.   If city A is 130 kilometers from city B, how many miles apart are they?

ANGLE MEASURE   *neat*

8.7   In advanced abstract geometry an angle is sometimes defined simply as a system of two rays (half-lines) emanating from a point. Any meaning which this system has must be inherent in the assumptions we make. We shall adopt a more concrete point of view. An angle may be defined either statically or dynamically. The latter way seems to be the more descriptive and subject to greater generality.

Accordingly: *If ray OA is rotated in a plane to position OB the angle AOB is thus generated.* The point *O* is the *vertex* of the angle. *OA* is the *initial side* and *OB* the *terminal side* of the angle. We specify that a counterclockwise rotation defines a *positive*, and a clockwise rotation a *negative*, angle.

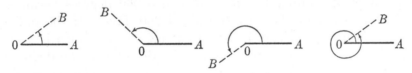

Figure 8.1   An angle is generated by a rotating ray.

Since an angle is by definition an amount of rotation, it seems reasonable that we base our units of angle measure either on a complete circle of rotation or on a half circle which will rotate the line back onto itself or, possibly, on a quarter circle.

The creators of the metric system originally planned to apply the idea to the calendar, to the subdivisions of the day, and to angular measure. Those phases of the idea failed to gain acceptance, however.

When we consider the establishment of standard units of time and angle measure, we are confronted with a problem fundamentally different from that posed by the selection of units of length and mass. If all the measuring devices in the world, including those preserved in various bureaus of standards, were suddenly destroyed it would be impossible to reconstruct our present standards into exactly what they are now. The unit of length is an arbitrarily chosen thing. We could use any length as our basic unit. Congress can pass a law, decreeing how long a yard must be, but it cannot decree how long a day or year lasts. The average length of a day and the duration of a year are beyond man's control. We could, of course, agree to subdivisions of the day different from hours, minutes, and seconds. The year could be subdivided into ten equal parts rather than twelve. As a matter of fact, there is at present considerable agitation for a radically different kind of calendar.   But the basic units of a day and year, from which the other units are derived, are determined by a higher Authority; we are not dependent on an arbitrary, man-made standard.

The same is true of angular measure.   Congress has no more control over the amount of rotation required to generate a circle than it has over the value of π.   If every right angle in the universe were suddenly destroyed, we could very easily construct a new one.   Its size is not dependent upon a man-made standard unit.

The familiar units of angle measure — degrees, minutes, and seconds — are not the only subdivisions of the circle.   Other units used in measuring angles are the radian and the mil.   All three systems of angle measure are, however, derived from either the circle or the right angle.

The circle was probably subdivided into 360 degrees because the Babylonians thought the year contained 360 days.   If the radius of the circle is used as a chord, it will cut off an arc which is $\frac{1}{6}$ of the circle, or 60°.   This may account for the division of the degree into 60 minutes and of the minute into 60 seconds.   The name *minute* originally meant literally a minute part (of a degree), and *second* meant the second minute part.   Babylonian records are not sufficiently complete for historians to be certain of the origin of these units, but it is definitely known that they had been fully developed by the Greeks at the beginning of the Christian Era.

RADIAN MEASURE *Know*

8.8   The radian is a less frequently used unit than the degree. However, custom has it that whenever the unit of measure of an angle is not specified the radian is the implied unit.   Angle $A = 1$ means A is one radian, not one degree or one mil.   The greatest usefulness of the radian does not stem from convenience of measurement or of computation.   It is almost indispensable in calculus and other ad-

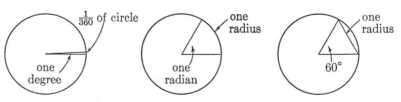

Figure 8.2   Angle measure.

vanced mathematics.   An angle of *one degree* is an angle which, if its vertex is placed at the center of a circle, subtends (cuts off) $\frac{1}{360}$ of the circumference of the circle.   An angle of *one radian* is an angle which, if its vertex is placed at the center of a circle, subtends an arc of the circumference whose length is equal to that of the radius of the circle. Since the ratio of the radius to the circumference of a circle is constant, the size of the circle has no effect on the size of a radian of angle.   The radian should not be confused with a 60° angle.   If the length of the *chord* is equal to the radius, the angle is not a radian, but 60°.   The length along the circle must equal the radius if the angle is to be a radian.

Since the circumference of a circle equals 2π times its radius, one complete revolution equals 2π radians.   But a complete revolution also equals 360°.   The relationship between the two units is then

$$360° = 2\pi \text{ radians}$$

or

$$180° = \pi \text{ radians}$$

If we use the approximation $\pi = 3.1416$, one radian equals approximately 57.3° and one degree equals approximately .0175 radian.

Since an angle of one degree subtends an arc $\frac{1}{360}$ of the circumference of the circle and the circumference is 2π times the radius, an arc corresponding to one degree of angle will have a length

$$\frac{1}{360} \cdot 2\pi \cdot r = \frac{\pi r}{180}$$

where r is the radius of the circle.   The length a of any arc is then

$$a = \frac{\theta \pi r}{180}$$

where θ is the angle, measured in degrees, corresponding to the arc.

If the angle is measured in radians, the number of radians in the angle and the number of radii the arc contains are numerically the same.   The length a of an arc corresponding to an angle θ is $a = \theta r$, when θ is measured in radians.

These two formulas for determining the length of an arc make it obvious that radian measure is more convenient for this purpose.

Example 1   Find the length of an arc of a circle, radius 12 feet, if the central angle is 35°.   We must substitute in the formula

$$a = \frac{\theta \pi r}{180}$$

giving

$$a = \frac{35 \times 3.1416 \times 12}{180} = 7.3304, \text{ or } 7.3 \text{ feet}$$

Example 2 Find the length of an arc of a circle, radius 12 feet, if the central angle is .65 radian.

Our formula in this case is $a = \theta r$, giving $a = .65 \times 12 = 7.8$ feet

MIL MEASURE

8.9   The third type of unit of angle, the *mil*, is defined as $\frac{1}{1600}$ of a right angle.   The mil is used extensively in gunnery.   Since the mil equals $\frac{1}{1600}$ of a right angle, it equals $\frac{90}{1600}$ of a degree.   If we recall that a degree is approximately .0175 radian we see that one mil equals $\frac{90}{1600} \times .0175$ radian.   This value very closely approximates .001. Then we may say that a radian is approximately 1,000 mils.   This accounts for the name, the Latin for 1,000 being *mille*.   The usefulness of the unit depends upon its size relative to the radian.   On a circle whose radius is 1,000 yards, an angle of one mil will subtend an arc whose length is one yard.   In general, if θ is the central angle in mils, a the length of the subtended arc, and r the radius of the circle,

$$a = \frac{\theta r}{1,000}$$

This relationship is approximately correct, since a radian is approximately 1,000 mils.

An arc of a circle is longer than its chord and shorter than the segment of the parallel tangent which is cut off by the radii cutting across the ends of the chord.   As the central angle gets smaller all

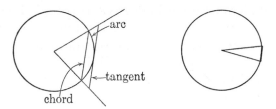

Figure 8.3   An arc is greater than its chord and less than its tangent.

three — chord, arc, and tangent — approach zero.   The arc and the tangent are very nearly equal in length for small angles.   The tangent is slightly longer, so if we use the arc length as the length of the tangent, the error in our approximation is a *deficiency*.   A mil is actually a little less than .001 radian, so when we assume 1,000 mils equal one radian the error in this approximation is an *excess*.   If we utilize both approximations, the two errors tend to cancel each other out and the combination of the two gives a still better approximation.   When we assume that the tangent and its arc are the same length, the error involved is a *variable*.   As the angle gets larger, the difference between the two increases rapidly.   The error involved when both approximations are used will not exceed 2 per cent for angles under 19°.

The usefulness of mil approximation in artillery fire is illustrated below.

Example   The gunner, firing at a range of 2,000 yards, hits 25 yards to the right of the target.   How much correction should he make in his aim?

If we assume the 25-yard offset to be the length *a* of the arc (it is really the length of the tangent), substitution in the formula

$$a = \frac{\theta r}{1,000}$$

yields the result $25 = \frac{2,000\theta}{1,000}$, or $\theta = 12\frac{1}{2}$

Therefore the gunner should turn his gun $12\frac{1}{2}$ mils to the left to bring it on the target.

———————   E   X   E   R   C   I   S   E   S   ———————

1. Through how many degrees does the minute hand of a clock rotate in 25 minutes?

2. Through how many degrees does the hour hand rotate in 1 hour and 15 minutes?

3. If we define an angle as being generated by the rotation of a line about a point (the vertex of the angle) on the line, what is the size of the largest possible angle?

4. What effect does the length of the line in Exercise 3 have on the size of the angle?

5. Express each of the following angles in radians.

(a) 30°	(d) 3 revolutions	(g) 2,000 mils
(b) 300 mils	(e) 90°	(h) 10 mils
(c) 150°	(f) 180°	

6. Express each of the following angles in degrees.

(a) $\pi/3$ radians	(d) 2π radians	(g) 2 revolutions
(b) 3,200 mils	(e) 1.5 radians	(h) $\frac{1}{2}$ revolution
(c) 1,000 mils	(f) 10 mils	

7. Express each of the following angles in mils.
(a) 15°   (d) 20°   (g) .01 radian
(b) 1.5 radians   (e) 1 revolution   (h) .001 radian
(c) π radians   (f) 90°

8. A flywheel is 3 feet in diameter. Find the speed of the belt over it in feet per minute if the wheel is turning at the rate of 200 revolutions per minute.

9. A sidewalk is built on the arc of a circle. If the arc subtends an angle of 35° and is 20 feet long, what is the radius of the circle?

10. An automobile is traveling at 60 miles per hour. If the wheels are 2.5 feet in diameter, find the rate at which the wheels are turning in revolutions per minute; in radians per second; in degrees per second.

11. In a circle, 16 inches in diameter, how long is an arc which subtends an angle of 1.3 radians?

12. Find the number of mils in a radian, correct to the nearest mil.

13. A gunner is firing at a target at a range of 5,000 yards. He is ordered to shift his fire 300 yards to the right. How many mils' correction in his direction of fire should he make?

14. An observer sights an enemy plane known to have a 110-foot wingspread. The plane subtends an angle of 20 mils from the point of observation. How far away is the observer?

INDIRECT MEASUREMENT

8.10 A surprisingly large proportion of all our measurements are indirect. We measure one thing directly in order to obtain another measurement indirectly. In Exercise 14 above, the angle of 20 mils was measured directly. From this measurement we obtain the indirect measurement of the distance from observer to plane. It would be impossible to measure directly the distance from the earth to the sun, or the speed of light, but both have been determined by measuring something else directly. The mileage gauge on an automobile records the number of miles the car has run, but the thing measured directly is the number of revolutions of the wheels. A major portion of numerical trigonometry (triangle measure) involves indirect measurement. In trigonometry, we determine certain parts of a triangle by measuring other parts. An analogue computer depends upon the concept of indirect measurement. For example, a clock measures time indirectly. The thing that is measured directly is the angle through which the hands turn.

Most linear measurements can be made directly. Straight lines, unless they are inaccessible, may easily be measured directly. However, it is usually easier to measure the circumference of a circle by determining the diameter and multiplying by π. One might think square measure could easily be done directly, but this is rarely the case.

AREA OF A RECTANGLE

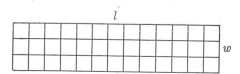

8.11   By definition, a square inch is a square that measures one inch on a side. Similarly for other square units. If we attempted to measure directly the number of square inches of area on this page, we would not use a ruler to get the dimensions of the page. We would measure the page with a one-inch square. Multiplying the length by the width is actually an indirect method of measuring area.

Figure 8.4   A rectangle l by w contains w rows of squares, l squares per row.

A *rectangle* is a quadrilateral (four-sided) figure all of whose angles are right angles.

$$Area \text{ of a } rectangle = length \times width$$
$$A = l \cdot w$$

The formula is obviously correct if both length and width are an integral number of linear units. Suppose the dimensions of the rectangle were $6\frac{1}{2}$ inches by $1\frac{1}{2}$ inches. We could then consider $\frac{1}{2}$ inch as our unit and the rectangle could be broken up into 3 rows of 13 squares, each square being $\frac{1}{2}$ inch by $\frac{1}{2}$ inch. We can similarly handle a rectangle of any dimensions provided they are rational multiples of the unit of measure. Suppose the ratio of length to width were 2 to $\sqrt{3}$. There would then be no unit which would exactly divide both length and width. The Greeks of Euclid's time recognized the difficulty involved when the sides were incommensurable; however, they succeeded in proving the correctness of the formula for all cases.

From the standpoint of measurement, the incommensurable case will not cause concern. Since all measurements are approximate, even if the sides of a figure were not commensurate, their measured approximations would be. The rectangle whose sides are exactly 2 and $\sqrt{3}$ would be measured as approximately 2 and 1.7. It is impossible to discover by measurement that the length of a given line is irrational. For, no matter how refined our measuring instrument may be, there is always a rational number between two successive readings.

AREA OF A PARALLELOGRAM

8.12   If we accept the formula for the area of the rectangle, other area formulas may be derived from it. A parallelogram has opposite sides which are both parallel and equal.

Area of a *parallelogram* = *base* × *altitude*

$$A = b \cdot a$$

where the base b represents a side, and the altitude a is the perpendicular distance from the base to its opposite side.

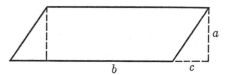

Figure 8.5   Area of a parallelogram.

In Figure 8.5, the two right triangles whose sides are a and c are congruent, that is, have the same shape and the same size. Thus the parallelogram has the same area as the rectangle formed by slicing off the triangle on the left and tacking it on the right. But the area of the rectangle is $a \cdot b$. Note that the area of the parallelogram could not possibly be determined by direct measurement, since one could never completely fill the parallelogram with squares, regardless of how small they were.

AREA OF A TRIANGLE

8.13   On the basis of the formula for the parallelogram we may justify the formula for the area of a triangle.

Area of a *triangle* = ½ *base* × *altitude*

$$A = \tfrac{1}{2}b \cdot a$$

If from the extremities of one side of the triangle we draw parallels
to the other two sides, the result is a parallelogram, composed of two

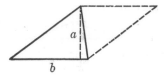

Figure 8.6 Area of a triangle.

congruent triangles.   Thus the area of the triangle is $\frac{1}{2}$ that of the
parallelogram.   Again, we observe that a triangle could not possibly
be filled with squares, however small.

——————————   E   X   E   R   C   I   S   E   S   ——————————

1.   If a rectangle is $5\frac{3}{4}$ feet by $7\frac{7}{8}$ feet, what is the largest unit which can be
      used in measuring the area directly?

2.   If the area of a triangle is 25 square meters and one of the sides is 10
      meters, what is the altitude to this side?

3.   If the area of a triangle is 48 square feet and one of the altitudes is 6 feet,
      how long is the side to which this altitude is drawn?

4.   If a second side of the triangle in Exercise 3 is 12 feet long, what is the
      altitude to this side?

5.   If two consecutive sides of a parallelogram are 7 feet and 10 feet and the
      distance between the two 7-foot sides is 9 feet, what is the distance be-
      tween the two 10-foot sides?

6.   Estimate the area of each of the triangles below by counting and approxi-
      mating the squares enclosed.

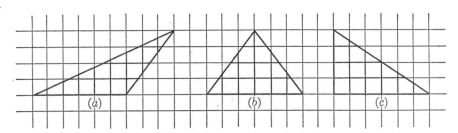

7.   Which of the triangles in Exercise 6 looks the larger.   (Disregard the
      estimate made by counting the squares.)   Find the area of each, using
      the formula on page 264.

8.   Estimate, as in Exercise 6, the area of each of the figures below.

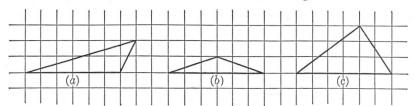

(a)   (b)   (c)

9.   Draw a parallelogram whose area is equal to that of the triangle below.

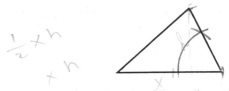

10.   Draw a rectangle whose area is equal to that of the parallelogram obtained in Exercise 9.

ZENO'S PARADOXES

8.14   It may come as somewhat of a surprise to learn that many of the formulas for area and volume which we studied in the elementary school cannot be satisfactorily established without the aid of some of the ideas of the calculus.   The limit concept is basic to the fundamental problems of the calculus.   One of the most important concepts of modern mathematics, its satisfactory formulation is only a little over two hundred years old.

A Greek philosopher named Zeno of Elia confounded his contemporaries with a set of now famous paradoxes which may be helpful in gaining a grasp of the limit concept.   To say the least, they caused his fellow mathematicians no end of trouble because they had not developed the idea of the limit process.

One of the paradoxes is known as "Achilles and the Tortoise." Achilles can run ten times as fast as the tortoise.   The tortoise has a 100-yard start.   Achilles can never catch the tortoise because by the time he reaches the point where the tortoise started the tortoise will be 10 yards farther on.   By the time Achilles covers that 10 yards the tortoise will have advanced 1 yard.   By the time Achilles covers that yard the tortoise will have gone $\frac{1}{10}$ yard farther.   This continues ad infinitum.   Therefore, Achilles never catches the tortoise.

Another one of Zeno's paradoxes asserts that motion is impossible. One of his adversaries attempted to disprove this by getting up and walking around the room. We do no better job of resolving the paradox than he did when we show that Achilles does in fact catch the tortoise after running $111\frac{1}{9}$ yards.

The "motion is impossible" paradox goes as follows. If you wish to walk across the room, you must reach the mid-point before you reach the end. But you must reach the $\frac{1}{4}$ point before you can get to the mid-point. The $\frac{1}{8}$ point must be reached before the $\frac{1}{4}$ point. This argument may be continued forever, since there is always another rational number between zero and the last one obtained. Therefore, since to reach any point we must first have passed other points, we can never start.

Both of these paradoxes are based on the idea that a line may be infinitely subdivided. If this is denied, still another paradox awaits you. This one is known as the "arrow." Consider an arrow in its flight. At every instant of its flight the arrow occupies a position. But while it is occupying a position it is motionless. Therefore, the arrow throughout its flight is motionless.

Zeno would have liked this question: Where was the farmer when he jumped off the roof of the barn? Not on the roof; that was before he jumped. Not in the air; that was after he jumped.

These paradoxes raise fundamental questions regarding the nature of space, time, and motion. Can a physical line be subdivided infinitely? Physical scientists are prone to think that matter cannot be infinitely subdivided. A *mathematical* line can be, however. There is no question here. When we create the mathematical line, we endow it with such a property. In Chapter VII it was pointed out that there is a one-to-one correspondence between the points of a line and the real numbers. This was a mathematical line. Whether or not a physical line has such properties is another matter. We like to think that the set of points of a physical line, the set of instants of time, and the set of real numbers have the same "numerousness," that they can be placed in one-to-one correspondence. Then an instant of time has the same duration that a point has length. The points of a line and the instants of time are continuous in the Dedekind Axiom sense of the word. From this point of view, motion has been defined as being in a state of rest in a continuous succession of positions for a continuous succession of instants. The arrow paradox vanishes, the arrow *is* in a state of rest throughout its flight.

Let us take another look at the Achilles paradox. Suppose I walk across the room half way, then half the remaining distance, then half that remainder, and continue walking half of each succeeding remainder. I will shortly reach the other side of the room, both actually and theoretically, if we assume that I move at a constant rate. On the other hand, suppose I walk half way today, half the remainder tomorrow, half that remainder the next day, and continue each succeeding day walking half the remainder from the previous day. In this case, after a sufficient number of days I would get so near the opposite wall that I could not move without touching it. But theoretically, if I could continue walking half the remainder each day, I would never reach the other side. What is different in these two situations? Suppose we call the width of the room *unity*. Then in each situation we are attempting to cover

$$\frac{1}{2} + \frac{1}{4} + \frac{1}{8} + \frac{1}{16} + \ldots + \frac{1}{2^n} + \ldots = 1 \text{ unit of length}$$

Let us say that we walk at such a rate as to require one minute to cover a room width. Then in the first situation we will reach the opposite wall in

$$\frac{1}{2} + \frac{1}{4} + \frac{1}{8} + \frac{1}{16} + \ldots + \frac{1}{2^n} + \ldots = 1 \text{ minute}$$

But in the other situation we will not have reached the opposite wall until $1 + 1 + 1 + \ldots + 1_n + \ldots$ days have elapsed. Now, if we admit the infinite divisibility of a line and of an interval of time, all three of the above series will have infinitely many terms in them. We say that the first two approach the limit 1. But the last one,

$$1 + 1 + 1 + \ldots + 1_n + \ldots$$

increases without any limit, or approaches infinity. The Achilles paradox owes itself to the fact that a line was considered infinitely divisible but an interval of time was not so considered.

THE LIMIT PROCESS

8.15   In the last section we said that $\frac{1}{2} + \frac{1}{4} + \ldots + 1/2^n + \ldots = 1$. In other words, we have an infinite number of terms whose sum is 1. We are guided by intuition in making such a statement. However, a little reflection will cause us to wonder. We cannot be using the word *sum* in the usual sense.   We cannot add *all* of infinitely many terms.   Then how can we be so sure about what we would get if we did?   Appealing once more to intuition, it seems that the general term $1/2^n$ could be made as close to zero as we chose, if n is sufficiently large.   You will notice that at any point in the series, if we repeat the last term and stop, the finite sum will be 1.   For example,

$$\tfrac{1}{2} + \tfrac{1}{4} + \tfrac{1}{8} + \tfrac{1}{8} = 1$$

and

$$\tfrac{1}{2} + \tfrac{1}{4} + \tfrac{1}{8} + \tfrac{1}{16} + \tfrac{1}{32} + \tfrac{1}{32} = 1$$

Assume that by taking enough terms we can make the last term as near zero as we please.   Assume, further, that the sum of any finite number of terms differs from 1 by an amount equal to the last term. Then we may certainly conclude that we can take enough terms of the series for the sum to be as close to 1 as we please.   It is not sufficient merely that the last term approach zero.   For example, in the series

$$1 + \tfrac{1}{2} + \tfrac{1}{3} + \tfrac{1}{4} + \ldots + 1/n + \ldots$$

we can take enough terms to make $1/n$ as near zero as we like yet this sum does not approach any limit.   It can be shown that we can add enough terms of this series and get a result larger than any specified number.

We shall attempt to state the foregoing ideas formally.   We denote an infinite *sequence* of numbers as

$$a_1, a_2, a_3, \ldots a_n, \ldots$$

The numbers are placed in one-to-one correspondence with the positive integers by means of the subscripts.   If this set of numbers is to be considered a sequence there must be a *general term*, a_n, which designates the manner in which all terms, after a finite number of them, are formed.

Consider the sequences:

Sequence 1: $\qquad\qquad 1, \dfrac{1}{2}, \dfrac{1}{3}, \ldots \dfrac{1}{n}, \ldots$

Sequence 2: $\qquad 3, 9, 4, \dfrac{5}{4}, \dfrac{6}{5}, \dfrac{7}{6}, \ldots \left(1 + \dfrac{1}{n}\right), \ldots$

Sequence 3: $\qquad\qquad 0, -5, 9, 16, \ldots n^2, \ldots$

The general term in Sequence 1 describes the formation of all its terms.   In Sequence 2 the general term describes all but the first three terms, and in Sequence 3 all but the first two are described by

n^2.   All terms of a sequence after a finite number of them, which must be shown, must be defined by the general term.

In Sequence 1 it appears that as the sequence continues the last term gets closer and closer to zero.   In the second, the final term approaches ever closer to 1.   But in the third, the last term gets larger and larger — and approaches no limit at all.   These statements are rather vague.   For example, we could also say of Sequence 1 that the general term continues to get closer to -10, or any number less than 0.   If we invert the terms in Sequence 2 we get

$$\frac{1}{3}, \frac{1}{9}, \frac{1}{4}, \frac{4}{5}, \frac{5}{6}, \frac{6}{7}, \cdots \frac{n}{n+1}, \cdots$$

This sequence also continues to get larger and larger; but it never reaches 1.   The situation here is basically different from that in Sequence 3, where we can find a term greater than any number we care to name.

The first two sequences above *converge* (Sequence 3 does not; a sequence that does not converge is said to *diverge*).   Convergence means that there exists some constant L such that a term may be found which differs from the constant by less than any number one chooses and, further, the same is true of all subsequent terms.   We say the general term a_n approaches L as limit.   This is written

$$\lim_{n \to \infty} a_n = L$$

We can say the same thing more concisely as follows.

Definition   If, corresponding to every positive ϵ there exists an n_0 such that $|L - a_n| < \epsilon$ for every $n > n_0$, then a_n approaches the limit L as n increases without limit, and the sequence is said to converge to the limit L.

The sum of the terms of an infinite sequence

$$a_1 + a_2 + a_3 + \ldots + a_n + \ldots$$

is called an *infinite series*.

$$S_n = a_1 + a_2 + a_3 + \ldots + a_n$$

designates the sum of the first n terms.   We then have a sequence of S_i's.

$$S_1 = a_1; \quad S_2 = a_1 + a_2; \quad S_3 = a_1 + a_2 + a_3; \quad \text{etc.}$$

If the sequence $S_1, S_2, S_3, \ldots S_n, \ldots$ converges to the limit S, then the series is said to *converge to S* and S is called the *sum* of the infinite series.

If we return briefly to the series

$$\tfrac{1}{2} + \tfrac{1}{4} + \tfrac{1}{8} + \ldots + 1/2^n + \ldots = 1$$

we do not claim to have added infinitely many terms and gotten the sum 1. What we do claim is that the sequence $(\tfrac{1}{2})$, $(\tfrac{1}{2} + \tfrac{1}{4})$, $(\tfrac{1}{2} + \tfrac{1}{4} + \tfrac{1}{8})$, $\ldots (\tfrac{1}{2} + \tfrac{1}{4} + \tfrac{1}{8} + \ldots + 1/2^n), \ldots$ converges to the limit 1 and we have defined the infinite sum to be this limit.

In order to prove that the above sequence, which may be written

$$\frac{1}{2}, \frac{3}{4}, \frac{7}{8}, \ldots \frac{(2^n - 1)}{2^n}, \ldots$$

converges to 1 we must show

$$\lim_{n \to \infty} \frac{2^n - 1}{2^n} = 1$$

$$\lim_{n \to \infty} \frac{2^n - 1}{2^n} = \lim_{n \to \infty} \left(1 - \frac{1}{2^n} \right) = 1 - \lim_{n \to \infty} \frac{1}{2^n}$$

We take the last step on faith. We have not proved it but it can be done. Our job now is to show

$$\lim_{n \to \infty} \frac{1}{2^n} = 0$$

If we choose n_0 such that $2^{n_0} = 1/\epsilon$ (remember that ϵ is picked in advance) then $\epsilon = 1/2^{n_0}$. But for any n greater than n_0, $1/2^n < 1/2^{n_0}$.

Therefore

$$\left| 0 - \frac{1}{2^n} \right| = \frac{1}{2^n} < \frac{1}{2^{n_0}} = \epsilon$$

and by definition

$$\lim_{n \to \infty} \frac{1}{2^n} = 0$$

————————   E   X   E   R   C   I   S   E   S   ————————

1. Given the numbers 1, 2, 4, determine three different rules for forming the sequence and write the next three terms in each sequence.

2. Write the first four terms of the sequence whose general term is

   (a) $\dfrac{1}{n + n^2}$ (b) 2^n (c) n^2 (d) $\dfrac{n + 1}{n^2}$

3.* Prove that the sequence $1, \tfrac{1}{2}, \tfrac{1}{3}, \tfrac{1}{4}, \ldots 1/n, \ldots$ converges to zero.

4. If a ball rebounds $\tfrac{3}{4}$ as high as it fell, would the ball theoretically ever stop? The time required to fall is directly proportional to the square root of the distance.

5. If a pendulum swings through $\frac{3}{4}$ as long an arc on any swing as on the preceding one, will it theoretically ever stop? The period, the time required for a complete swing, depends entirely upon its length.

6. Consider the infinite series $1 - 1 + 1 - 1 + 1 - \ldots + (-1)^{n+1} + \ldots$. If the terms are grouped as follows, what does the sum of the series appear to be?
$$(1 - 1) + (1 - 1) + (1 - 1) + \ldots$$
What does the sum appear to be if we group as follows?
$$1 - (1 - 1) - (1 - 1) - \ldots$$

7. Does the following sequence appear to approach any limit?
$$1, 1 - 1, 1 - 1 + 1, 1 - 1 + 1 - 1, 1 - 1 + 1 - 1 + 1, \ldots$$

8. Prove that the sequence $1, 1, 1, \ldots 1^n, \ldots$ converges, but that the corresponding series $1 + 1 + 1 + \ldots + 1^n + \ldots$ does not converge.

9. Write $\frac{1}{3}$ as an infinite series. Can we say that any endless decimal is an infinite series? Explain.

AREA OF A CIRCLE

8.16 The ancients recognized the fact, proved by the Greeks, that the ratio of the diameter to the circumference of a circle is constant. The Egyptians used a rule for finding the area of the circle which implies that the ratio is $\frac{32}{9}$. According to the Bible (I Kings, chapter 7), the ratio is taken as 3; "... and he made a molten sea, ten cubits from the one brim to the other: it was round all about, ... and a line of thirty cubits did compass it round about." The Greeks attempted to find the exact value of the ratio which we now designate as π. Archimedes showed that its true value lies between $3\frac{10}{70}$ and $3\frac{10}{71}$. The problem of the determination of π was not completely disposed of until 1882, when Ferdinand Lindemann proved that π is a transcendental number.

In Section 8.13 the observation was made that squares, no matter how small, could not completely fill a triangle. A circle could not be completely filled with any kind of polygon (plane figure bounded by straight lines) or combination of polygons. In other words, we cannot derive a formula for the circle in a manner similar to that used to derive the formulas for the area of parallelograms and triangles.

We shall define the area of a circle in terms of the area of a polygon, but first we must define an inscribed polygon. *An inscribed polygon is a polygon whose sides are chords of a circle.* We now state the following definition: *The area of a circle is the limit of the area of a polygon inscribed in the circle as the number of sides of the polygon increases without limit.* This definition assumes the existence of the limit; otherwise a circle has no area. It is intuitively evident that the limit exists. In fact, the area lies between the area of the inscribed polygon of n equal sides and that of the circumscribed polygon of n sides. Regular polygons (equal sides) are easier to compute with when one is approximating, but as far as the definition and the limit process are concerned it makes no difference whether they are equal or not. Archimedes' approximation of π was found by increasing the number of sides of the inscribed and circumscribed polygons, the circumference of the circle lying between their perimeters.

Suppose, as in Figure 8.7, we start with an inscribed square. If we draw radii to each vertex, the polygon is split into four triangles. If we double the number of sides of the polygon and draw radii, we get eight triangles. Let this process continue without limit. Each chord approaches zero but the sum of all the chords, the perimeter of the polygon, approaches the circumference of the circle. The altitude of the triangle approaches the radius of the circle. The area of the polygon of n sides is the sum of the areas of the triangles obtained by drawing radii to the vertices. The

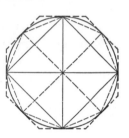

Figure 8.7 The inscribed polygon approaches the circle as its limit.

limit of this area is by definition the area of the circle. We may summarize as follows:

The area of the inscribed polygon, whose n sides are the chords $b_1, b_2, b_3, \ldots b_n$ with distances from the center of the circle $a_1, a_2, a_3, \ldots a_n$, is given by $P = (\frac{1}{2})a_1b_1 + (\frac{1}{2})a_2b_2 + (\frac{1}{2})a_3b_3 + \ldots + (\frac{1}{2})a_nb_n$. If we let n increase without limit, the area P of the polygon approaches the area A of the circle, a_i approaches the radius r, and we have

$$\lim_{n \to \infty} P = A = \lim_{n \to \infty} (\tfrac{1}{2})rb_1 + (\tfrac{1}{2})rb_2 + (\tfrac{1}{2})rb_3 + \ldots + (\tfrac{1}{2})rb_n$$

$$= \lim_{n \to \infty} (\tfrac{1}{2})r(b_1 + b_2 + b_3 + \ldots + b_n)$$

$$= (\tfrac{1}{2})r \lim_{n \to \infty} (b_1 + b_2 + b_3 + \ldots + b_n)$$

But the last limit is the circumference of the circle. Then we have the formula for the area of a circle:

$$A = (\tfrac{1}{2})r \cdot c$$

Since π is the ratio of the circumference c to the diameter $d = 2r$, we have

$$c = 2\pi r$$

and the area becomes

$$A = (\tfrac{1}{2})r \cdot 2\pi r = \pi r^2$$

AREAS OF CURVED SURFACES

8.17   Although plane surfaces abound in three-dimensional space, we know that many surfaces are not planes.   Three of the more common simple curved surfaces are the *cone*, the *cylinder*, and the *sphere*.

A conical surface is generated by the rotation of a line about a point (called the vertex) on the line.   If the rotating line traces a circle on a plane, one of the conical surfaces cut off by the plane is called a *circular cone* (see Figure 8.8).   If the perpendicular from the vertex to the plane is at the center of the circular base, the cone is called a *right circular cone*.

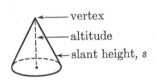

Figure 8.8 A right circular cone.

The lateral area, that is, the area of the curved surface of the cone, is determined somewhat as is the area of a circle.   If we imagine the surface as being cut into many small pieces by lines from the vertex to the perimeter of the circular base, these small pieces will approximate triangles, all of whose altitudes as well as sides are the distance s from vertex to the perimeter of the base. This distance is called the *slant height* of the cone.   We define the lateral area of the cone as the limit of the sum of the areas of these triangles as the number of triangles increases without limit.   But the sum of the bases of these triangles approaches the circumference of the base of the cone as the number of triangles increases without limit. Then the lateral area of the cone will equal $\tfrac{1}{2}$ the slant height times the circumference of the base:

$$A = (\tfrac{1}{2})s \cdot 2\pi r = \pi r s$$

A cylindrical surface is generated by a line moving so as to remain parallel to its original position.   If the line traces a circle on a plane that is perpendicular to the generating line, then any two planes thus placed will cut off a right circular cylinder.   If we draw lines perpendicular to the bases, these lines, together with the chords cutting along the bases, will form rectangles.   We define the lateral area of the cylinder as the limit of the areas of these rectangles as the number of rectangles increases without limit.   But the height of the cylinder, which is one dimension of all the rectangles, is fixed and the sum of the second dimension of the rectangles is the sum of the sides of an inscribed polygon.   Then as the number of rectangles increases without limit, the sum of these sides approaches the circumference of the circular base.   Then the limit of the sum of the areas of the rectangles is the height h of the cylinder times the circumference, $2\pi r$, of the base, and we have for the lateral area of the cylinder

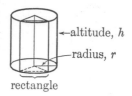

altitude, h

radius, r

rectangle

Figure 8.9 A right circular cylinder.

$$A \;=\; 2\pi rh$$

The sphere is a surface in space such that every point on it is equidistant from a fixed point, its center.   We may think of the sphere as being generated by rotating a circle about its diameter.   A derivation of the formula for the area of a sphere, to be really satisfying, requires applications of integral calculus. There also the limit process is crucial.   We state the result

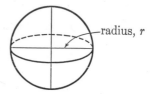

radius, r

Figure 8.10   A sphere.

$$A \;=\; 4\pi r^2$$

and note that the area of the sphere is four times the area of the circle that is formed by passing a plane through the center of the sphere.

VOLUME FORMULAS

8.18   The basic unit of volume is a cube whose edge is the unit of length.   We may extend the idea of the area of a rectangle to three dimensions and obtain the formula for the volume of a rectangular solid, called a *parallelepiped*.   If the edges are l, w, and h, we have for the volume of the parallelepiped

$$V \;=\; lwh$$

We may think of the height h as split into h units, giving h layers, each 1 unit thick, consisting of $l \cdot w$ cubes.   Then all h such layers will contain $l \cdot w \cdot h$ cubes.

Figure 8.11
A parallele-
piped.

When we think of extending the triangle to three dimensions, we get a *triangular prism*. A prism is a solid that has parallel and congruent bases. So its sides must be parallelograms. If the bases are perpendicular to the sides, the sides are rectangles. If we cut the height h into h units, we slice the prism into layers 1 unit thick. The volume of each of the layers is then the area of the base b times unity. Since there are h such layers we get for the total volume:

Figure 8.12
A triangular prism.

$$V = bh$$

If we pass a plane through a vertex of one base of a triangular prism and the opposite side of the other base, we cut off a *pyramid*. A pyramid is a solid whose sides, other than the base, are triangles all having a common vertex. When we cut the pyramid from the prism,

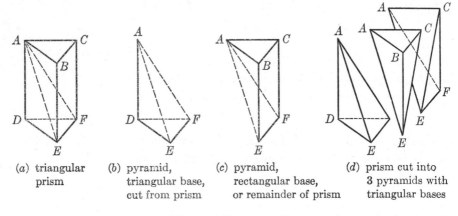

| (a) triangular prism | (b) pyramid, triangular base, cut from prism | (c) pyramid, rectangular base, or remainder of prism | (d) prism cut into 3 pyramids with triangular bases |

Figure 8.13   Pyramids.

a rectangular pyramid remains. This may be cut into two more triangular pyramids by passing a plane through the same vertex and the diagonal of the remaining (rectangular) face of the prism. We may infer from this that the volume of the pyramid is $\frac{1}{3}$ that of the prism, or

$$V = \tfrac{1}{3}bh$$

In fact, this formula is correct whether the pyramid has a triangular base or not.

We define the volume of a cone as the limit of the volume of a pyramid as the base of the pyramid approaches a circle.   The volume of the cone is

$$V = \tfrac{1}{3}bh = \tfrac{1}{3}\pi r^2 h$$

We define the volume of a cylinder as the limit of the volume of a prism as the base of the prism approaches a circle.   Then its volume is given by the formula

$$V = \pi r^2 h$$

As in the question of the surface area of a sphere, we again merely put our faith in the calculus and state the result.   The volume of a sphere is given by the formula

$$V = \tfrac{4}{3}\pi r^3$$

─────────   E   X   E   R   C   I   S   E   S   ─────────

1. A packing carton is 16 inches long, 12 inches wide, and 8 inches high. It is to be filled with smaller boxes 2 inches by 2 inches by 3 inches. How many boxes can be packed in the carton?

2. Disregarding lap, how many square inches of material will be required to make the carton described in Exercise 1?

3. A circular sidewalk is built around a pond which is 50 feet across at its greatest width.   The walk is 2 feet wide.   Find its total area.

4. The walk described in Exercise 3 is 4 inches thick.   Find the volume of concrete necessary to construct it.

5. If an ice cream cone is 6 centimeters wide at the top and 18 centimeters high, will you get more ice cream when you have the cone level full or when you have a hemisphere of ice cream sitting on top of the cone?

6. Find the area of the metal required to make a tin can 6 inches high with a 3-inch radius.   Find its volume.

7. Find the area of the metal required to make a tin can 12 inches high with a radius of 1.5 inches.   Find its volume.   Compare these results with those of Exercise 6.

8. The dome of a building is in the form of a hemisphere with a radius of 10 feet.   At $5 per square yard, what will it cost to gild the dome?

9. One quart of paint will cover 150 square feet.   Find the paint required to paint the walls and ceiling of a room 12 feet by 18 feet, ceiling 9 feet high.   Disregard openings.

10. The diameter of a cylindrical can is equal to its height.   A spherical ball just fits into the can.   Prove that the area of the ball is equal to the area of the side of the can.

11. A conical lamp shade is 20 inches wide at the bottom and 16 inches wide at the top. The slant height of the cone from which it is cut is 40 inches. The slant height of the shade is 8 inches. Find its area.

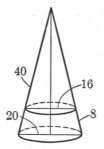

12. A silo is built in the shape of a cylinder with a cone on top. The diameter of the cylindrical base is 20 feet, its height is 15 feet. The height of the conical top is 8 feet. How many cubic feet of feed will it hold?

13. If the hose of a gasoline tank has an inside diameter of 1 inch and the hose is 10 feet long, how many gallons of gasoline will the hose hold? One gallon equals 231 cubic inches.

14. What is the total area of the outside of the silo described in Exercise 12?

15. A triangular lot fronts 50 feet on the street and tapers to a point 60 feet from the street. What is the area of the lot?

16. If the entire area of the lot described in Exercise 15 is to be utilized for a building and we must excavate 10 feet deep for its foundation, how many yards of dirt must be removed?

17. Compare the area of a sphere and the area of the cube into which it will fit exactly.

18. Compare the volumes of the cube and the sphere described in Exercise 17.

19. Compare the area of a square whose perimeter is 40 feet with the area of a circle whose circumference is 40 feet.

20. If the radius of the earth is taken as 4,000 miles, what is its surface area? Its volume?

21. The diameter of a bottle of olives is 1 inch; its height is 8 inches.   How many cubic inches does it hold?

22. Another bottle 2 inches in diameter and 6 inches high costs twice as much as the one described in Exercise 21.   Which is the better buy?

DO YOU KNOW

The difference between an exact and an approximate number?

The difference between the precision of a measurement and the accuracy of a measurement?

That a measurement may be correct and yet have an error involved?

The difference between an error and a mistake?

What significant digits are?

How to write a number in scientific notation?

What logarithms are?

What they are used for?

What a slide rule is and why it works?

CHAPTER IX

MEASUREMENT COMPUTATION

In this chapter we shall learn how to compute with approximate numbers. We shall see how logarithms may be used as a tremendous saver of time and work in approximate computation. We shall find that the slide rule, a further aid in computation, is only an application of the principle of logarithms.

APPROXIMATE NUMBERS

9.1 The nature of measurement is such that all measurements are approximate. No measurement can be more nearly exact than the instrument used; its accuracy is further limited with the care and skill of the person using the instrument. Although we have but one set of numbers they are used in two distinctly different ways. *Exact* numbers arise from counting. *Approximate* numbers are *estimates*. We can usually tell to which use numbers are being put. When one goes to the store and buys a dozen eggs he expects to get *exactly* 12 eggs. He can count them to verify that there are exactly 12. On the other hand, when a man says he is 6 feet tall, he does not mean that his height is exactly 6 feet. The 6 is used as an approximate number.

Usually one can tell from a given context whether a number is exact or approximate, but this is not always the case. If John's mother sends him to the store to buy 3 pounds of bacon, the 3 could be either exact or approximate. If the implication is that John is to purchase three 1-pound packages of bacon, the 3 is exact. On the other hand, if he buys a 3-pound slab of bacon, the 3 is approximate.

In general, if a number is the result of counting it is exact.   This is not always the case, however.   Consider census figures.   Let us say the population of a given state is $3\frac{1}{2}$ million.   We probably mean that its population is between 3,450,000 and 3,550,000 or that, to the nearest hundred thousand, it is 3,500,000.   This is admittedly not an exact number; it was obtained by approximating another number. On the other hand, suppose the census report shows this state to have 3,476,128 persons.   Is that an exact number?   True, it is the result of an enumeration.   But in all likelihood it is not exact simply because in all probability 3,476,128 is not *exactly* the number of persons in our state at a particular time.   Although the figure is the result of an enumeration, many births and deaths occur while the count is in progress.

Any time we use an approximate number we should know the closeness of the approximation.   Unfortunately, this cannot always be obtained from the context.   What does the man who says he is 6 feet tall mean?   He might mean he is nearer 6 feet than 5 feet or 7 feet.   He might mean that he is 6 feet tall to the nearest inch or half inch, or even something more precise.   If we knew what kind of measuring device was used to obtain his height, we might make a more intelligent guess as to the degree of precision.   If a stick a yard long with no subdivisions on it were used, precision to the nearest half foot would be all we could expect.   If a yardstick were used with sufficient care, we might expect precision to the nearest eighth of an inch.

The way in which an approximate number is written should indicate how close the approximation is.   The approximate numbers 10 and 10.0 are not the same.   The first represents a quantity anywhere from 9.5 up to but not including 10.5.   We are saying that the quantity is nearer 10 than 9 or 11.   On the other hand, 10.0 means a quantity which is at least 9.95 but less than 10.05.   In other words, the quantity described is 10 to the nearest tenth of a unit.   To indicate more precision than the facts justify is just as much a misrepresentation as to indicate the wrong quantity.   Suppose we have a measurement which is 12.4 units.   This means we know the measurement to the nearest tenth.   We know the true measurement is nearer 12.4 than 12.3 or 12.5.   If we write the measurement as 12, we are not misrepresenting the situation.   We may not be telling the whole truth, but we are telling the truth.   For, if the measurement is 12.4 to the nearest tenth, it is certainly 12 to the nearest whole unit.   On the other hand, if we record the measurement as 12.400, we are claiming to know something we know nothing about.   We have no information on how many hundredths and thousandths of a unit are present, but 12.400 asserts that the measurement is 12 units and 400 thousandths of a unit more.

There is no fixed relationship between the kind of number (integer, rational, irrational) and the use to which it is put (approximate or exact).   When we use 0.66 instead of $\frac{2}{3}$, assuming that the $\frac{2}{3}$ is exact, we use 0.66 as an approximation of $\frac{2}{3}$.   On the other hand, you pay 18¢ for a can of peas which are priced at 2 for 35¢.   In this case the integral 18¢ is an approximation of the exact price $17\frac{1}{2}$¢.   The familiar π is an exact number, because although one could never measure exactly the circumference and diameter of a circle, the ratio of circumference to diameter of all circles is exactly the same; it is exactly π. When we use $3\frac{1}{7}$ or 3.1416 or some other value for π, we are using a rational approximation of the exact irrational number π.

Although every measurement is an approximation, it does not follow that every approximation is the result of a measurement.   An approximate number may well result from computation with exact numbers, either because we cannot get an exact result or because we prefer the approximation.

Whenever we deal with approximate numbers we should be concerned with the question: How good an estimate of the exact quantity is this approximate number?   There are two aspects of this question of a "good" approximation, namely precision and accuracy.

——————   E   X   E   R   C   I   S   E   S   ——————

1.   State whether each number in the following items is approximate or exact.   Give reasons for your opinion.
   (a)   Union representatives reject company offer of $.05 raise.
   (b)   State Department backs $100 million foreign aid bill.
   (c)   Rainfall for 24 hours, 0.   Total this month, 1.20.   Total this year, 36.74.   Deficiency this month, 2.20.   Excess this year, 4.53. *Nation's Weather,* page 6.
   (d)   Midnight Frolic and Morning Rose topped a class of 32 mares and foals.
   (e)   600 Shriners go to Atlantic City meeting.
   (f)   100,000 A.U.W. members get $.14 raise.
   (g)   26 more fired as security risks.

2.   State whether each of the following is possible. Give an example of each that is possible.

(a)   An exact number which is not the result of a count
(b)   A measurement which is an exact number
(c)   An approximate number which is the result of neither counting nor measuring
(d)   A count which is not an exact number

PRECISION OF A MEASUREMENT

9.2   The *precision* of a measurement is judged in terms of the maximum amount it can vary from the exact number it approximates, called its *maximum error*.   Suppose a mile runner is clocked for the mile at 4 minutes 2.4 seconds.   This means that the runner's time was actually somewhere between 4 minutes 2.35 seconds and 4 minutes 2.45 seconds.   Then the time of 4 minutes and 2.4 seconds cannot differ from the runner's actual time by more than .05 second.   The measurement is precise to the nearest 0.1 second.   This is the smallest of the units, minutes, seconds, tenths of a second, used in the measurement.   The maximum error is one half of the smallest unit in a measurement.   The more precise of two measurements is the one whose maximum deviation from its true value is the smaller.

The precision of a measurement may be indicated in one of three ways.

(1)   The smallest unit used in the measurement may be explicitly stated.

Example   The distance from city A to city B is 150 miles, correct to the nearest 5 miles.   This means that the true distance from A to B is somewhere between $147\frac{1}{2}$ and $152\frac{1}{2}$ miles.

(2)   The maximum error may be given as a plus-or-minus correction.

Example   The distance from city A to city B is 150 $\pm$ 4 miles.   Here we are saying our measurement may be in error by as much as 4 miles; the true distance from A to B is somewhere between 146 and 154 miles.

(3)   The maximum error may be indicated by the position of the last significant digit (see Section 9.4).

Example   A weight of 12.3 pounds has a maximum error of .05 pound. The decimal point tells us the size of the smallest unit in the measurement. The smallest unit in the weight 12.3 pounds is one tenth of a pound; half of this is .05 pound, the maximum error.

A measurement of 149.4 feet correct to the nearest 0.1 foot; 149.4 ± .05 feet; and 149.4 feet — all express the same degree of precision: the maximum error is .05 foot.

ACCURACY OF A MEASUREMENT

9.3   If a 100-yard distance is measured as 99.7 yards, the error is 0.3 yard. The ratio of the error to the true measure is 0.3/100. We should like to express the accuracy of a measurement as the ratio of the error to the true value. However, the true value and, conse-quently, the actual error of the magnitude to be measured are unob-tainable. In the first place, if we know exactly how long a distance is, why measure it? Even so, the point is that there are plenty of distances that are exactly 100 yards long, but we can never verify by measurement that a given distance is one of them. Our best guess of the true value is the one we obtain by measurement. Since we do not know the actual error we use the maximum error.

Definition   The accuracy of a measurement is the ratio of the maximum error to the measurement itself.

Thus the measurement of 4 minutes 2.4 seconds (= 242.4 seconds) has an accuracy which is expressed by the ratio .05/242.4 = .0002. This is approximately one part in 5000. This ratio is called the *relative error* of the measurement. Accuracy is also given in *per cent of error*, which is 100 times the relative error; in this case, .02 per cent. The smaller the relative error of a measurement, the more accurate the measurement.

Since precision is concerned with the *amount* of variation from the true value, and accuracy is a comparison of this amount of variation with the total measurement, neither implies anything about the other. Given two measurements, the more precise may or may not be the more accurate. The commonly accepted value of the distance from the earth to the sun is 93,000,000 miles. This measurement is precise to the nearest 1,000,000 miles. The first joint of a man's thumb is one inch long. This measurement is precise to the nearest inch, much more precise than the distance to the sun. Yet 93,000,000 miles is much more accurate. Its relative error is 500,000/93,000,000 = .0054; but the relative error of the one-inch thumb is 0.5/1 = 0.5.

Which is more important, precision or accuracy?   The only answer to that question is that they are both important.   There is no satisfactory answer to the question of how accurate and/or how precise a measurement must be in order to be acceptable.   That all depends on the situation.   Less precision would be required in making a survey of a farm to be sold at $50 per acre than that required for a city lot which sells at $1,000 per front foot.   The buyer of scrap iron is not too concerned with precision; an error of a hundred or so pounds is not very important when buying or selling several hundred tons of scrap.   But it is another story when this same scrap has been reprocessed into watch springs, cylinder heads, and ball bearings.   Mass production would be impossible without a high degree of precision.

We cannot compare the precision of two measurements involving different kinds of units.   A length of 15.4 feet is precise to the nearest tenth of a foot; a weight of 15.4 pounds is precise to the nearest tenth of a pound.   We cannot properly say either is more precise than the other.   But a weight of 15.4 ounces is more precise than 15.4 pounds: they are the same kind of unit, weight, and the former has a maximum error $\frac{1}{16}$ that of the latter.   On the other hand, it is possible to compare the accuracy of any two measurements.   Accuracy, being a ratio, is independent of the unit of measure.   All three of the above, the 15.4 feet, 15.4 pounds, and 15.4 ounces, have the same degree of accuracy.

SIGNIFICANT DIGITS

9.4   An understanding of *significant digits* is helpful when one is considering either precision or accuracy.

Definition   A significant digit of a number is a digit that serves a purpose other than merely placing the decimal point.

In other words, if a digit is used only to give other digits their correct place value we do not call it a significant digit.   However, we should not assume that digits that are not significant are thereby unimportant or insignificant.

All nonzero digits are significant.   All zeros which lie between significant digits are significant.   In the number 105, the one and the five are of course significant; the zero is also significant because it not only gives the number one its proper value but states that there are no tens present.   If we know how many units and how many hundreds are present, we necessarily know about the number of tens present — none in this case.

Terminal zeros following the decimal point are always significant. Unless we know how many hundredths and thousandths of a unit are present there is no excuse for the two final zeros in 14.600.   The writing of these zeros implies that we *do* know there are no hundredths of a unit and no thousandths of a unit.

The terminal zeros in an integer are not significant.   When we write 93,000,000 miles as the distance to the sun, the implication is that we are expressing the distance to the nearest million miles; we do not specify how many hundreds of thousands of miles or tens of thousands, and so forth, there are.   The zeros merely give the 9 and the 3 their correct place value, that is, they place the decimal point. Suppose we wish to express the fact that the measurement 15,000 is correct to the nearest ten units.   We could write 15,000 ± 5.   But in terms of significant digits this can be done by underscoring the zero in the tens digit thus: 15,0_0_0.   An underscored terminal zero indicates that it is significant.   Since all zeros between significant digits are significant, this will make all zeros preceding an underscored zero significant also.   It would be impossible to know how many tens are present and not know about the number of hundreds.

In a number less than one, zeros immediately following the decimal point are not significant.   When we write .045 the zero is used merely to place the decimal point so that the 4 and 5 have their correct place value.   It is true that here we know that we have no tenths, but the zero is no more needed to indicate that fact than a zero is needed to show that we have no hundreds in 56.   We do not write 56 as 056.

--------- E X E R C I S E S ---------

1. Explain the difference in meaning of the approximate numbers $12\frac{1}{2}$, 12.5, 12.50.

2. Each of the following approximate numbers is used to indicate a magnitude falling within what range?
   (a) 1 yard   (b) 4.852 miles   (c) $6\frac{4}{7}$ pounds

3. A gasoline engine has a cylinder bore 2.000 inches in diameter.   If the piston which must fit into this bore is to have a diameter of 1.998 inches, what is the maximum tolerance permissible?

4.   Between what two values does each of the following measurements approximate: 5,280 feet, 1 mile, 20.3 seconds, $3\frac{9}{8}$ inches, $5\frac{3}{16}$ pounds?

5.   Which in the following pairs has the greater precision? Which has the greater accuracy?
   (a)   3.0 feet — .0030 inch
   (b)   15.6 inches — 15.60 inches
   (c)   880 yards — $\frac{1}{2}$ mile
   (d)   The diameter of a cent, $\frac{3}{4}$ inch — the diameter of the earth, 8,000 miles.
   (e)   Distance light travels per second, 186,000 miles — distance sound travels per second, 1,100 feet.

6.   Determine the number of significant digits in each of the following measurements.

   (a)   37
   (b)   309
   (c)   .0057
   (d)   10.05
   (e)   1,050

   (f)   760,000
   (g) $3\frac{1}{7}$
   (h)   3.1416
   (i)   2,600
   (j)   2,600.0

7.   Which of the following most nearly agrees with $4\frac{1}{8}$ inches in terms of accuracy?   4 feet, 33 miles, 4.12 inches, $4\frac{2}{16}$ pounds.

8.   If you know a measurement has been made to the nearest thousandth of a unit, does this tell you its accuracy or its precision? What else must you know to obtain the other?

9.   Find the maximum allowable error, the relative error, and the per cent of error in each of the following measurements.
   (a)   The diameter of the moon, 2,160 miles
   (b)   Speed limit, 65 miles per hour
   (c)   Boiling point of hydrogen, -252.7 centigrade
   (d)   Area of Mr. Smith's farm, 342 acres

ADDING AND SUBTRACTING APPROXIMATE NUMBERS

9.5   Suppose we wish to find the total weight of a car weighing 3,200 pounds and its occupants weighing 186 pounds, 12$\underline{0}$ pounds, and 56 pounds.   The weight of the car is known to the nearest hundred pounds and the weight of the occupants to the nearest pound.   The total weight could be as low as $3,150 + 185.5 + 119.5 + 55.5 = 3,510.5$ pounds, and it could be as high as $3,250 + 186.5 + 120.5 + 56.5 = 3,613.5$ pounds.   We are sure the total weight is 4,000 pounds to the nearest thousand pounds.   We are not sure to the nearest hundred pounds but we know it is either 3,500 or 3,600.   In this case there is very little to choose from but, since the value midway between the upper and lower limit is 3,562 pounds, our best answer seems to be 3,600 pounds. The result, 3,600 pounds, implies that the answer lies between 3,550 pounds and 3,650 pounds. In this particular case, we are sure of the upper limit but may be off on the lower limit. This is characteristic of an approximate number. We should be certain of all but the last significant digit, and we should be sure that it is within 1 of the correct value.

How then shall we treat approximate numbers in addition and subtraction? Obviously, the answer can be no more precise than the least precise of our measurements. In the above example, we could not hope to know the sum any closer than to the nearest hundred pounds, since the weight of the car alone might cause that great an error. One method consists of adding (or subtracting) the numbers as if they were exact, then expressing the result to the same degree of precision as the least precise of all the measurements used. By this rule, our problem would be solved as $3,200 + 186 + 120 + 56 = 3,562$, and since this is nearer 3,600 than 3,500 we take for our answer 3,600 pounds. An easier and, usually, equally satisfactory method consists of expressing each measurement to the same degree of precision as the least precise measurement and adding the results. Following this scheme, our problem has this solution: $3,200 + 200 + 100 + 100 = 3,600$ pounds.

MULTIPLYING AND DIVIDING APPROXIMATE NUMBERS

9.6 We cannot add measurements unless they are expressed in the same units, so a determination of the precision of each offers no difficulty. In general, we do not multiply measurements of the same denomination. Gallons multiplied by gallons is meaningless. It is true that we do speak of multiplying feet by feet, but the product is not feet. We see that in multiplication it is not so simple to compare the precision of the product with the precision of the factors. Suppose we attempt to find the area of a room which is 12 feet 4 inches by 10 feet 6 inches or, expressed in feet, 12.3 feet by 10.5 feet. (Note that if we know the length to the nearest inch only we must express 12 feet 4 inches as 12.3 feet, not 12.333 . . . .) The smallest possible area of the room whose dimensions are 12.3×10.5 is obtained by multiplying 12.25 by 10.45, which gives 128.0125 square feet. On the other hand, the largest possible area is $12.35 \times 10.55 = 130.2925$

square feet. Obviously, we would not expect to find the area to the nearest ten thousandth of a square foot. That means a square, one hundredth of a foot on a side, and we know our dimensions only to the nearest tenth of a foot. We might argue that since we have each dimension to the nearest tenth of a foot, we should be able to obtain the area to the nearest hundredth of a square foot because $0.1 \times 0.1 = 0.01$. However, the above results show the error of such a conclusion. We are sure of the result to the nearest ten square feet but not the nearest square foot. To the nearest square foot, the area may be 128, 129, or 130 square feet. Then our best estimate is probably 129 square feet. In the example, each factor, 12.3 and 10.5, contains three significant digits; the product of 129 also contains three significant digits. Suppose we multiplied the numbers as if they were exact: $12.3 \times 10.5 = 129.15$. If this result is expressed to three significant digits, we get 129 square feet, our best estimate. Then if we multiply approximate numbers *with the same number of significant digits*, the product should be expressed to this same number of significant digits.

Let us investigate a problem in which the factors have different numbers of significant digits. Suppose we wish to find the weight of 5.2 quarts of an oil which weighs 2.13 pounds per quart. The minimum weight is $5.15 \times 2.125 = 10.94375$ pounds. The maximum weight is $5.25 \times 2.135 = 11.20875$ pounds. Our best estimate to the nearest pound is evidently 11 pounds. In this case, the factors have two and three significant digits respectively and the product has the smaller number, two significant digits. We may conclude that in multiplying approximate numbers, regardless of the number of significant digits of the factors, the product should be expressed with the same number of significant digits as that factor which contains the smallest number of significant digits. The same rules may be applied to the division of approximate numbers as have been applied to their multiplication.

It is instructive to examine the last example a little more closely. Suppose we adjoin a 9 to 2.13, making 2.139, and find the product.

$$
\begin{array}{r}
2.13\text{⑨} \\
5.2 \\
\hline
42\text{⑦⑧} \\
106\text{⑨⑤} \\
\hline
11.\text{①②②⑧}
\end{array}
$$

We see that, by circling the adjoined 9 and those digits in the partial products and in the final answer which were affected by the 9, its effect reaches only to the first digit beyond the last significant digit of the result.   Since the thing that controls the significant digits in the product is the other factor, 5.2, the addition of more digits to 2.13 could not possibly have any effect on the result.   We may modify our rule for multiplication and division to the extent that we round off (Section 9.8) all other factors to one more significant digit than those of the least accurate number, then multiply (or divide) and express the answer to the same number of significant digits as the least accurate factor.

To summarize:

In addition and subtraction of approximate numbers we are concerned with precision.   Express all terms to the same degree of precision as the least precise one, then add or subtract.

In multiplication and division, our concern is with accuracy as this is indicated by significant digits.   Express all factors to one more, at most, significant digit than the number of significant digits of the least accurate factor, multiply or divide, then express the result to the number of significant digits possessed by the least accurate factor.

The above are not to be thought of as theorems capable of mathematical proof.   They are satisfactory working rules.   In unusual cases, the results may be slightly off in the last digit.   The important thing to remember in working with approximate numbers is that we should obtain results which are justified from the given data.   We should never imply greater precision or accuracy than the data justify.

MULTIPLICATION — SOME FACTORS ARE EXACT

9.7   Quite frequently operations are performed with numbers, some of which are approximate and others exact.   For example, if it is found that a bushel of apples weighs 53 pounds, what is the weight of 100 bushels?   Here the 100 is an exact number; we are concerned with the weight of exactly 100 bushel hampers filled with apples.   Our result is, of course, 5,300 pounds.   Now the question is: How many significant digits does the answer possess?   Do we know the weight to the nearest hundred pounds or ten pounds or pound?   The only approximate number in the computation is 53; therefore, according to our rule, there should be two significant digits in the result, and we know that the total weight is 5,300 pounds to the nearest hundred pounds.   This result is consistent with common sense.   The variation in the weight of each bushel being one pound, we should expect no more than 100 times that possible variation in 100 bushels. As a matter of fact, we have every right to expect considerably less. We should expect some bushels to hold a little over 53 pounds, and others a little under. These are compensating errors. But we cannot be sure of a total any closer than to the nearest hundred pounds. On the other hand, quite frequently we are required to use an approximation for some exact number involved in our problem. Suppose we are required to find the circumference of a circle whose diameter is 6 feet. The answer is 6π feet. The question is: What approximation for π should we use: 3, 3.1, 3.14, 3.142, or 3.1416? Here we may be guided by our rule. Since there is only one significant digit in the diameter, we should use 3.1 as our approximation for π. Thus $6 \times 3.1 = 18.6$ feet is the circumference, but to what degree of accuracy shall we leave the result? To the nearest foot we get 19, but this is quite questionable. Since the diameter is given to only one significant digit we take for our answer 20 feet, a one-significant-digit result. If we bear in mind that the diameter is known only to the nearest whole foot, it is not surprising that we are justified in asserting only that the circumference is nearer 20 feet than 10 feet or 30 feet. The point is that when we must use an approximation for an exact number, it is useless to use an approximation which is more refined than that implied by the other data. There would be no justification for using 3.1416 for π in the above situation. At times we use an approximation to an exact number simply because it is more convenient and has no effect on the answer. For example, suppose we are required to multiply the exact number 1,728, the number of cubic inches per cubic foot, by the approximate number 33. The product can be expressed to only two significant digits and we can approximate 1,728 as 1,730 without affecting the result.

ROUNDING OFF

9.8   The process of dropping digits in order that our result may reflect the desired number of significant digits is known as *rounding off* the number. Our definition of significant digits makes it obvious that any digits dropped must *always* be replaced by zeros if the number is an integer. Thus, if 175,623 be rounded off to hundreds, the result becomes 175,600. On the other hand, the dropped digits should never be replaced with zeros if the number is a fraction: 17.5628 becomes 17.56 when rounded to the nearest hundredth. If the last digit dropped is 5, 6, 7, 8, or 9, the first digit retained is increased by one. If the last digit dropped is 0, 1, 2, 3, or 4, the remaining digits are unchanged. If, in a whole number, the first digit retained is zero, it should be underscored to indicate that it is a significant digit.

Examples   6,981 = 6,980 to three significant digits
6,981 = 7,000 to two significant digits
6,981 = 7,000 to one significant digit
6,546 = 6,550 to three significant digits
6,546 = 6,500 to two significant digits
6,550 = 6,600 to two significant digits

The last three examples illustrate the fact that the rounding process should be done all at once, not one digit at a time.

17.238 = 17.24 to four significant digits

17.238 = 17.2 to three significant digits

17.238 = 17 to two significant digits

17.238 = 20 to one significant digit

The procedure described above will yield a result containing the least possible error, with one possible exception.   When 17.238, which represents an exact quantity between 17.2375 and 17.2385, is rounded to 17.24, we then have an approximate number which represents an exact quantity between 17.235 and 17.245.   If the exact quantity is the smallest possible value, 17.2375, the error involved in using 17.24 is .0025, but if we use 17.23 the error becomes .0075.   The exceptional case arises when the only nonzero digit dropped is 5 and it occupies the highest position of the dropped digits; for example, consider 102.5 or 102.50, rounded to three digits.   But neither 102.05 nor 102.51 fits the exceptional case.   If they are rounded to three digits, the results, 102 and 103 respectively, are the three-digit numbers containing the least possible error in each case.   On the other hand, if we round 102.5 to 103, the maximum error is .55; this would occur if the true measure were 102.45.   If we round to 102, the maximum error is also .55; this would be the case if the true measure were 102.55.   We arbitrarily adopt the convention that under these circumstances we always round to the closest *even* digit.   Thus we increase the last digit retained in about half of such cases.

We should get the same effect if we chose to round to the closest *odd* digit; but the other choice is customarily made.

The above procedure is correct if we wish to *minimize error*. In business practice it is seldom followed. It would be a rare thing to be able to purchase a single article for 12¢ that is priced at 2 for 25¢. Here the more common practice is to round off any fraction of a cent to the next cent higher.

COMMON FRACTIONS

9.9   When measurements are given in common fractions rather than decimals, the denominator should be used to indicate the degree of precision. The two measurements $8\frac{1}{2}$ inches and $8\frac{16}{32}$ inches are not the same. The former indicates precision to the nearest half inch; it approximates an exact distance somewhere between $8\frac{1}{4}$ inches and $8\frac{3}{4}$ inches. The latter, $8\frac{16}{32}$, represents an exact value within the range $8\frac{31}{64}$ to $8\frac{33}{64}$. The accuracy of $8\frac{1}{2}$ inches is $\frac{1}{4}/8\frac{1}{2} = 1/34 = .029$, that of $8\frac{16}{32}$ is $\frac{1}{64}/8\frac{16}{32} = 1/544 = .0018$. If the measures are expressed as $8\frac{1}{2} = \frac{17}{2}$ and $8\frac{16}{32} = \frac{272}{32}$, then the number of digits in the numerator gives comparable indications of degree of accuracy as does the number of significant digits in decimal notation.

In actual practice it is well to remember that we are expected to be able to infer something about implied precision and accuracy from context. This is especially true of common fractions. If a customer orders $3\frac{1}{4}$ yards of material to make a dress, precision to the nearest $\frac{1}{4}$ yard is implied. The clerk might feel justified in giving her 3 yards 5 inches — but she would probably get fired anyway. (For another example concerning implied precision and accuracy, see Exercise 14, following Section 9.10.)

ERRORS

9.10   We have said that all measurements are estimates and as such are approximate. The variations in our estimates are due to errors. Errors and mistakes are not synonymous. We may properly say that a mistake is an error but an error is not necessarily a mistake. A mistake occurs when the measuring instrument is improperly used. If a scale indicates 56 units but the operator reads it 54 units, he has made a mistake. All that need be said of mistakes is that they are unnecessary and can be avoided. Other errors are inevitable; they are of two kinds, *constant* and *random*. Constant errors may be due to incorrect calibration of the measuring instrument. For instance, a clock may run fast or slow consistently. It may be due to a faulty technique. There was a striking example of this type of error in a political poll a number of years ago. The sample of persons whose opinions were obtained was gotten from telephone directories. It just so happens that people who cannot afford telephones also vote. This fact caused the results of the poll to be completely at variance with the actual election results. This may well be called a mistake on the part of the pollster; nevertheless, it was a constant error which proved disastrous. Constant errors, if they are discovered, can be controlled or eliminated. Otherwise, they may be such as to counteract each other when some make an estimate too large and others make it too small. Random errors are those that are due to unknown or uncontrollable conditions; they are as apt to operate in one direction as in the other. Such errors are always present and their effect may be determined by statistical analysis. A measurement is correct if no mistakes have been made. A measurement may well be both imprecise and inaccurate and yet be correct.

——————— E X E R C I S E S ———————

1. Round off each of the following to two significant digits.
   (a) 13,602   (c) 504   (e) 500.92
   (b) 86   (d) 17.039

2. Which of the following numbers have most nearly the same accuracy?
   8; .0160; 186,000; 3.2; 8,000; .003

3. Determine the maximum allowable error, the relative error, and per cent of error of the following measures: 1.4 centimeters, $4\frac{9}{8}$ inches, 937.563 miles per hour.

4. A transit is an instrument for measuring horizontal angles. The instrument is so constructed that it is possible to turn an angle, then clamp the scale, and return to the initial sight and turn the angle again. This gives, in effect, the size of an angle twice as large as that which one wishes to measure. The process may be repeated as many times as wished. Will this process enable one to increase the precision with which the angle is measured? Give reasons for your opinion.

5. The sides of a triangle are measured at 12.5, 37.25, and 20. What is the least possible perimeter of this triangle? The greatest possible? What is its perimeter, expressed to the degree of precision which the data justify?

6. Add the following groups of approximate numbers.
   (a) 15.3, 6.5, 12.4, 14.0
   (b) 0.153, 6.5, 12.4, 0.14
   (c) 0.153, 6.5, 1.24, 1,400

7. Find the areas of the following figures.
   (a) A rectangle 35.4 inches by 20.0 inches
   (b) A triangle whose base is 12 inches and altitude 4 inches
   (c) A circle whose diameter is 22.3 inches

8. The formula for the volume of a cone is $V = \frac{1}{3}bh$ where V = volume, b = area of base, and h = altitude. The radius of the circular base of a cone is 6.0 inches, its altitude is 12.4 inches. How many quarts will it hold if a gallon equals 231 cubic inches?

9. The surface area of a sphere is given by the formula $A = 4\pi r^2$, where A = area and r = radius. How much leather does it take to cover a baseball if its diameter is $3\frac{1}{2}$ inches?

10. We wish to paint the ceiling and walls of a room whose dimensions are 18.4 feet by 26.0 feet, ceiling 9.6 feet high. If a quart of the paint we wish to use will cover 500 square feet of surface and sells for $1.55 per quart or $5.25 per gallon, how much should we purchase?

11. The speedometer of an automobile is graduated to the nearest mile per hour. Determine the degree of precision, in feet per second, with which the speed of the automobile may be determined from the speedometer reading.

12. What is the error if we use the approximation 0.66 instead of the exact $\frac{2}{3}$?

13. What is the error if we use $\frac{2}{3}$ as an approximation for 0.66?

14. In terms of approximate numbers, how should you interpret a sign which reads "Speed Limit 30 M.P.H."?

SCIENTIFIC NOTATION

9.11 The practice of underscoring a terminal zero to indicate that it is significant is not universally followed. Very large and very small approximate numbers, though not necessarily confusing, can be quite cumbersome. For example, newspapers prefer to refer to a $78 billion budget rather than a $78,000,000,000 budget. It is not at all uncommon for astronomers to deal with numbers like 9600000000000000000000, which is the number of centimeters across our galaxy. Nuclear physicists commonly deal with numbers like .00000001 centimeter, the size of the hydrogen atom.

There is a much more convenient way of writing very large or very small numbers which also removes any ambiguity as to significant digits. This is known as *scientific notation* or *standard form*. Moving the decimal point in a number merely multiplies the number by some integral power of 10. If we move to the right we multiply by a positive power to 10, and if to the left, by a negative power. Thus, if we start with 36.05 and shift the decimal point three places to the right, we get 36,050, which is $1,000 = 10^3$ times as large. If we shift to the left we get .03605, which is $\frac{1}{1000} = 10^{-3}$ times as large. It is always possible to shift the decimal point so that it is immediately to the right of the first nonzero digit, then multiply by the power of 10 which is equivalent to the shift back to the starting point. For example, suppose we have the number 186,000, the speed of light in miles per second. We shift the decimal point to the position just to the right of the one: 1.86000. We have moved the decimal point five places to the *left*, which means that we have multiplied the original number by 10^{-5}. Since $10^{-5} \cdot 10^5 = 10^0 = 1$ (Section 3.8 page 62), we must now multiply by 10^5 in order that the original number may remain unchanged:

$$186,000 = 1.86000 \times 10^5$$

In this manner, it is always possible to write a number as 1 or more and less than 10, times an integral power of 10. If the number between 1 and 10 is written so as to show *only* significant digits, then the number is written in scientific notation. Thus

$$186,000 = 1.86 \times 10^5$$

Definition   A number is written in scientific notation when written as the product of a number, 1 or more and less than 10, times an integral power of 10, the first factor showing only significant digits.

Under this scheme we can show that 100 means a number to the nearest unit by writing 1.00×10^2, whereas 1.0×10^2 means 100 to the nearest 10 units and 1×10^2 means 100 to the nearest hundred units.

There are a number of devices which may be used to keep the sign of the exponent of 10 straight. Perhaps the most meaningful approach is to remember that we are both multiplying and dividing the original number by the same power of 10. When we shift the decimal point we multiply by some power of 10. When we multiply by a power of 10 whose exponent is minus that implied by the shift, we are actually dividing by the original power of 10.

Example $597,300 = 5.973 \times 10^5$

Here we have moved the decimal point five places to the left, which is equivalent to multiplying the number by 10^{-5}. Then when we multiply by 10^5, this is equivalent to dividing by 10^{-5}.

Since it is possible to express any number as a number between 1 and 10, times some integral power of 10, we could express any number as a power of 10 if we knew to what powers 10 must be raised to get the numbers between 1 and 10. Recall that $a^2 \cdot a^3 = a^{2+3} = a^5$ and in general $a^m \cdot a^n = a^{m+n}$. Then it appears that $10^m \cdot 10^n = 10^{m+n}$. Now if 10^n represents our integral power of 10 and we can find m such that 10^m represents our number between 1 and 10 we have the required power of 10 by merely adding m and n. Consider the number 316,000. In scientific notation this is 3.16×10^5. The square root of 10, which is the same as $10^{.5}$, is 3.16. Therefore $3.16 \times 10^5 = 10^{.5} \times 10^5 = 10^{5.5}$, and we can express the original $316,000 = 10^{5.5}$ as a power of 10.

Even though we can extract the square root of 10, it does not follow that we can find the power of 10 which corresponds to any number between 1 and 10. However, it can be done and has been, but the method involves more advanced mathematics than we are now prepared for.

Assume for the moment that we have at our disposal the powers of 10 which correspond to numbers between 1 and 10. As was seen above, it is then possible to express any number as a power of 10. Since $10^a \cdot 10^b = 10^{a+b}$ we can find the power of 10 corresponding to the product of two numbers by adding the exponents of the powers of 10 corresponding to each factor.

Example   Multiply 3,750 by 13.7.

$$3,750 = 3.75 \times 10^3$$
$$13.7 = 1.37 \times 10^1$$

If $\qquad 3.75 = 10^{.5740}$ and $1.37 = 10^{.1367}$

we have $\qquad 3,750 = 10^{.5740} \times 10^3 = 10^{3.5740}$

$$13.7 = 10^{.1367} \times 10^1 = 10^{1.1367}$$

and $\qquad 3,750 \times 13.7 = 10^{3.5740} \times 10^{1.1367} = 10^{4.7107}$

but $\qquad 10^{4.7107} = 10^4 \times 10^{.7107}$

Now if we can perform the inverse of finding the power of 10 corresponding to a number between 1 and 10, namely, find the number corresponding to a given power of 10, then we can find our product. It happens that $10^{.7107} = 5.14$. Then our product is $5.14 \times 10^4 = 51400$.

———————— E   X   E   R   C   I   S   E   S ————————

1. Write the following in scientific notation.
    (a) .00305   (d) .305   (f) .008732
    (b) 3050000   (e) 8732   (g) 87.32
    (c) 30.5

2. Convert the following to ordinary notation.
    (a) 9.31×10^{-3} (d) 6.338821×10^{-8}
    (b) 8×10^5 (e) 3.33×10^2
    (c) 8.00×10^5 (f) 1×10^{-12}

3. Express the following in scientific notation and find the result to the justified degree of accuracy; all numbers are approximate.

$$\frac{128000 \times .00015}{352 \times .073}$$

4. Light travels 186,000 miles per second. The distance traveled by light in one year is known as a light-year. Using scientific notation, find the number of miles per light-year.

5. Astronomers have estimated that it takes about 5×10^8 years for light to reach the earth from the most distant stars that have so far been observed. How many miles away is this? Write your answer in both scientific notation and ordinary decimal notation.

6. An angstrom unit is a unit of length equal to 1×10^{-8} centimeters. The largest atom, that of uranium, is estimated to have a diameter of about 1/100,000,000 of an inch. If one centimeter equals .3937 inch, find the diameter of the uranium atom in angstrom units.

7. One gram equals .002 pound. Find the mass of the earth in pounds if its mass is 6.0×10^{27} grams.

8. The diameter of the earth is 1.3×10^9 centimeters, that of the sun is 1.4×10^{11} centimeters. If the mass of the sun is 2.0×10^{33} grams, the density of the sun is how many times that of the earth? (Density is mass per unit volume.)

LOGARITHMS ARE EXPONENTS

9.12   The exponents of the powers of 10 that we have been discussing are called logarithms.

Definition   The logarithm of a number is the exponent to which another number, called the base, must be raised to produce the number.

Thus the logarithm of 64 to base 4 (written $\log_4 64$) is 3, because $4^3 = 64$.   The base 10 logarithm of 100 ($\log_{10} 100$) is 2, because $10^2 = 100$.

Although we could use any number we chose for base, there are only two bases in wide usage.   Natural logarithms have the constant e for base.   This constant is an irrational number and has the approximate value 2.7.   By definition, e is the limit which the expression $(1 + 1/x)^x$ approaches, as x increases without limit.   Natural logarithms are extremely useful in the calculus and more advanced mathematics.

Common logarithms have 10 for base.   Their usefulness is derived from the fact that their base agrees with the base of our system of numeration.   Logarithms, in no small measure, are the result of the pioneering work of the Scot, John Napier, during the seventeenth century.   The existence of logarithms has saved scientists and engineers untold amounts of time and labor.   They rank with Hindu-Arabic notation and decimal fractions as aids to computation.   We shall confine our attention to common logarithms.   When no base is indicated it is to be understood that the base of the logarithm is 10.

––––––––––   E   X   E   R   C   I   S   E   S   ––––––––––

1.   Find the following.
   (a) $\log_7 49$ (d) $\log_3 27$ (g) $\log_a 1$
   (b) $\log_2 16$ (e) $\log_{13} 1$ (h) $\log_c c$
   (c) $\log_5 5$ (f) $\log_{10} 1000$

2.   Find the bases for which the following equalities are true.
   (a) $\log 10 = 1$ (c) $\log a^5 = 5$ (e) $\log 4 = \frac{1}{2}$
   (b) $\log 64 = 3$ (d) $\log 81 = 2$ (f) $\log 2 = \frac{1}{2}$

3.   Determine the numbers which have the following logarithms.
   (a) $\log_4 \underline{\quad} = \frac{1}{2}$ (c) $\log_{10} \underline{\quad} = 2$ (e) $\log_a \underline{\quad} = 1$
   (b) $\log_5 \underline{\quad} = 3$ (d) $\log_4 \underline{\quad} = 4$ (f) $\log_x \underline{\quad} = 0$

4.   What is the logarithm of 1 regardless of the base of the logarithm?

5.   Regardless of the base of the logarithm, what is the logarithm of the base?

6.   (a)   Find the value of $(1 + 1/x)^x$ for the following values of x: 1, 2, 3, 4.
      (b)   Find the differences between successive values of $(1 + 1/x)^x$ for $x = 1, 2, 3, 4$.

7.   Write in exponential form:
   (a) $\log_{10} 1000 = 3$ (c) $\log_a x = y$
   (b) $\log_6 36 = 2$ (d) $\log_4 2 = \frac{1}{2}$

8.   Write in logarithmic form:
   (a) $10^0 = 1$ (c) $4^3 = 64$
   (b) $c^x = y$ (d) $10^{1.5502} = 35.5$
9.   Solve for x:
   (a) $2^x = 4^{\frac{3}{2}}$ (b) $8^x = 4^{\frac{1}{3}}$ (c) $5^{x-3} = 25^{\frac{1}{2}}$

LOGARITHMS OF NUMBERS BETWEEN 1 AND 10

9.13   If we remember that $10^1 = 10$ and $10^0 = 1$ (which means log 10 = 1 and log 1 = 0) we conclude that the logarithms of numbers between 1 and 10 are numbers greater than zero but less than one. When we consider scientific notation, it is evident that the logarithm of any number consists of an integer, the exponent of the integral power of 10, plus a fraction, the exponent of the power of 10 corresponding to the number between 1 and 10.

The integral part of a logarithm is called its *characteristic*. The fractional part is called the *mantissa*.

Example   Find the logarithm of 8750.

$$8750 = 8.75 \times 10^3$$
But if $\qquad\qquad 8.75 = 10^{.942}$
then $\qquad\qquad 8750 = 10^{.942} \times 10^3 = 10^{3.9420}$

Therefore, the logarithm of 8750 is written log 8750 = 3 + .9420 = 3.9420.

Given the logarithms of numbers between 1 and 10 we can, by means of scientific notation, determine the logarithm of any number. Table 9.1 gives the logarithms of numbers between 1 and 10. The numbers are given to only three significant digits and the logarithms to four decimal places. Logarithms are never used when exact results are required; the logarithms themselves are approximate numbers. Most exact logarithms are irrational; the values in the table are rational approximations to these exact irrational numbers. Our table can be used when the computation requires three-place accuracy (three significant digits). Four-place accuracy can be obtained from this table by a process known as interpolation (Section 9.15). If greater than four-place accuracy is required, a more refined table must be used.

All decimal points have been omitted from the table. We should remember that each logarithm is less than unity; a decimal point precedes each of them. The logarithms are the numbers within each of the columns of the table which are headed 0 through 9. The numbers corresponding to the logarithms are numbers between 1 and 10:

therefore, a decimal point belongs between the first and second digits from the left.   The first two digits of the numbers corresponding to the logarithms are located in the extreme left column headed N; the third digit is found at the top of the table as the column heading.

Table 9.1   Logarithms of numbers from 1 to 10.

N	0	1	2	3	4	5	6	7	8	9
10	0000	0043	0086	0128	0170	0212	0253	0294	0334	0374
11	0414	0453	0492	0531	0569	0607	0645	0682	0719	0755
12	0792	0828	0864	0899	0934	0969	1004	1038	1072	1106
13	1139	1173	1206	1239	1271	1303	1335	1367	1399	1430
14	1461	1492	1523	1553	1584	1614	1644	1673	1703	1732
15	1761	1790	1818	1847	1875	1903	1931	1959	1987	2014
16	2041	2068	2095	2122	2148	2175	2201	2227	2253	2279
17	2304	2330	2355	2380	2405	2430	2455	2480	2504	2529
18	2553	2577	2601	2625	2648	2672	2695	2718	2742	2765
19	2788	2810	2833	2856	2878	2900	2923	2945	2967	2989
20	3010	3032	3054	3075	3096	3118	3139	3160	3181	3201
21	3222	3243	3263	3284	3304	3324	3345	3365	3385	3404
22	3424	3444	3464	3483	3502	3522	3541	3560	3579	3598
23	3617	3636	3655	3674	3692	3711	3729	3747	3766	3784
24	3802	3820	3838	3856	3874	3892	3909	3927	3945	3962
25	3979	3997	4014	4031	4048	4065	4082	4099	4116	4133
26	4150	4166	4183	4200	4216	4232	4249	4265	4281	4298
27	4314	4330	4346	4362	4378	4393	4409	4425	4440	4456
28	4472	4487	4502	4518	4533	4548	4564	4579	4594	4609
29	4624	4639	4654	4669	4683	4698	4713	4728	4742	4757
30	4771	4786	4800	4814	4829	4843	4857	4871	4886	4900
31	4914	4928	4942	4955	4969	4983	4997	5011	5024	5038
32	5051	5065	5079	5092	5105	5119	5132	5145	5159	5172
33	5185	5198	5211	5224	5237	5250	5263	5276	5289	5302
34	5315	5328	5340	5353	5366	5378	5391	5403	5416	5428
35	5441	5453	5465	5478	5490	5502	5514	5527	5539	5551
36	5563	5575	5587	5599	5611	5623	5635	5647	5658	5670
37	5682	5694	5705	5717	5729	5740	5752	5763	5775	5786
38	5798	5809	5821	5832	5843	5855	5866	5877	5888	5899
39	5911	5922	5933	5944	5955	5966	5977	5988	5999	6010
40	6021	6031	6042	6053	6064	6075	6085	6096	6107	6117
41	6128	6138	6149	6160	6170	6180	6191	6201	6212	6222
42	6232	6243	6253	6263	6274	6284	6294	6304	6314	6325
43	6335	6345	6355	6365	6375	6385	6395	6405	6415	6425
44	6435	6444	6454	6464	6474	6484	6493	6503	6513	6522
45	6532	6542	6551	6561	6571	6580	6590	6599	6609	6618
46	6628	6637	6646	6656	6665	6675	6684	6693	6702	6712
47	6721	6730	6739	6749	6758	6767	6776	6785	6794	6803
48	6812	6821	6830	6839	6848	6857	6866	6875	6884	6893
49	6902	6911	6920	6928	6937	6946	6955	6964	6972	6981
N	0	1	2	3	4	5	6	7	8	9

Table 9.1   (Continued)

N	0	1	2	3	4	5	6	7	8	9
50	6990	6998	7007	7016	7024	7033	7042	7050	7059	7067
51	7076	7084	7093	7101	7110	7118	7126	7135	7143	7152
52	7160	7168	7177	7185	7193	7202	7210	7218	7226	7235
53	7243	7251	7259	7267	7275	7284	7292	7300	7308	7316
54	7324	7332	7340	7348	7356	7364	7372	7380	7388	7396
55	7404	7412	7419	7427	7435	7443	7451	7459	7466	7474
56	7482	7490	7497	7505	7513	7520	7528	7536	7543	7551
57	7559	7566	7574	7582	7589	7597	7604	7612	7619	7627
58	7634	7642	7649	7657	7664	7672	7679	7686	7694	7701
59	7709	7716	7723	7731	7738	7745	7752	7760	7767	7774
60	7782	7789	7796	7803	7810	7818	7825	7832	7839	7846
61	7853	7860	7868	7875	7882	7889	7896	7903	7910	7917
62	7924	7931	7938	7945	7952	7959	7966	7973	7980	7987
63	7993	8000	8007	8014	8021	8028	8035	8041	8048	8055
64	8062	8069	8075	8082	8089	8096	8102	8109	8116	8122
65	8129	8136	8142	8149	8156	8162	8169	8176	8182	8189
66	8195	8202	8209	8215	8222	8228	8235	8241	8248	8254
67	8261	8267	8274	8280	8287	8293	8299	8306	8312	8319
68	8325	8331	8338	8344	8351	8357	8363	8370	8376	8382
69	8388	8395	8401	8407	8414	8420	8426	8432	8439	8445
70	8451	8457	8463	8470	8476	8482	8488	8494	8500	8506
71	8513	8519	8525	8531	8537	8543	8549	8555	8561	8567
72	8573	8579	8585	8591	8597	8603	8609	8615	8621	8627
73	8633	8639	8645	8651	8657	8663	8669	8675	8681	8686
74	8692	8698	8704	8710	8716	8722	8727	8733	8739	8745
75	8751	8756	8762	8768	8774	8779	8785	8791	8797	8802
76	8808	8814	8820	8825	8831	8837	8842	8848	8854	8859
77	8865	8871	8876	8882	8887	8893	8899	8904	8910	8915
78	8921	8927	8932	8938	8943	8949	8954	8960	8965	8971
79	8976	8982	8987	8993	8998	9004	9009	9015	9020	9025
80	9031	9036	9042	9047	9053	9058	9063	9069	9074	9079
81	9085	9090	9096	9101	9106	9112	9117	9122	9128	9133
82	9138	9143	9149	9154	9159	9165	9170	9175	9180	9186
83	9191	9196	9201	9206	9212	9217	9222	9227	9232	9238
84	9243	9248	9253	9258	9263	9269	9274	9279	9284	9289
85	9294	9299	9304	9309	9315	9320	9325	9330	9335	9340
86	9345	9350	9355	9360	9365	9370	9375	9380	9385	9390
87	9395	9400	9405	9410	9415	9420	9425	9430	9435	9440
88	9445	9450	9455	9460	9465	9469	9474	9479	9484	9489
89	9494	9499	9504	9509	9513	9518	9523	9528	9533	9538
90	9542	9547	9552	9557	9562	9566	9571	9576	9581	9586
91	9590	9595	9600	9605	9609	9614	9619	9624	9628	9633
92	9638	9643	9647	9652	9657	9661	9666	9671	9675	9680
93	9685	9689	9694	9699	9703	9708	9713	9717	9722	9727
94	9731	9736	9741	9745	9750	9754	9759	9763	9768	9773
95	9777	9782	9786	9791	9795	9800	9805	9809	9814	9818
96	9823	9827	9832	9836	9841	9845	9850	9854	9859	9863
97	9868	9872	9877	9881	9886	9890	9894	9899	9903	9908
98	9912	9917	9921	9926	9930	9934	9939	9943	9948	9952
99	9956	9961	9965	9969	9974	9978	9983	9987	9991	9996
N	0	1	2	3	4	5	6	7	8	9

If we look down the column headed N and find 34, then opposite the 34 and in the column headed 6 we find the number 5391. This tells us that log 3.46 = .5391. If the numbers whose logarithms we want have more than three significant digits, they should be rounded off to this degree of accuracy before we find their logarithms unless, by interpolation, we use a fourth digit.

In case we know the logarithm of a number and wish to find the number, we locate the logarithm in the body of the table — the first two digits of the required number are found in the column headed N and the third digit is the heading of the column in which the logarithm is located. Find the number whose logarithm is .6955. We find 6955 opposite 49 in the N column and in the column headed 6. Therefore, our number, called the *antilogarithm*, is 4.96. Since log 4.96 = .6955, antilog .6955 = 4.96 — meaning the number whose logarithm is .6955 is 4.96.

In case the given logarithm is not in the table we use the logarithm nearest its value. Find the number whose logarithm is .8601. The number 8601 is not in the table, but we find 8597 below and 8603 above. Since 8603 is the closer of the two to 8601, we take for our answer 7.25. We know the correct answer is between 7.24 and 7.25. Since it is nearer 7.25, the correct answer, to three significant digits, is 7.25. As in the inverse process, we can find a fourth digit by interpolation.

E   X   E   R   C   I   S   E   S

---

1.   Find the logarithms of the following numbers.
   (a)   6.72   (e)   7.468
   (b)   3.8742   (f)   3.725
   (c)   1.383   (g)   10,000
   (d)   9.759   (h)   .0001

2.   Find the numbers which have the following numbers as logarithms.
   (a)   .9112   (e)   .5911
   (b)   .2650   (f)   6
   (c)   .7611   (g)   3
   (d)   .8888   (h)   −5

3.   Find the following.
   (a)   log 3.4   (d)   antilog .675
   (b)   antilog .34   (e)   log 2.111
   (c)   log 6.75   (f)   antilog .2111

LOGARITHMS OF ANY POSITIVE NUMBER

9.14   By utilizing scientific notation and our table we may now find the logarithm of any positive number, assuming the number is rounded to three significant digits.   Let us find the logarithm of 7286431.   If we round off the number to conform to the accuracy of our table we get 7290000.   If we write this result in scientific notation we get 7.29×10^6.   Opposite 72 in the N column and in the column headed by 9 we find 8627.   Then our logarithm is $6 + .8627 = 6.8627$.   Suppose we find the logarithm of .00583.   In scientific notation, this is 5.83×10^{-3}.   From the table, the logarithm of $5.83 = .7657$.   Then log $.00583 = -3 + .7657$.   The negative integer and the positive fraction can be combined into the negative number -2.2343.   However, all mantissas, since they are the logarithms of numbers from 1 to 10, are *positive*.   It is very advantageous to maintain the positive fractional part of all logarithms since negative fractions cannot be identified in the table.   For this reason, we express $-3 + .7657$ as $7.7657 - 10$.   We could write it as $.7657 - 3$, or $16.7657 - 19$, or in any other form having integers whose sum is -3.   But the above scheme is frequently advantageous in computation with logarithms.

LINEAR INTERPOLATION

9.15   As a number increases, its logarithm also increases, but they do not increase at the same rate.   The logarithm of $4 = .6021$ is very near exactly twice the logarithm of $2 = .3010$.   Here it appears that the logarithm is doubled when the number is doubled.   Accordingly, we might expect log 6 to be 3 times log 2, log 8 to be 4 times log 2, and so on.   Examination of the table of logarithms shows that this is not the case.   Log 4 is twice log 2, not because 4 is twice 2, but because $4 = 2^2$.   However, if we find the difference between consecutive entries in the table there seems to be almost a constant difference.   The first line of logarithms in the table gives differences of 43, 43, 42, 42, 42, 41, 41, 40, and 40.   The differences of the logarithms on the line with the entry 80 in the N column are 5, 6, 5, 6, 5, 5, 6, 5, and 5.   We may conclude that, although the number and its logarithm do not change at the same rate, the successive entries going down the table very nearly do.   This makes linear interpolation possible.   Interpolation is a process of finding intermediate values between given ones in a series or function.   Since 3.427 is $\frac{7}{10}$ of the way between 3.42 and

3.43, we assume that log 3.427 is also $\frac{7}{10}$ of the way between log 3.42 and log 3.43.   From the table we find log 3.42 = .5340 and log 3.43 = .5353.   The difference between these logarithms is .0013, the amount the logarithm increases in moving from 3.42 to 3.43.   Then $\frac{7}{10}$ of this increase, or .0009, is the amount log 3.42 must increase to become log 3.427.   Accordingly, log 3.427 = .5340 + .0009 = .5349.   Note that we took $\frac{7}{10}$ of .0013 to be .0009 rather than .00091.   We should never use more digits than the number found in the table.   Interpolation makes it possible to find the logarithms of numbers containing four significant digits.

We may also, by interpolation, find to four significant digits the number corresponding to a given logarithm.   We wish to find the number whose logarithm is .2135.   This logarithm is not in the table, but we find .2122 = log 1.63 and .2148 = log 1.64.   The difference between these two logarithms is .0026.   The difference between .2122 and the given .2135 is .0013.   Then the number whose logarithm is .2135 lies .0013/.0026 = .5 of the way between 1.63 and 1.64; it is 1.635.

You will probably find it helpful to arrange your work in tabular form when interpolating.   However, this is a crutch which should be abandoned as soon after you grasp the idea as possible.   The above problem of finding the logarithm of 3.427 can be arranged like this:

$$\log 3.43\ \ = .5353$$
$$\log 3.427 = .5340 + .0009 = .5349$$
$$\log 3.42\ \ = \frac{.5340}{.0013} \times \tfrac{7}{10} = .0009$$

To find antilog .2135 we may write:

$$.2148 = \log 1.64$$
$$.2135 = \log (1.63 + .005) = \log 1.635$$
$$.2122 = \log 1.63$$
$$\frac{.0013}{.0026} = .5$$

———————— E   X   E   R   C   I   S   E   S ————————

1.   Find the following.
   (a)   log .000756
   (b)   log 156000
   (c)   log 1.8900

   (d)   log 89.000
   (e)   log 387

2.   Express in exponential form:
(a)   log 73.6 = 1.8669   (c)   log 1000000 = 6
(b)   log .00025 = 6.3979 − 10   (d)   log .000001 = − 6

3.   Find the number whose logarithm is:
(a)   3.1818   (c)   −2   (e)   9.8774 − 10
(b)   5.0086   (d)   0.3711   (f)   1.9859

4.   Find the following by interpolation.
(a)   log 179.4   (c)   antilog 3.4935
(b)   log .084307   (d)   antilog 8.6600 − 10

COMPUTATIONS WITH LOGARITHMS

9.16   From the definition of logarithms, we know that *logarithms are exponents.*   Accordingly, they obey the laws of exponents.

Property 1   Since $10^a \cdot 10^b = 10^{a+b}$
$$\log (x \cdot y) = \log x + \log y$$

Proof:

Let $10^a = x$ and $10^b = y$.

Then the original statement becomes

$$xy = 10^{a+b}$$

Take the logarithm of each side

$$\log xy = \log 10^{a+b} = a + b$$

But if $10^a = x$, then $a = \log x$, and if $10^b = y$, then $b = \log y$.   Then substituting these values for a and b, we get

$$\log xy = \log x + \log y$$

In words, this result states that the logarithm of a *product* is equal to the *sum* of the logarithms of the factors.   This property was utilized in finding the logarithm of any number, given the logarithms of numbers from 1 to 10.

Property 2   Since $10^a \div 10^b = 10^{a-b}$
$$\log x/y = \log x - \log y$$

Proof:

Let $10^a = x$ and $10^b = y$.

Then from the original statement

$$x/y = 10^{a-b}$$

Take the logarithm of each side

$$\log x/y = \log 10^{a-b} = a - b$$

But if $10^a = x$, then $a = \log x$, and if $10^b = y$, then $b = \log y$. Therefore, substituting these values for a and b, we get

$$\log x/y = \log x - \log y$$

This result tells us that we may find the logarithm of a *quotient* by *subtracting* the logarithm of the divisor from the logarithm of the dividend.

The two principles above show that with the aid of logarithms, we can reduce multiplication and division to addition and subtraction respectively.

Property 3   Since $(10^a)^b = 10^{ab}$
$$\log (x^y) = y \log x$$

Proof:
Let $10^a = x$ and $b = y$.
Then $x^y = 10^{ab}$
and $\log (x^y) = \log 10^{ab} = ab = ba$
But if $10^a = x$, then $a = \log x$, and since $b = y$, then $\log (x^y) = ba = y \log x$.

From this we may conclude that the logarithm of any power of a number is the same as the exponent of the power times the logarithm of the number. The logarithm of 2^{15} is equal to 15 times the logarithm of 2.

When we recall that any root of a number can be expressed as a fractional exponent, $\sqrt{10} = 10^{\frac{1}{2}}$, $\sqrt[5]{a} = a^{\frac{1}{5}}$, $\sqrt[n]{a} = a^{1/n}$, the above principle can be extended to include the finding of any root of a number. The logarithm of any root of a number is equal to the logarithm of the number divided by the index of the root.

Logarithms *cannot* aid one in performing addition and subtraction.

Refer to the definition of a logarithm. What is the logarithm of -25? To what power must we raise 10 to get -25?

$$10^x = -25$$

We know that if x is greater than 1, then 10^x is greater than 10. If x is negative, $10^x = 1/10^{-x}$, which means a fraction — a 1 over some positive number. We cannot raise 10 to a positive, a zero, or a negative power and get -25, or any other negative number. Negative numbers do not have *real logarithms*. It is only the logarithms which are real numbers that interest us here, so for our purposes we may consider negative numbers (and zero) as not having logarithms. That does not prevent our using logarithms to compute with negative quantities. We merely ignore the signs until the answer is determined except for its sign. Then we may take its negative factors into consideration to determine the sign of the result.

A few examples will illustrate the foregoing principles of logarithms.

Example 1   Find the side of a square whose area is equal to that of a circle with a 16.5-foot radius. The problem requires that we evaluate $\sqrt{16.5^2 \times 3.14}$.

$$\log 16.5^2 = 2 \log 16.5$$
$$\log (16.5^2 \times 3.14) = \log 16.5^2 + \log 3.14 = 2 \log 16.5 + \log 3.14$$
$$\log \sqrt{16.5^2 \times 3.14} = \log (16.5^2 \times 3.14)^{\frac{1}{2}}$$
$$= \tfrac{1}{2} \log (16.5^2 \times 3.14)$$
$$= \tfrac{1}{2}(2 \log 16.5 + \log 3.14)$$
$$= \log 16.5 + \frac{\log 3.14}{2}$$
$$= 1.2175 + \tfrac{1}{2}(.4969)$$
$$= 1.2175 + .2485$$
$$= 1.4660$$

Then the logarithm of our answer is 1.4660; antilog 1.4660 = 29.2.

Example 2   Evaluate $\dfrac{17.3 \times .00627}{65.1 \times .87}$.

We shall find the logarithm of the numerator, the logarithm of the denominator, then subtract:

log 17.3 = 1.2380	log 65.1 = 1.8136
log .00627 = 7.7973 − 10	log .87 = 9.9395 − 10
log numerator 9.0353 − 10	log denominator 11.7531 − 10

$$\text{log numerator} - \text{log denominator} = 7.2822 - 10$$
$$\text{antilog } 7.2822 - 10 = .00192$$

Any time the logarithm to be subtracted has the larger positive component, the other logarithm should be changed so as to make its positive component the larger by adding and subtracting the necessary multiple of 10.

Example 3   Evaluate $\dfrac{.00486 \times 3.52}{.0199 \times 24}$.

log .00486 = 7.6866 − 10	log .0199 = 8.2989 − 10
log 3.52 = 0.5465	log 24 = 1.3802
log numerator 8.2331 − 10	log denominator 9.6791 − 10

Since 8.2331 is less than 9.6791, we write the logarithm of the numerator as 18.2331 − 20.

$$
\begin{array}{ll}
\text{log numerator} & 18.2331 - 20 \\
\text{log denominator} & \underline{9.6791 - 10} \\
& 8.5540 - 10
\end{array}
$$

antilog 8.5540 − 10 = .0358

When dividing a negative logarithm we must be careful that the negative integer is an exact multiple of the divisor; otherwise a negative fraction will be introduced.

Example 4   Evaluate $\sqrt[3]{\dfrac{43.6 \times 1.008}{.735 \times 937.6}}$.

$$
\begin{array}{ll}
\text{log } 43.6 = 1.6395 & \text{log } .735 = 9.8663 - 10 \\
\text{log } 1.008 = \underline{0.0034} & \text{log } 937.6 = \underline{2.9720} \\
\text{log numerator } 1.6429 & \text{log denominator } 12.8383 - 10
\end{array}
$$

log fraction = (11.6429 − 10) − 2.8383 = 8.8046 − 10

We cannot divide 3 into −10 an even number of times but we can change 8 − 10 to 28 − 30:

$$\tfrac{1}{3} \text{ log fraction} = \tfrac{1}{3}(28.8046 - 30) = 9.6015 - 10$$
$$\text{antilog } 9.6015 - 10 = .3995$$

An *exponential equation* is an equation wherein the variable appears as an exponent.   For example,

$$8.12^{x-3} = 2^{2x}$$

is an exponential equation.   Logarithms may be employed in solving such equations.

Example   Solve $3^{x-1} = 5^{\frac{1}{3}}$ for x.

Taking the logarithm of both numbers, $\log 3^{x-1} = \log 5^{\frac{1}{3}}$
By Property 3, $(x - 1) \log 3 = \tfrac{1}{3} \log 5$

$$x - 1 = \frac{\tfrac{1}{3} \log 5}{\log 3} = \frac{\log 5}{3 \log 3} = \frac{\log 5}{\log 3^3}$$

$$x = \frac{\log 5}{\log 27} + 1$$

$$x = 1.488$$

Although logarithms simplify computation by reducing multiplication to addition, division to subtraction, and raising to a power to multiplication, we should remember that computation with logarithms gives only approximate results.

THE SLIDE RULE

9.17   The slide rule is a useful adaptation of logarithms. Many kinds of rules with special scales have been developed. The most common type, the rectilinear rule, was invented in 1622 by William Oughtred, an Englishman.   In its simplest form, the slide rule consists of two movable scales so constructed that one may be moved alongside the other.   The scales are graduated not at equal intervals, but logarithmically.   The idea may be demonstrated most easily with the aid of our logarithm table.   If we divide our scale into 1,000 equal divisions, then by referring to the table we see the beginning of the scale (the zeroth division) is marked 1, since the logarithm of 1 is zero.   Similarly, the 301st division is marked 2 because the logarithm of 2 is .301 to three significant digits; the 477th division is 3; the 602nd division is 4; the 699th is marked 5; the 778th is marked 6; the 845th is marked 7; the 903rd is marked 8; the 954th is marked 9; and the 1,000th on the other end is marked 1.

If we add distances on two such scales, we are evidently adding logarithms and the numbered distance corresponding to the sum will give the product of the two numbers.   Similarly, if we subtract distances on the scales, we are subtracting logarithms and therefore dividing.

The slide rule is quite useful when the required accuracy is not too great.   It provides a rapid means of calculating, and is quite useful in checking results.

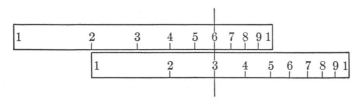

Figure 9.1   A slide rule consists of two movable scales graduated logarithmically.

The illustration in Figure 9.1 shows the indicator, 1, on the lower scale opposite the 2 on the upper scale.   Opposite 3 on the lower scale we find 6 on the upper scale.   Here we have added the distance corresponding to the logarithm of 2 and the distance corresponding to the logarithm of 3, getting the distance corresponding to the logarithm of 6.   Multiplication on the slide rule is thus accomplished by adding logarithms.   Division is performed by subtracting distances on the logarithmic scale.

——————— E X E R C I S E S ————————

1.   Evaluate by means of logarithms:
   (a) $(73.08)(.00931)(567.43)$
   (b) $\dfrac{(4967)(.053)}{(214)(.0873)}$
   (c) $\dfrac{(593)(6.74)}{(3.15)(12.5)}$
   (d) $\sqrt[3]{1590}$
   (e) $(543)(1.05)^{21}$
   (f) $\sqrt[5]{.0049}$
   (g) $\dfrac{(83.7)^2(5.006)^3}{(.0093)^4}$

2.   Use logarithms to solve the following:
   (a)   The formula $A = p(1 + r)^n$ shows the amount, A, which p dollars will yield at compound interest in n interest periods at an interest rate, r, per period. If \$1,500 is left at compound interest for 10 years at 4 per cent compounded semiannually, the amount, A, is given by $A = 1,500(1 + .02)^{20}$.   Find A.
   (b)   If a bank pays 3 per cent interest, compounded annually, how much money should one deposit now in order to have \$10,000 ten years from now?
   (c)   A ball rebounds $\frac{1}{2}$ the distance it has dropped. If the ball is dropped from a 100-foot height, how far does it travel in coming to rest?
   (d)   A \$2,400 automobile depreciates \$600 the first year.   If the annual rate of depreciation is constant, that is, during any year the depreciation is a fixed per cent of its value at the beginning of the year, what is the automobile worth at the end of three years?   Ten years?

3.   Complete the following table from the logarithm Table 9.1.

x	.1	.2	.3	.4	.5	1	2	3	4	5	10
log x											

4.   Use the values obtained in Exercise 3 to construct a graph of $y = \log x$.

5.   Solve the following:
   (a) $10^x = \frac{2}{5}$
   (b) $5.12^{x+3} = 6.7$
   (c) $6.4^{x-1} = 4.8^{x+2}$

LOGARITHMIC SCALE IN GRAPHS

*9.18 When constructing a graph, although different scales may be used on the horizontal and vertical axes, the same unit should be used throughout on each axis.   However, there are times when it is advantageous to plot the units on the vertical axis logarithmically rather than uniformly.   Ordinarily, we wish our graph to picture the trend of the variables in terms of the corresponding changes in the two variables.   If the graph rises as we move to the right, we know that both variables are increasing; if it falls, we know that the dependent variable is decreasing as the independent variable increases.   If the graph is a straight line, the ratio of the two variables is always the same.   There are some situations in which it is more important to know the rate at which one of the variables is changing than to know the ratio between the two variables.   This is particularly true of certain time series.

You will recall from Section 9.16 that $\log x/y = \log x - \log y$.   If x and y are any two successive values of the dependent variable and their ratio x/y is constant, then $\log x/y$ and $\log x - \log y$ are also constant.   Then if we use a logarithmic scale on a vertical axis, the graph of a function in which successive values of the dependent variable are in a constant ratio will appear in a straight line.   The use of a logarithmic scale enables us to picture rates of change in the same manner that the uniform scale pictures absolute changes.

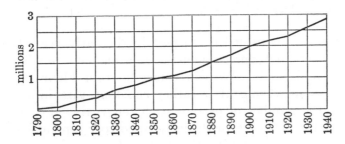

Figure 9.2   Population of the state of Tennessee, 1790–1940. Equal interval scale is used.

Figure 9.2 shows the population of the state of Tennessee from 1790 through 1940, using a uniform scale.   Figure 9.3 shows the same information, using a logarithmic scale.

If the population had increased by the same amount for each ten-year interval, the graph of Figure 9.2 would have appeared as a straight line.   On the other hand, if the per cent of increase in the population had been constant at each census then Figure 9.3 would have appeared as a straight line.   According to these two charts, did the state grow faster in recent years than in the early 1800's?   Figure 9.2 seems to show a fairly constant rate of growth with a slight acceleration from 1870.   Figure 9.3 seems to imply the most rapid growth in the earliest years.   This is because Figure 9.2 pictures the rate of growth as a function of the increase in the number of people per unit of time, whereas Figure 9.3 pictures the growth as the rate of increase over the previous census. In any ten-year interval in which the population doubled, the graph of Figure 9.3 would show the same amount of rise. This is not true of Figure 9.2. In Figure 9.2 any interval having an increase of 100,000 would show the same amount of rise.

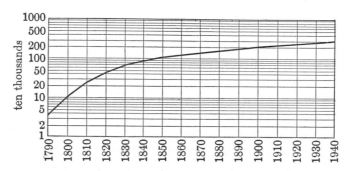

Figure 9.3 Population of the state of Tennessee, 1790–1940. Logarithmic scale is used.

The curve in Figure 9.3 is steepest in the early years because the population increased, percentagewise, at a higher rate when the state was young and small. We can conclude from Figure 9.2 that the population is increasing at a rather constant rate in terms of the increase in the number of persons each ten years. From Figure 9.3 we see that the rate of growth, in terms of per cent of increase over the previous census, is constantly slowing down.

──────────── * E   X   E   R   C   I   S   E   S ────────────

1. Explain why the flattest part of the graph in Figure 9.2 corresponds to the steepest part in Figure 9.3.

2. The curve in Figure 9.3 is rising and concave downward. What does this tell us about the way in which the population is changing? What would be happening if the curve were rising and concave upward? If rising in a straight line?

3. If the curve of Figure 9.3 drops between 1950 and 1960 will that of Figure 9.2 necessarily drop? What will be happening to the population if this occurs?

4. Under what condition would graphs similar to those in Figures 9.2 and 9.3 be exactly the same?

5.   If the graph in Figure 9.3 were rising in a straight line describe the corresponding graph in Figure 9.2.   If the graph in Figure 9.2 were rising in a straight line describe the corresponding graph in Figure 9.3.

DO YOU KNOW

The difference between a selective sample and a random sample?

There are many kinds of averages?

The difference between a mean and a median?

What a standard deviation is?

What a normal distribution is?

The difference between betting odds and probability?

What "Pascal's Triangle" is?

What it has to do with probability?

What a correlation coefficient indicates?

When the harmonic mean is more appropriate than the arithmetic mean?

Why the use of the wrong average can be misleading?

STATISTICAL MEASURES

The seventeenth century was one of the most productive eras in all history in so far as mathematical development is concerned. Modern statistics had its beginning in this century. A French gambler has the distinction of having instigated its development. He proposed a problem known as the "Problem of Points" to Blaise Pascal. The problem was essentially this: Two gamblers are playing a game where points are scored. The one gaining a specified number of points first wins the stake. The game is interrupted before either player wins enough points. If the number of points won by each player is known, how should the stakes be divided? Pascal related the problem to Pierre Fermat. They each solved it, but went much further. Their work, resulting from this problem, laid the foundation for the theory of probability which in turn is the framework on which modern statistics is based.

Statistics represents a vast, ever expanding field of applied mathematics. It is constantly finding wider use in such fields as engineering, business, medicine, education, and agriculture. There are two main aspects of statistics. One is the organization, classification, and interpretation of a mass of collected data. This is known as *descriptive statistics*. The other consists of studying a total population by analyzing a sample of that population. When properties of the sample are projected to the total population, we are making a *statistical inference*. This is the realm of inductive conclusions, probable truths. A good illustration of the first type of activity is the work of the U.S. Census Bureau. From the data collected by the census takers, information is obtained about the average size of an American family, its average income, the age distribution of the population, occupation distribution, and so forth.   Public opinion polls are a familiar illustration of the other type of activity.   The poll taker obtains the opinions of a sample of the population on the question under investigation — for example, whom they favor for President.   From the opinions of the sample, the poll taker predicts the opinion of the total population.

The success of such undertakings depends on the extent to which the sample is an accurate miniature of the total.   Two methods of obtaining the sample may be used.   A *random sample* is one that is so obtained that every member of the population has an equal chance of being selected.   A *selective sample* is one that is obtained so that all relevant differences in the population shall be represented in the proper proportion.   In the opinion poll such factors as age, education, occupation, sex, and geographical location are considered.   One might wonder, "Why take a sample?   Why not use the whole population?"   One answer is obvious: the population is too large.   Another answer is that the sample sometimes must be subjected to tests which alter or destroy it.   For example, if the breaking strength of concrete beams is to be determined, the sample beams must be broken in the process. Quality control is maintained for many products by subjecting samples of the product to chemical analysis.

The use of statistical terminology in nontechnical literature is increasing, and it is essential that the general reader have a correct understanding of the more common terms and ideas.

MEASURES OF CENTRAL TENDENCY

10.1   A measure of central tendency is a single measure representative of all the measures, the one measure which from some point of view is the most typical of the elements in the group.   There are three such measures in common use: the *arithmetic mean,* usually referred to merely as the *mean,* the *median* or mid-score, and the *mode.*   All three measures are averages.   Each has its advantages and limitations.   The nature of the particular distribution of measures, as well as the purpose for which the average is chosen, will determine which average should be used.

The term, arithmetic mean, is also used in a somewhat different sense than the above.   We may find any desired number of arithmetic means between two numbers.   For example, three arithmetic means between 12 and 24 are 15, 18, and 21.   The connection between these two uses of the term should become evident presently.

THE ARITHMETIC MEAN

10.2   The arithmetic mean of a group of measures is obtained by adding the measures and dividing by the number of measures.   The following are the weights to the nearest pound of the members of a football team: 185, 203, 240, 190, 211, 189, 170, 203, 165, 180, and 180 pounds.   If we add the eleven weights and divide by 11 we get the mean weight of the members of the team.

$$\frac{2116}{11} = 192 \text{ pounds, to the nearest pound}$$

If we designate the weight of a player as X, the variable X may take on each of the eleven values given above.   The values of the individual measurements in the group of measurements are called *variates*.   The symbol X_i indicates any one of the variates.   In the above example, $X_1 = 185$, $X_2 = 203$, ... $X_{11} = 180$.   The symbol Σ, which is the Greek letter sigma, is used to indicate a sum.   Thus $\sum_{i=1}^{11} X_i$ means the sum of the variates $X_1 + X_2 + \ldots + X_{11}$.   The symbol $\sum_{i=1}^{11} X_i$ is read "the sum, from $i = 1$ to 11 of X_i."   The arithmetic mean is designated $\overline{X}$ (read X-bar).   The formula for the arithmetic mean is then

$$\overline{X} = \frac{1}{N} \sum_{i=1}^{N} X_i$$

where N = the number of variates (or measurements or scores).

If N is quite large a considerable amount of work may be saved in the computation of the mean.   We illustrate the method in computing the mean weight of the members of the football team.

First, we assume a value of the mean, say 200 pounds.   Next we find how much each score differs from the assumed mean.   This is called the deviation from the mean.   These differences are -15, $+3$, $+40$, -10, $+11$, -11, -30, $+3$, -35, -20, -20.   Then we obtain the mean of the deviations

$$\frac{-15 + 3 + 40 - 10 + 11 - 11 - 30 + 3 - 35 - 20 - 20}{11}$$

$$= \frac{-84}{11} = -8, \text{ to the nearest pound}$$

Adding this correction to the assumed mean, we obtain the true mean, $200 - 8 = 192$ pounds.

If we designate the assumed mean as X_0 and the deviations of the X_i's from X_0 as Y_i, the above method implies that the mean of the variates, $\overline{X}$, is equal to the assumed mean, X_0, plus the mean of the deviations, $\overline{Y}$:

$$\overline{X} = X_0 + \overline{Y}$$

To prove this we first note that $Y_i = X_i - X_0$, and

$$\overline{Y} = \frac{1}{N} \sum_{i=1}^{N} (X_i - X_0)$$

Then

$$X_0 + \overline{Y} = X_0 + \frac{1}{N} \sum_{i=1}^{N} (X_i - X_0)$$

$$= X_0 + \frac{1}{N} [(X_1 - X_0) + (X_2 - X_0) + \ldots + (X_N - X_0)]$$

$$= X_0 + \frac{1}{N} (X_1 + X_2 + \ldots + X_N - NX_0)$$

$$= X_0 + \frac{1}{N} (X_1 + X_2 + \ldots + X_N) - X_0$$

$$= \frac{1}{N} \sum_{i=1}^{N} X_i$$

$$= \overline{X}$$

In case our assumed mean, X_0, happens to be the true mean, $\overline{X}$, we get

$$\overline{X} = \overline{X} + \overline{Y}$$
$$0 = \overline{Y}$$

But $\overline{Y}$ is, in this case, the mean of the deviations from the mean of the scores; therefore

$$0 = \frac{1}{N} \sum_{i=1}^{N} (X_i - \overline{X})$$

or, multiplying by N

$$0 = \sum_{i=1}^{N} (X_i - \overline{X})$$

or *the sum of the deviations of the scores from their mean is zero.*

THE MEDIAN

10.3   The median of a group of measures is the middle one when they are arranged in order of size.   The weights of the members of the football team are in order of size: 165, 170, 180, 180, 185, *189*, 190, 203, 203, 211, 240.   The mid-score, 189, is the median weight.

If the number of measures is even, it is customary to assign a value midway between the two middle scores as the median.   Fifty per cent of the scores fall below, and 50 per cent above, the median.

This is not precisely true when there is an odd number of scores, for if 50 per cent were above and 50 per cent below, the total would be 100 per cent of the scores plus the middle score.

THE MODE

10.4   The *mode* of a group of measures is the measure that occurs most frequently.   It is possible for a set of measures to have more than one mode.   If two or more measures occur with the maximum frequency each measure is properly called a mode.   The group of measures given in Section 10.3, the weights of the football players, is a bimodal one, since 180 and 203 occur the same number of times and more frequently than the other weights.   In this example, the mode is rather useless, not because the distribution is bimodal, but because there is no tendency of the weights to fall in clusters.

WHICH AVERAGE IS BEST?

10.5   Why have the three averages, mean, median, and mode?   Each of them best typifies the total set in a different way.   The mean is a magnitude average.   It is the value each measure would have if they were all equal.   The median is a positional average.   The number of measures greater than the median is the same as the number that is less.   The mode is a frequency average.   It is the most "stylish," most "popular" measure.   If a measure is selected at random from the set, the mode is most likely to be selected.

In many distributions all three of these measures are almost the same.   However, each has its own properties and under some circumstances one is more meaningful than the others.   In fact, the use of the wrong measure can be quite misleading. For example, a church is trying to pay off its building mortgage. From 200 pledges $15,000 has been raised. When Mr. Average Guy is contacted he inquires how much is usually pledged. The mean pledge up to now is $75. However, Mr. Big started the campaign off with $5,000 and the other 199 pledges have ranged from $10 to $100, averaging about $50. The mean is obviously misleading in this instance. The median or the mode would be a much more appropriate measure of central tendency. In general, the mean is the best measure because it takes into account the magnitude of all the measures. It is not appropriate when a few extremely small or extremely large measures unduly affect the result.

The following grades were reported for a class of twelve students: 95, 90, 90, 85, 80, 80, 80, 80, 80, 80, 70, 50. Both the sixth and the seventh scores are 80; therefore the score midway between them, also 80, is the median. But there are twice as many scores higher than 80 as there are lower than 80. We certainly cannot infer that half the class scored better than 80. The median as a measure of central tendency would be misleading in this case.

The manager of a hat store does not care a rap about the mean hat size sold in his store. It would probably come out as a value between two sizes. The median is just about worthless. But he probably could profit from knowing the mode, the size most frequently bought.

The appropriateness of the average used will depend upon the nature of the data as well as upon which of its characteristics is the most significant. The reader should be wary when an "average" is cited without stating what kind of average it is. "Figures don't lie, but liars do figure." An inappropriate average is sometimes deliberately used in order to give an erroneous impression.

The mean is the most frequently used average. It can always be precisely determined. Unless there are a few very large or very small scores to distort the mean, its value is representative of the group. As we shall see later, it is necessary in the determination of many other statistical measures.

──────── E X E R C I S E S ────────

1. Criticize the following statements — typical of many you see and hear.
   (a) Six out of ten adults who wear glasses are smokers. Smoking is injurious to the eyesight.

(b)   Eighty per cent of the students at Universal University make grades of B or higher.   The grade C represents average work.

(c)   In a certain city last year, five times as many men as women were involved in automobile accidents.   These statistics prove women are the more careful drivers.

(d)   The average annual temperature for Tennessee is 58°; that of North Dakota is 39°.   Therefore in midsummer it is hotter in Tennessee than in North Dakota.

(e)   Mortality tables tell us that over five times as many Americans die at 40 years of age than at 80 years of age.   This proves that 80-year-olds are either healthier or more careful.

(f)   Mr. Brown sold two houses.   On one he made a 10 per cent profit and on the other a 20 per cent profit, for an average gain of 15 per cent.

(g)   The median nicotine content of cigarette A was found to be .85 per cent; that of cigarette B was .81 per cent.   Company B advertised that the results of this test proved conclusively that their cigarette is the less harmful.

2.   A factory manager and a union representative are attempting to determine the reasonable rate of production on a particular piecework job. The daily output of fourteen workers was checked, with the following number of pieces turned out: 111, 115, 116, 118, 118, 119, 122, 128, 128, 130, 135, 140, 152, 170.   Should they use the median or the mean in determining the production rate?

3.   In which of the following sets of measures is the median of any value? Is the median a better measure than the mean in any of them?
(a)   15, 17, 42, 20, 70, 35, 27, 40
(b)   1.8, 1.0, .9, .9, .5, .2, 1.5, 1.7, .6, 1.5, 1.4, .9, .9
(c)   221, 224, 218, 218, 222, 221, 216, 225, 220, 217, 219, 213, 230
(d)   18.6, 17.3, 18.4, 16.7, 17.9, 20.4, 19.3, 48.2, 53.1

4.   Will a concentration of extremely high scores in a distribution cause the mean or the median to be higher?

5.   The mean score of Section A, Math 100, was 79 and the median was 73. The mean score for Section B was 74 and the median 77.   What can you infer about the two classes?

THE WEIGHTED MEAN

10.6   There are times when each variate is not the same in importance.   The variates may then be *weighted* by assigning a number to each to indicate its relative importance.   In a certain factory the following hourly wages are paid: $1.25, $1.75, $2.00, $2.90.   What is the mean hourly wage?   The mean of the four hourly rates would not give a meaningful average unless the same number of hours is worked at each of the rates of pay. If we assume that each man works the same number of hours, we can assign weights to each rate which will indicate the proportion of the total force receiving that rate. If $\frac{1}{3} = \frac{4}{12}$ of the men receive $1.25, $\frac{1}{4} = \frac{3}{12}$ of them get $1.75, $\frac{1}{4} = \frac{3}{12}$ get $2.00, and the remaining $\frac{1}{6} = \frac{2}{12}$ receive $2.90, we assign the weights 4, 3, 3, and 2 respectively to the wage rates $1.25, $1.75, $2.00, $2.90. If N men are employed, the mean wage would be

$$\frac{\dfrac{N}{3} \times \$1.25 + \dfrac{N}{4} \times \$1.75 + \dfrac{N}{4} \times \$2.00 + \dfrac{N}{6} \times \$2.90}{N}$$

$$= \frac{\$1.25}{3} + \frac{\$1.75}{4} + \frac{\$2.00}{4} + \frac{\$2.90}{6}$$

$$= \frac{4 \times \$1.25 + 3 \times \$1.75 + 3 \times \$2.00 + 2 \times \$2.90}{12}$$

But the numerator is the summation of the products of each hourly wage times its weight and the denominator is the summation of the weights. The formula for the weighted mean $\overline{W}$ is

$$\overline{W} = \frac{\sum\limits_{i=1}^{N} W_i X_i}{\sum\limits_{i=1}^{N} W_i}$$

THE HARMONIC MEAN

*10.7   Another average that is sometimes used is the *harmonic mean*. The harmonic mean of a set of measures is the number whose reciprocal is the arithmetic mean of the reciprocals of the measures. Suppose we have measures 3, 3, 4, 5, 6, 9 whose reciprocals are $\frac{1}{3}, \frac{1}{3}, \frac{1}{4}, \frac{1}{5}, \frac{1}{6}, \frac{1}{9}$. The arithmetic mean of these reciprocals is

$$\frac{\frac{1}{3} + \frac{1}{3} + \frac{1}{4} + \frac{1}{5} + \frac{1}{6} + \frac{1}{9}}{6} = \frac{251}{1080}$$

Then the harmonic mean of the original set 3, 3, 4, 5, 6, 9 is $\frac{1080}{251}$. The usefulness of the harmonic mean is not immediately apparent.

It is a well-known fact that the value of a dollar is anything but constant. This economic principle has been recognized in labor-management agreements which provide for cost-of-living adjustments in wage rate.   In determining a cost-of-living index, it is more important to know how much bacon a dollar buys than what a pound of bacon costs.   Every merchant knows that by lowering the price sufficiently he can sell a given article.   The cost of an article is, in general, inversely related to the amount sold.

Suppose the cost of bacon for three consecutive months is 50¢, 60¢, and 85¢.   The mean cost for this period is 65¢.   But as the price advances consumption drops.   Consequently, the relative importance of this item in a cost-of-living index is less.   A more meaningful average would be obtained if we found the *weighted* mean.   At the above prices, a dollar will buy 2 pounds, $1\frac{2}{3}$ pounds, and $1\frac{3}{17}$ pounds of bacon respectively.   Then if we assign the weights of 2, $1\frac{2}{3}$, and $1\frac{3}{17}$ to the three prices, 50¢, 60¢, and 85¢, the weighted mean price of bacon for the three months is

$$\frac{2 \times 50 + 1\frac{2}{3} \times 60 + 1\frac{3}{17} \times 85}{2 + 1\frac{2}{3} + 1\frac{3}{17}} = \frac{300}{\frac{247}{51}} = \frac{15300}{247} = 62¢$$

The harmonic mean of the three prices is obtained by finding the mean of their reciprocals,

$$\frac{1}{3}\left(\frac{1}{50} + \frac{1}{60} + \frac{1}{85}\right) = \frac{247}{3(5100)}$$

and taking the reciprocal of the result

$$\frac{1}{\frac{247}{3(5100)}} = \frac{3(5100)}{247} = \frac{15300}{247} = 62¢$$

In general, the harmonic mean is equal to the weighted mean if the weights are inversely proportional to the variates.   If the variates a, b, c have weights $\frac{k}{a}, \frac{k}{b}, \frac{k}{c}$ their weighted mean is

$$\frac{a \cdot \frac{k}{a} + b \cdot \frac{k}{b} + c \cdot \frac{k}{c}}{\frac{k}{a} + \frac{k}{b} + \frac{k}{c}} = \frac{3k}{k\left(\frac{1}{a} + \frac{1}{b} + \frac{1}{c}\right)} = \frac{3}{\frac{1}{a} + \frac{1}{b} + \frac{1}{c}}$$

But the harmonic mean of a, b, c is

$$\frac{1}{\frac{1}{3}\left(\frac{1}{a} + \frac{1}{b} + \frac{1}{c}\right)} = \frac{3}{\frac{1}{a} + \frac{1}{b} + \frac{1}{c}}$$

———————— E X E R C I S E S ————————

1. If you travel 1 hour at 30 miles per hour, 1 hour at 40 miles per hour, and 1 hour at 50 miles per hour, what is your average speed? If you travel 100 miles at 30 miles per hour, 100 miles at 40 miles per hour, and 100 miles at 50 miles per hour, what is your average speed?

2. Find the arithmetic mean and the harmonic mean of the following:
    (a) 2, 4   (b) 1, 2, 3, 4, 5   (c) $\frac{1}{2}, \frac{1}{3}, \frac{1}{4}$

3. The average price per ton of coal for three consecutive years was $6, $8, $13. Find the average price per ton for the three-year interval assuming (a) the same amount of coal was purchased each year and (b) the amount purchased was inversely proportional to its price.

GROUPED DATA

10.8   If the number of variates is very large, computation of the mean and other statistical measures can be greatly facilitated by grouping the variates into a *frequency distribution*. Class intervals of equal widths are determined so that the class boundaries separate the variates. The number of classes is usually 12 to 15. Each variate is tallied in the class interval in which it falls. For example, if the boundaries of an interval are 74.5 and 79.5 all integral-valued variates that are 75 or greater but less than 80 are counted in the interval.

Table 10.1 illustrates the process of forming a frequency distribution. The intelligence scores of 283 freshmen are found to range from 96 to 143. The total span of the class intervals must be at least 47. This suggests a class width of 4. We use 13 intervals rather than 12 in order that the extreme scores may be near the center of the interval. The first 100 scores are indicated in the *tally* column. The *frequency* column shows the total 283 scores.

The figures in the class mark column are the mid-points of each interval. Once the frequency distribution is set up the identity of the individual scores is lost. All scores in an interval are considered to have the value of the class mark. This is equivalent to the assumption that the mid-point of each interval is the mean of the scores within it. The errors which this assumption introduces are random and tend to cancel each other out.

We may now find the mean of the scores by finding the weighted mean of the class marks. The class frequency is its weight. For

Table 10.1   Frequency distribution of intelligence scores of 283 freshmen.

Class mark	Class boundaries	Tally	Frequency
	93.5		
95.5		1	5
	97.5		
99.5		111	10
	101.5		
103.5		⊢⊢⊢ 1	28
	105.5		
107.5		⊢⊢⊢ ⊢⊢⊢ ⊢⊢⊢ 111	41
	109.5		
111.5		⊢⊢⊢ ⊢⊢⊢ ⊢⊢⊢ ⊢⊢⊢ ⊢⊢⊢ 1	76
	113.5		
115.5		⊢⊢⊢ ⊢⊢⊢ ⊢⊢⊢ 111	54
	117.5		
119.5		⊢⊢⊢ ⊢⊢⊢ 1111	23
	121.5		
123.5		⊢⊢⊢ 1	17
	125.5		
127.5		111	14
	129.5		
131.5		11	12
	133.5		
135.5		1	2
	137.5		
139.5			0
	141.5		
143.5		1	1
	145.5		

Table 10.2   Mean intelligence score of 283 freshmen.

Class mark	f	x	fx	Class mark	f	x	fx
95.5	5	-5	-25	123.5	17	2	34
99.5	10	-4	-40	127.5	14	3	42
103.5	28	-3	-84	131.5	12	4	48
107.5	41	-2	-82	135.5	2	5	10
111.5	76	-1	-76	139.5	0	6	0
115.5	54	0	0	143.5	1	7	7
119.5	23	1	23	Sums	283		-143

example, 95.5 has the weight 5, 119.5 has the weight 23. To find the mean we find the sum of the products of each class mark times its frequency and divide by the sum of the frequencies.

A further simplification may be obtained by a change of scale, Table 10.2. The f column gives the frequency of each class. We arbitrarily select some class mark as the assumed mean, in this case 115.5. The numbers in the x column indicate the deviations, *in interval steps*, of the classes from the assumed mean. We wish to find the weighted mean of the x deviations, the corresponding f being the weight. In the fx column we have the product of each deviation times its weight. The weighted mean of x is $\dfrac{f_i x_i}{f_i}$ or, in the example, $\dfrac{-143}{283}$. If this is multiplied by 4, the width of the interval, we have the correction which must be added to the assumed mean.

EXERCISES

1. If a class width of 5 units had been used with the data in Table 10.2 the following frequencies would have resulted. Compute the mean from the frequency distribution.

Class mark	95	100	105	110	115	120	125	130	135	140	145
Frequency	5	12	46	80	69	26	21	20	3	0	1

2. Construct a bar graph depicting the data in Exercise 1.

3. In terms of class marks what is the mode of the distribution in Exercise 1? What is the median if we assume the variates all evenly distributed in each class interval?

4. Determine whether the arithmetic mean or harmonic mean is the greater if the variates are
   (a) 6, 10, 12   (b) 1, 5, 7, 9   (c) 3, 5

5.* Prove: If a and b are positive numbers, $a \neq b$, their harmonic mean is less than their arithmetic mean.

MEASURES OF VARIABILITY

10.9 A mathematics class made the following grades on Test 1: 95, 85, 80, 75, 75, 75, 75, 70, 65, 65, 65, 55, 40, 40, 40. The mean grade is found to be 66.6, which we round off to 67. On Test 2 the same class made the following grades: 80, 75, 75, 75, 70, 70, 70, 70, 65, 65, 65, 60, 60, 55, 55.   The mean is again 67.   If we knew only the mean we would be apt to assume that the class did the same on each test.   This is obviously not the case.

There were both higher grades and lower grades on the first test. The second test shows less variability within the class.   Had each member of the class made 67 on the second test the instructor certainly would not have considered this performance comparable to that on the first test.   We need, in addition to a measure of central tendency, a statistical measure to indicate the extent to which the variates tend to spread out.   Such measures are called measures of *variability*.

The simplest measure of variability is the *range*.   It is merely the difference between the highest and lowest measures.   The range on the first test above is $95 - 40 = 55$.   On the second test the range is $80 - 55 = 25$.   This indicates considerably more variability on the first test.

Although the range is an easy and useful measure it has serious limitations.   Suppose our class takes a Test 3, with these results: 95, 90, 90, 90, 90, 85, 65, 60, 60, 50, 50, 50, 45, 40, 40.   Both the average, 67, and the range, 55, are the same as for the first test.   The range does not take into account how much each score varies from the point of central tendency, but merely the total over-all spread of the scores.   An isolated score at either extreme of the distribution of scores will unduly affect the range.   What is needed is a measure which takes into account the amount each measure deviates from the mean score.

A number of such measures have been devised; among them are the *mean deviation, variance,* and *standard deviation*.   We shall confine our attention to the most widely used of these, the standard deviation, denoted by the Greek letter sigma, σ.   The standard deviation not only is a very satisfactory measure of variability but it is extensively used in deriving other statistical measures.   *The standard deviation is the square root of the mean of the squares of the deviations of each score from their mean:*

$$\sigma = \sqrt{\frac{1}{N} \sum_{i=1}^{N} (X_i - \overline{X})^2}$$

This is not as formidable as it sounds.   We shall compute the standard deviations for the first and third test results given above.

Table 10.3   Scores, deviations, deviations squared,
for determination of standard deviation of Test 1.

Score	Deviation from mean = 66.6	Deviations squared
95	28.4	806.5
85	18.4	338.5
80	13.4	179.5
75	8.4	70.56
75	8.4	70.56
75	8.4	70.56
75	8.4	70.56
70	3.4	11.56
65	−1.6	2.56
65	−1.6	2.56
65	−1.6	2.56
55	−11.6	134.6
40	−26.6	724.2
40	−26.6	724.2
40	−26.6	724.2
N = 15		Total 3922.18

$$\sigma = \sqrt{\frac{3922.18}{15}} = 16.2$$

If we substitute the values from Table 10.3 in the standard deviation formula we get

$$\sigma = \sqrt{\frac{3922.18}{15}} = 16.2$$

as the standard deviation of the class scores on Test 1.   The values from Table 10.4 give

$$\sigma = \sqrt{\frac{6166.28}{15}} = 20.3$$

as the standard deviation of the scores on Test 3.   These two results indicate that the third test, with the higher standard deviation, gave more variable results than the first test.   That is, the scores on the third test had a greater tendency to diverge from the mean score and a greater tendency to make both high scores and low scores.   In general, a relatively small standard deviation indicates that the scores tend to cluster close to the mean and a relatively high one shows that the

Table 10.4   Scores, deviations, deviations squared,
for determination of standard deviation of Test 3.

Score	Deviation from mean = 66.6	Deviations squared
95	28.4	806.5
90	23.4	547.5
90	23.4	547.5
90	23.4	547.5
90	23.4	547.5
85	18.4	338.5
65	−1.6	2.56
60	−6.6	43.56
60	−6.6	43.56
50	−16.6	275.5
50	−16.6	275.5
50	−16.6	275.5
45	−21.6	466.7
40	−26.6	724.2
40	−26.6	724.2
$N = 15$		Total 6166.28

$$\sigma = \sqrt{\frac{6166.28}{15}} = 20.3$$

scores are widely scattered from the mean.   A more specific and more meaningful interpretation of the standard deviation will be possible after we have examined the *normal distribution.*

———————   E   X   E   R   C   I   S   E   S   ———————

1. Find the standard deviation of the distribution in Exercise 1, Section 10.8.

2. How many standard deviations below the mean is the lowest score in the distribution, Exercise 1, Section 10.8?   The highest score is how many standard deviations above the mean?

3. Prove: Each variate X_i is equal to $\overline{X}$ if and only if $\sigma = 0$.

4. Find σ for the following distribution:

X	1	2	3	4	5	6	7	8	9	10	11
F	5	5	5	5	5	5	5	5	5	5	5

5. A basketball player's individual scores were 16, 24, 21, 17, 10, 19, 23, 20, 15, and 12. What is his mean average per game? Find the standard deviation of the scores.

6. The following grades were made in a class of 25 students. Find the median, mean, mode, range, and standard deviation of these grades: 98, 65, 90, 80, 85, 70, 75, 60, 90, 80, 85, 70, 74, 88, 91, 65, 72, 78, 83, 70, 90, 60, 75, 76, 50.

7. A machine turns out six-inch bolts. Samples taken at intervals through the day were measured with a micrometer with the following results: 6.03, 6.05, 5.99, 5.96, 6.02, 6.06, 5.95, 5.98, 6.08, 6.02, 5.94, 5.98, 6.01, 6.00, 6.04, 5.97, 6.07. Find the mean and standard deviation of this sample.

STANDARD DEVIATION DETERMINED FROM GROUPED DATA

10.10 The formula for the standard deviation may be expressed in another form than that given in the preceding section.

If we expand the binomial square we get

$$\sigma = \sqrt{\frac{1}{N} \sum_{i=1}^{N} (X_i^2 - 2X_i\bar{X} + \bar{X}^2)}$$

$$= \sqrt{\frac{1}{N} \left(\sum_{i=1}^{N} X_i^2 - 2\bar{X} \sum_{i=1}^{N} X_i + N\bar{X}^2 \right)}$$

But since $\bar{X} = \dfrac{\sum X_i}{N}$ or $\sum X_i = NX$, by substituting for $\sum X_i$

$$\sigma = \sqrt{\frac{1}{N} \left(\sum_{i=1}^{N} X_i^2 - N\bar{X}^2 \right)}$$

$$= \sqrt{\sum_{i=1}^{N} \frac{X_i^2}{N} - \bar{X}^2}$$

If we express this result as the deviation of step interval scores from a frequency distribution we have

$$\sigma = \sqrt{\frac{\sum f_i x_i^2}{\sum f_i} - \left(\frac{\sum f_i x_i}{\sum f_i} \right)^2}$$

The standard deviation may now be computed from a frequency distribution by adding one column, fx^2, to the table for computing the mean, Table 10.2, Section 10.8. Table 10.5 illustrates the process.

Table 10.5   Computation of standard deviation from grouped data.

Class marks	f	x	fx	fx^2	Class marks	f	x	fx	fx^2
95.5	5	−5	−25	125	123.5	17	2	34	68
99.5	10	−4	−40	160	127.5	14	3	42	126
103.5	28	−3	−84	252	131.5	12	4	48	192
107.5	41	−2	−82	164	135.5	2	5	10	50
111.5	76	−1	−76	76	139.5	0	6	0	0
115.5	54	0	0	0	143.5	1	7	7	49
119.5	23	1	23	23	Sums	283		−143	1285

$$\text{Mean} = 113.5$$

$$\sigma = 4\sqrt{\frac{1285}{283} - \left(\frac{-143}{283}\right)^2}$$

$$\sigma = 8.3$$

Since the formula gives the standard deviation in step interval scores, the result must be multiplied by the interval width — 4 in the example — to convert the result to the original scale.

PROBABILITY

10.11 If you toss an unweighted coin the odds are even (1 to 1) that it will fall heads.   The correct odds that an honest die will land with any one of its six faces up are 1 to 5, one favorable chance to five unfavorable.   Probability is not defined in the same way as are betting odds.

Definition   If an event can occur in N equally likely ways, S of which are favorable, the probability, P, of a favorable event is S/N.

Betting odds are the ratio of success to failure.   Probability is the ratio of success to success plus failure.   The probability that a tossed coin will land heads up is $\frac{1}{2}$.   The probability that a die will land with a given face up is $\frac{1}{6}$.   The range of possible values of P is 0 to 1.   If none of the events are favorable, $P = 0/N = 0$.   A probability of zero means certain failure.   If all N events are successful, $P = N/N = 1$. A probability of 1 indicates certain success.

Example 1   What is the probability of drawing an ace or a king in one draw from a deck of 52 cards?

Solution: Since there are 4 aces and 4 kings in the deck, $P = \frac{8}{52} = \frac{2}{13}$.

Example 2   What is the probability of drawing an ace and a king in drawing 2 cards from a deck?

Solution: We can draw an ace in any one of 4 ways and with each of these, a king in any one of 4 ways.   Then we can draw an ace and then a king in $4 \times 4 = 16$ ways.   But we might draw a king and then an ace.   This can be done in 16 ways.   A favorable event may occur in $16 + 16 = 32$ ways. The total number of events is 52×51 since we may draw any one of 52 cards and then any one of the 51 remaining cards on the second draw. The probability of drawing an ace and a king is then

$$P = \frac{32}{52 \times 51} = \frac{8}{663}$$

Example 3   A drawer contains 6 black and 6 white socks.   If two socks are drawn at random, what is the probability that a pair is drawn?

Solution: We may draw a black sock in 6 ways, then a black in 5 ways, or a black pair in $6 \times 5 = 30$ ways.   We may draw a white pair in 30 ways more.   Then a successful event may occur in 60 ways.   The total number of events is 12×11 since we may draw any one of 12 socks and then any one of the 11 remaining socks.   Therefore

$$P = \frac{60}{12 \times 11} = \frac{5}{11}$$

A Simpler Analysis: Regardless of the color drawn first it must be matched on the second draw.   There are 5 more socks of the same color as that drawn first, and there are 11 more socks altogether.   Then the drawing of the second sock may occur in 11 ways, 5 of which are successful.   The probability of success is $\frac{5}{11}$.

There are rules for counting involving *permutations* and *combinations* which are quite helpful in more complicated problems of probability. These are discussed in any good college algebra book.

The above examples are illustrations of *mathematical probability*. We can predict the probability through an analysis of the possibilities of occurrence of events all of which are equally likely.   This is called *a priori probability*, probability at a prior time.   In statistics we are just as concerned with *empirical* or *a posteriori probability*.   This probability is based on past experience.   If we toss a coin 10,000 times and get 5,100 heads and 4,900 tails, the a posteriori probability that the coin would fall heads is $\frac{51}{100}$.   We would not expect the coin to fall heads one time and tails one time every time a coin is tossed twice. We would not be surprised if we got heads quite a few times in succession.   But as the number of tosses becomes very large, we would expect the ratio of heads to the total tosses to approach the predicted value $\frac{1}{2}$ more and more closely.   If we are to place much confidence in empirical probability we must have many cases.   There are, however, many practical situations in which it is impossible to make a mathematical prediction and empirical probability is essential.   The professional gambler's stock in trade is a priori probability.   His odds are not determined by the past performance of a given pair of dice or a roulette wheel.   It has been aptly said that "dice have no memory." However, life insurance companies have a different problem when they set the rates for an insurance policy.   We cannot calculate in advance the probability that a 35-year-old man will survive for 20 years in the same manner that we can determine the probability that an 11 will be obtained from one throw of a pair of dice.   The insurance company obtains its probability from past experience with similar 35-year-olds. The *American Experience Mortality Table* is based on years of experience with many insured persons.   The table shows the number of persons still living, of an original 100,000 aged 10, at each age above 10 years. The number dying each year is also given.   The table shows 81,822 of the original 100,000 still living at age 35.   At age 55 there are 64,563 still living.   On the basis of these figures the probability that a 35-year-old will live for at least 20 years is 64,563/81,822.   It is upon information of this kind that life insurance premium rates are based.   New evidence has accumulated which is at variance with the table.   In 1941 a new mortality table, the *Commissioners 1941 Standard Ordinary Mortality Table*, was adopted.   It showed some changes in life expectancy and caused some adjustments in rates.   Automobile liability rates are set in a similar manner.   A marked change in the accident rate will quickly be reflected in a corresponding change in the premium rate.

————————— E   X   E   R   C   I   S   E   S —————————

1.   What is the probability of drawing a heart when drawing one card from a deck of 52 playing cards?

2.   What is the probability of "filling a flush" in hearts, that is, drawing a heart in one draw when you are holding four hearts and one nonheart? (Since you can see only your own hand, assume that you draw one card from $52 - 5 = 47$ cards.)

3.   A drawer contains 6 black and 6 white socks.   If the room is totally dark and you put on two socks from the drawer, what is the probability that you do not have on a pair?

4.   Three couples sit at a table which is round.   They are seated at random, except that the boys and girls alternate.   If you are in the party, what is the probability that you are seated next to your partner?   What is the probability that each person in the party is next to his partner? What is the probability that no one will be next to his partner?

5.   Why is it impossible for the probability of an event to be 2?

6.   Distinguish between a priori probability and empirical probability. Which is the primary concern of the statistician?   Why?

7.   According to the *Commissioners 1941 Standard Ordinary Mortality Table*, of 1,000,000 persons at age 1 there will be 906,554 living at age 35.   Of these 4,161 will die within a year.
(a)   What is the probability that a 1-year-old will live to be at least 35 years old?
(b)   What is the probability of dying during one's thirty-sixth year?
(c)   What is the probability that a 35-year-old will die within a year?

8.   Tom flips a coin to see whether he goes fishing or mows the lawn.   If it lands heads, he goes fishing.   Since he is going fishing anyway, he flips until he gets heads.   What is the probability that he must flip exactly 3 times?

THE BINOMIAL THEOREM

10.12 The following results may be verified by direct multiplication:

$$(a + b)^0 = 1$$
$$(a + b)^1 = a + b$$
$$(a + b)^2 = a^2 + 2ab + b^2$$
$$(a + b)^3 = a^3 + 3a^2b + 3ab^2 + b^3$$
$$(a + b)^4 = a^4 + 4a^3b + 6a^2b^2 + 4ab^3 + b^4$$
$$(a + b)^5 = a^5 + 5a^4b + 10a^3b^2 + 10a^2b^3 + 5ab^4 + b^5$$

A number of facts may be observed:

1.   The power to which the binomial $(a + b)$ is raised is always one less than the number of terms in the expansion.   For example, the expansion of $(a + b)^3$ has *four* terms, the expansion of $(a + b)^5$ has *six* terms.

2.   The exponent of a decreases by 1 from term to term, starting with the exponent of $(a + b)^n$ and ending with zero.   The first term in the expansion of $(a + b)^4$ is a^4.   The last term may be thought of as a^0b^4.

3.   The exponent of b increases by 1 from term to term, starting with zero and ending with the exponent of $(a + b)^n$.

4.   The sum of the exponents of a and b in any term of the expansion of $(a + b)^n$ is n.

5.   The coefficients are arranged symmetrically; the first and last terms have coefficients 1, coefficients of the second and next to last terms are always the same as the exponent of $(a + b)^n$.

6.   Each coefficient after the first may be determined from the preceding term as follows.   The exponent of a in any term times the coefficient of the term divided by the number of the term (first, second, third, and so on) gives the coefficient of the next term.   For example, the coefficient of the third term of the expansion of $(a + b)^4$ may be obtained from the *second* term, $4a^3b$, as $(3 \times 4)/2$.

If we assume these properties hold for any value of n we can write the expansion of the binomial $(a + b)^n$:

$$(a + b)^n = a^n + \frac{n}{1} a^{n-1}b + \frac{n(n - 1)}{1 \cdot 2} a^{n-2}b^2 +$$

$$\frac{n(n - 1)(n - 2)}{1 \cdot 2 \cdot 3} a^{n-3}b^3 +$$

$$\cdots \frac{n(n - 1)(n - 2) \cdots (n - r + 2)}{1 \cdot 2 \cdot 3 \cdot \cdots (r - 1)} a^{n-r+1}b^{r-1} +$$

$$\cdots + \frac{n(n - 1) \cdots 1}{1 \cdot 2 \cdot 3 \cdot \cdots n} a^0 b^n$$

THE BINOMIAL, n, NOT A POSITIVE INTEGER

10.13 We can prove by mathematical induction that the expansion of the binomial given in Section 10.12 is correct for all positive integral values of n.   When n is negative or fractional, the expansion becomes endless, it never terminates.   Do you see why?   If this infinite series converges our formula is still correct.   We shall not attempt to state the conditions under which the binomial series converges.   However, it is necessary but not sufficient for succeeding terms of the series to get smaller if the series is to converge (see Section 8.15).   We know that $(1 + 1)^{-1} = \frac{1}{2}$ but if we attempt to expand $(1 + 1)^{-1}$ according to the binomial theorem we get

$$(1 + 1)^{-1} = 1^{-1} + (-1) \cdot 1^{-2} \cdot 1 + \frac{(-1)(-2)}{2} 1^{-3} \cdot 1^2 +$$

$$\frac{(-1)(-2)(-3)}{1 \cdot 2 \cdot 3} 1^{-4} \cdot 1^3 + \cdots = 1 - 1 + 1 - 1 + \cdots$$

This is a series which does not converge.

On the other hand, we get a convergent series and can approximate the square root of 10 nicely if we apply the expansion to $(9 + 1)^{\frac{1}{2}}$.

$$(9 + 1)^{\frac{1}{2}} = 9^{\frac{1}{2}} + \frac{1}{2} \cdot 9^{-\frac{1}{2}} \cdot 1 + \frac{\frac{1}{2}(-\frac{1}{2})}{2} 9^{-\frac{3}{2}} \cdot 1^2 + \cdots$$
$$= 3 + \frac{1}{6} - \frac{1}{216} + \cdots$$
$$= 3.16$$

─────── E X E R C I S E S ───────

1. Expand $(H + T)^7$.

2. Find, without expanding, the term of the expansion of $(a + b)^8$ which contains a^5.

3. Find 99^3 by expanding $(100 - 1)^3$.

4. Find the sum of the coefficients in the expansion of $(a + b)^4$; of $(a + b)^5$. Compare these results with 2^4 and 2^5.

5. Find $\sqrt{2}$ to three digits by expanding $(1 + 1)^{\frac{1}{2}}$.

6. Find $\sqrt[5]{11}$ to three significant digits.

7. Find 9^{-7} to three significant digits by expanding $(10 - 1)^{-7}$.

8. Use logarithms to check Exercises 5, 6, and 7.

BINOMIAL DISTRIBUTION

10.14 If we write the coefficients of the expansion of $(a + b)^n$, where n is a non-negative integer, in the triangular array

$$
\begin{array}{ccccccc}
 & & & 1 & & & \\
 & & 1 & & 1 & & \\
 & & 1 & 2 & 1 & & \\
 & 1 & 3 & 3 & 1 & & \\
 1 & 4 & 6 & 4 & 1 & & \\
 - & 5 & - & 10 & - & 1 & \\
\end{array}
$$

· · · · · · ·

the result is known as Pascal's Triangle. The top row contains the coefficients in the expansion of $(a + b)^0$. The numbers in the second row are the coefficients in the expansion of $(a + b)^1$. The third row has the coefficients of the expansion of $(a + b)^2$. Generalizing, the nth row contains the coefficients of the expansion of $(a + b)^{n-1}$. Compare this with the expansions on page 334.   It is a simple matter to continue the triangle for any desired number of rows.   Notice that each number except the top 1 is the sum of the numbers immediately above and to the right and left.   To illustrate:

The sixth row is partially filled.   The 5 is the sum of the 4 and the 1 immediately above and to the right and left.   The 10 is obtained from the 6 and the right-hand 4 in the line above.   Since there is no number to the right of the 1, our procedure requires that the number to its left in the line above, namely 1, be placed there.

Do you see why the sum of the numbers in any row must be two times as great as the sum in the row above?   The outside diagonals always consist of 1's.   All other numbers can be found by adding two consecutive numbers in the row above and placing the sum midway between them in the next row.   The triangle will give the correct sequence of coefficients in the expansion of any positive integral power of the binomial $(a + b)$.

The binomial theorem has many interesting and useful applications. Suppose we toss two coins.   They may fall 2 heads, 1 head and 1 tail, or 2 tails.   The probabilities of each combination's appearing on any one toss are $\frac{1}{4}$, $\frac{1}{2}$, and $\frac{1}{4}$ respectively.   Suppose we toss a dime and a cent. The dime can fall either of two ways, then the cent can fall either of two ways, making a total of four ways (heads-heads, heads-tails, tails-heads, tails-tails).   If we toss the coins four times, the most likely occurrence would be 2 heads one time, 1 head and 1 tail two times, and 2 tails one time.   Similarly, if we toss three coins we may get 3 heads, 2 heads and 1 tail, 1 head and 2 tails, or 3 tails.   The first of the three coins can fall heads or tails, so can the second, and then the third. We have a total of eight possibilities: $H_1H_2H_3$, $H_1H_2T_3$, $H_1T_2H_3$, $H_1T_2T_3$, $T_1H_2H_3$, $T_1H_2T_3$, $T_1T_2H_3$, $T_1T_2T_3$, where the subscript indicates the identity of each coin.   If the three coins are tossed eight times, the most likely occurrence will be 3 heads one time, 2 heads and 1 tail three times, 1 head and 2 tails three times, and 3 tails one time.   These frequencies, 1, 2, 1 and 1, 3, 3, 1 are the coefficients of the expansions of the binomials $(a + b)^2$ and $(a + b)^3$.   In fact, the coefficients of the expansion of $(a + b)^n$ give the frequency of occurrence of n, $n - 1$, $n - 2, \ldots 1$ heads when n coins are tossed 2^n times, 2^n being the sum of the coefficients of the terms of the expansion of $(a + b)^n$.   We shall prove this to be true in a later exercise.   They are the *relative* frequencies of the occurrence of these events regardless of the number of tosses.

THE NORMAL DISTRIBUTION

10.15 If we toss five coins simultaneously all five may fall heads, or we may get 4 heads and 1 tail, 3 heads and 2 tails, 2 heads and 3 tails, 1 head and 4 tails, or no heads and 5 tails. Let us examine the terms of the expansion of $(H + T)^5$:

$$(H + T)^5 = H^5 + 5H^4T + 10H^3T^2 + 10H^2T^3 + 5HT^4 + T^5$$

The sum of the coefficients is

$$1 + 5 + 10 + 10 + 5 + 1 = 32 = 2^5$$

If we toss five coins 32 times these coefficients give the theoretical number of times we shall get the various combinations of heads and tails. For example, the coefficient 1 in the first term indicates that we should get 5 heads (the exponent of H is 5 in the first term) on one of the 32 tosses. We should expect 4 heads five times, 3 heads ten times, 2 heads ten times, 1 head five times, and no heads one time. Of course we would not expect to get exactly the number of occurrences indicated above in 32 tosses. But we would be quite surprised if we got all heads every other time and all tails the rest of the time. In fact, we would expect our results to approximate those given above. The more times the coins were tossed the more closely we would expect the ratio of frequency of occurrence to agree with the theoretical frequencies. The predicted relative frequencies may be stated in terms of probability. Since we expect to get 5 heads one time in 32, the probability of doing so on any toss is $\frac{1}{32}$. The probability of getting 4 heads is $\frac{5}{32}$, 3 heads $\frac{10}{32}$, 2 heads $\frac{10}{32}$, 1 head $\frac{5}{32}$, and no heads $\frac{1}{32}$.

Conclusions similar to the above may be drawn when $(H + T)^5$ is replaced with $(H + T)^n$, where n is a positive number. If n coins are tossed the probability of n heads is $1/2^n$, the probability of $n - 1$ heads is $n/2^n$, the probability of $n - 2$ heads is $\dfrac{n(n - 1)/2}{2^n}$, and so on.

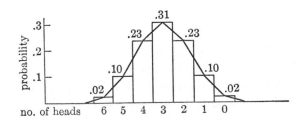

Figure 10.1 Theoretical distribution of number of heads when six coins are tossed simultaneously.

The numerators are the coefficients of the terms of the expansion of $(H + T)^n$ and the denominator is the fixed value of 2^n.

The bar graph, Figure 10.1, shows the probability of getting 6, 5, 4, ... 0 heads when six coins are tossed. The expansion of $(H + T)^6$ is

$$(H + T)^6 = H^6 + 6H^5T + 15H^4T^2 + 20H^3T^3 +$$
$$15H^2T^4 + 6HT^5 + T^6$$

The sum of these coefficients is $2^6 = 64$. The probability of 6 heads is $\frac{1}{64}$, 5 heads $\frac{6}{64}$, 4 heads $\frac{15}{64}$, 3 heads $\frac{20}{64}$, 2 heads $\frac{15}{64}$, 1 head $\frac{6}{64}$, and no heads $\frac{1}{64}$. The sum of these probabilities is

$$\tfrac{1}{64} + \tfrac{6}{64} + \tfrac{15}{64} + \tfrac{20}{64} + \tfrac{15}{64} + \tfrac{6}{64} + \tfrac{1}{64} = \tfrac{64}{64} = 1$$

which is what we expect since the occurrence of some one of the above events is certain.

The bar graph of Figure 10.1 is called a *histogram*. Since the sum of the above probabilities is unity, so is the sum of the areas of the rectangles in the histogram. The rectangles are of equal widths, each width representing unity, and have heights corresponding to the different probabilities. If we join the mid-points of the tops of successive rectangles, the resultant broken-line graph is known as a *frequency polygon*. If we extend the broken-line graph to the mid-points of the next intervals beyond the histogram on the base line, the area of the frequency polygon will be unity, since equal triangles will have been added to and subtracted from the histogram.

Regardless of the value we assign to n in $(H + T)^n$, the sum of the probabilities of n, $n - 1$, ... 0 heads will be unity. As n increases without limit, the polygon of area unity will approach a smooth curve which is the graph of the normal density function, or what is called the *normal curve*. As is true of all the binomial distributions we have examined, the mean, median, and mode are identical. For instance, in $(H + T)^6$, 3 heads and 3 tails occurred 20 times — more than did any other combination; therefore the "score" of 3 heads is the mode. But it is also at the middle of the distribution; it is the median. And since the distribution is perfectly symmetrical it is also the mean. It will be observed that the curve is approximately bell-shaped, it is symmetric with respect to the mean, and it approaches, but does not touch, the base line at its extremes.

If the average weight of American men is 165 pounds, we would expect to find fewer men weighing 265 pounds than 170 pounds. In general, the further from the mean a given weight is, the fewer men we would expect to find having that weight. However, the distribution of men's weights is found to approach very near to the normal distribution. Numerous examples of distributions found in nature conform to this pattern. It is for this reason that it is called the *normal* distribution. It is a basic assumption in statistical analysis that differences due to chance errors tend to distribute themselves normally. However, it should be observed that a nonnormal distribution is not prima facie abnormal. Many important distributions fail to approximate the normal distribution.

It is beyond our scope here to derive the normal curve analytically or to establish a proof for its properties. However, there is a close connection between it and the standard deviation, one which we shall state without proof. For a normal distribution, scores one standard deviation above and one standard deviation below the mean will include approximately two-thirds of all the scores of the distribution; the standard deviation becomes much more meaningful as a measure of variability.

Let us return to the test results for which we computed the standard deviation (Section 10.9). On the first test, the standard deviation of 16.2 means that if the distribution is normal about two-thirds of the scores will be found between 50.4 and 82.8. In this case, 10 of the 15 scores are within this range. On the third test, about two-thirds of the scores should be found between 46.4 and 86.8. Even with this larger standard deviation, we find in this case only 7 of the 15 scores in this range. Not only are the results of the third test more variable than those of the first test, but they are much further from a normal distribution.

One of the most persistent misconceptions concerning statistics relates to the normal distribution. Some people seem to think that any sample must distribute itself normally, relative to any characteristic. There is no basis for assuming normality in a sample unless variations in the trait measured are due to chance. This implies that the inclusion or exclusion of an individual in the sample is a matter of chance. Furthermore, the sample must be relatively large if we expect to get an accurate representation of the total population. There is no reason to expect a small, highly selective group to form a normal distribution. Some educators assume that the grades earned in each class must be distributed into the various grade classifications in a predetermined proportion. Such a Procrustean procedure requires that standards of performance be determined after the course is completed.

———————   E   X   E   R   C   I   S   E   S   ———————

1. Determine the theoretical distribution of heads when six coins at a time are tossed 64 times.   Construct a histogram showing your results.

2. Toss six coins at a time 64 times and tabulate the number of heads on each toss.   Superimpose a histogram over that of the above exercise, showing the results of these tosses.

3. Combine your results with those of nine other members of the class, divide the frequencies by ten, and compare with your results and the theoretical distribution.

4. Complete Pascal's Triangle to eight rows.

5. Notice that the outside diagonal of Pascal's Triangle consists of all 1's and the second diagonal consists of the consecutive integers.   The third diagonal consists of what is known as triangular numbers:

$$(1, \quad 3, \quad 6, \quad 10, \quad \text{etc.})$$

Can you infer from this what kind of number the sum of the first n consecutive integers is?

6. Prove by mathematical induction that $1 + 2 + 3 + \ldots + n = n(n + 1)/2$.

7. Start at any diagonal and add down the diagonal as far as you wish. Where do you find this sum?

8. The sum of the numbers in the first row is 1, in the second row $1 + 1 = 2$, in the third row $1 + 2 + 1 = 4$.   Find the sums of the numbers in each of the first eight rows.   What can you infer about the sum of the numbers in the nth row?

9. Prove the sum of the coefficients in the expansion of $(a + b)^n$ equals 2^n, assuming that Pascal's Triangle always yields the correct coefficients.

STANDARD ERROR

10.16 The standard error is another statistical measure which one frequently encounters in reading.   Although the standard error of the mean is a standard deviation, it should not be confused with the standard deviation of the scores of the sample.   Its significance can best be illustrated with an example.   Suppose from a random sample of 1,000 men we find their mean height to be 68.3 inches.   This distribution has a standard deviation of 4.1 inches.   If we select one of the 1,000 men at random, about two times in three the individual selected will have a height of between 64.2 and 72.4 inches. If we select another random sample of 1,000 men, the mean and standard deviation of this sample will be very likely to differ from the first. In fact, if we continue to get very many such samples, the means of all these samples will themselves constitute a distribution. Now, the sample of 1,000 men is supposed to be a miniature of the total population from which it is drawn. But how good a miniature of the total population is it? If we had a distribution of the means of many such samples and could obtain the standard deviation of this distribution of means, then we should have a basis for judging how much reliance could be placed on the sample. However, it is usually not feasible to obtain a large number of samples. What is needed is a measure obtainable from a single sample which will give some indication of how well it represents the total population. The standard error of the mean, written $\sigma_{\bar{x}}$, is such a measure. It may be interpreted as the standard deviation of a distribution of means of many samples drawn from the population. The standard error of the mean of the above sample is .13; that is, the chances are two in three that the mean height of the total population from which the sample was drawn differs from the obtained mean of 68.3 by not more than .13, or the true mean lies between 68.17 and 68.43 inches. The chances are better than 99 in 100 that the mean of the population lies between 67.91 and 68.69 inches. This result is usually written 68.3 ± .39, meaning that the true mean is the obtained mean plus or minus three times its standard error. The standard error, as well as many other statistical measures, can be found from the standard deviation. We give without proof the formula for the standard error of the mean,

$$\sigma_{\bar{x}} = \frac{\sigma_{\text{pop}}}{\sqrt{N}}$$

where σ_{pop} is the standard deviation of the population from which the sample comes. However, since we usually do not know the standard deviation of the population we may estimate, using the standard deviation of the sample. The formula then becomes

$$\sigma_{\bar{x}} = \frac{\sigma}{\sqrt{N - 1}}$$

The use of $N - 1$ instead of N is relatively unimportant when N is large.

CORRELATION

*10.17 Up to this point our discussion of statistical measures has been
concerned with the analysis of a single group of variates.   Most
practical applications of statistics are not as simple; very likely a
statistical problem will be concerned with more than one group and
more than one characteristic.   The idea of correlation is of fundamental importance in many statistical problems.   Although there are
numerous extensions of the concept of correlation we shall confine our
discussion to its simplest aspect.

Suppose a group of students is given a test in mathematics and a
test in reading.   Is there any relationship between the two sets of
grades?   We would expect some relationship to exist.   In general, we
might expect those students who scored high on one of the tests to score
high on the other.   Correlation is a measure that indicates the extent to
which this trend, or the reverse, occurs.   Table 10.6 gives the grades

Table 10.6   Mathematics achievement and
reading grades made by a group of students.

Student	Mathematics	Reading	Student	Mathematics	Reading
A	80	75	I	86	75
B	60	80	J	70	65
C	93	89	K	75	85
D	55	60	L	60	50
E	85	70	M	85	90
F	65	83	N	90	80
G	95	95	O	65	70
H	73	82	P	70	85

which a group of students made on the mathematics test and the
reading test.

If a perfect relationship existed between the two sets of scores, the person
who made the highest score on one test
would be highest on the other, another
student would be second highest on
both tests, and so on.

Figure 10.2 shows a *scatter diagram.*
Each individual's scores are indicated
by a point, located so that its distance
along each axis corresponds to the scores
of the two tests.   For example, student

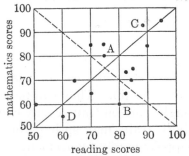

Figure 10.2 Scatter diagram of the
scores given in Table 10.6.

A made a score of 80 in mathematics and 75 in reading. Point A is located on the diagram by going out the horizontal (reading) scale to 75 and then up, parallel with the mathematics scale, to 80. The first four students' points are labeled in the diagram.

If all the points of the diagram fell on a straight line, a perfect (linear) relationship would exist between the two traits. Two traits could be so related that a high score on one trait implied a low score on the other. In this case they would be correlated negatively. All points would be on a line sloping downward, the dotted line in Figure 10.2. The value of the correlation coefficients ranges from $+1$ to -1. A coefficient $+1$ indicates a perfect correlation between the two traits; -1 indicates a perfect negative relationship, highest on one trait implying lowest on the other; and so on. A coefficient of zero implies the absence of a linear relationship between the two traits.

The formula for the coefficient of correlation, which we shall not derive here, may be expressed in terms of both the mean and the standard deviation of both sets of scores. The coefficient of correlation, r, is given by

$$ r = \frac{1}{N} \sum \frac{(X_i - \overline{X})}{\sigma_X} \frac{(Y_i - \overline{Y})}{\sigma_Y} $$

Each of the two factors, $\dfrac{X_i - \overline{X}}{\sigma_X}$ and $\dfrac{Y_i - \overline{Y}}{\sigma_Y}$, expresses each score as the number of standard deviations it lies from its mean. The correlation coefficient is itself a mean. It is the mean of the products of each X score times the corresponding Y score, the scores expressed in standard deviation units.

INTERPRETATION OF CORRELATION

*10.18 Caution should be exercised in interpreting a correlation coefficient. The existence of a high correlation does not establish the existence of a cause and effect relationship between the two traits. The coefficients can only state quantitatively the existence of a co-relationship. They can never explain *why* the relationship exists. A high score on trait A may cause a high score on trait B, high scores on both traits may spring from a common cause, or the situation may appear purely by accident.

What is a "high" correlation coefficient? There is no pat answer to this question. We must rely on past experience in making our in-

terpretation.   It has been found that mental traits tend to agree rather
well.   If a reasonably large group were given two different intelligence
tests, an *r* of .90 would not be considered unusually high.   On the
other hand, if we obtained the shoe sizes and number of coins of change
in the pockets of the first 100 men we met on the street, we would
attribute to pure chance a correlation coefficient which differed very
much from zero.

——————————   E   X   E   R   C   I   S   E   S   ——————————

1.   A group of boys has a mean intelligence quotient of 103.9 with standard
deviation of 10.3.   The chances are one in six that a boy selected at
random has an I.Q. above what figure?

2.   Find the standard error of the mean in Exercise 1 if there are 100 boys
in the group; 25 boys; 1,000 boys.   In which of these three cases, if any,
can we be almost certain (99 times in 100) that the true mean of the
population from which the samples were taken is not over 105?

3.   The average life of a certain type of light bulb is 1,025 hours, standard
deviation 115 hours.   What is the minimum life you can expect from
such a bulb, 99 times in 100?

4.   If a group of 100 students have weights and intelligence quotients which
have a correlation coefficient of $-.75$, can you conclude that the smaller
a person is the smarter he is?   How would you expect these two traits
to correlate?

5.   Would you expect a high or low correlation between keenness of vision
and marksmanship?   Discuss the possibilities.

The difference between analytic geometry and synthetic geometry?

We can define a point as a pair of numbers?

The Pythagorean Theorem is not necessarily true?

How many kinds of curve you can get if you let a plane intersect a cone?

There are geometries in which a triangle does not have an angle sum of 180°?

There are geometries in which there is no such thing as a square?

A line may have only seven points on it?

There is such a thing as parallel points?

There is more than one geometry that describes physical space?

Geometries need not pertain at all to physical space?

CHAPTER XI

GEOMETRIC SYSTEMS

In Chapter I a mathematical system was described as consisting of (1) *undefined terms*, (2) *axioms*, (3) *defined terms*, and (4) *theorems*. As we have seen in our study of groups and fields, these four categories include *relations* such as equality and order, and *operations* such as addition and multiplication.

In this chapter we shall examine geometry as a deductive system. Prior to the Greek era, geometry consisted of mensuration formulas, empirically determined and often incorrect. The Greeks made geometry a deductive science. Even so, at that time axioms were "self-evident truths." There was no doubt that Euclid's conclusions were *the* true description of physical space. The seventeenth century saw the advent of *analytic geometry*, which enables one to apply algebraic techniques to geometric problems and geometric techniques to algebraic problems. But it was not until the nineteenth century that geometry was freed from physical space. Geometry is now a completely abstract system concerned, not with truth, but with validity. The earlier physical geometry is now merely a model for some abstract geometric system.

ANALYTIC GEOMETRY

11.1 In the early seventeenth century two French mathematicians, Pierre Fermat and René Descartes, independently hit upon an idea which is one of the most important landmarks in the history of mathematics. Essentially, the idea was the isomorphism between real number pairs and points in a plane. Since we can associate each ordered pair of real numbers with a unique point in the plane, it is possible to picture geometrically a relation between the real variables x and y. We have seen this technique utilized in our study of functions and equations. This makes it possible to attack algebraic problems geometrically.

Suppose, for example, we wish to find the real simultaneous solutions of the system of equations

$$\begin{cases} x^2 + y^2 = 25 \\ x - y = 4 \end{cases}$$

Careful plotting of representative (x, y) pairs which satisfy the relation $x^2 + y^2 = 25$ is sufficient to suggest that its graph is a circle whose center is the origin.

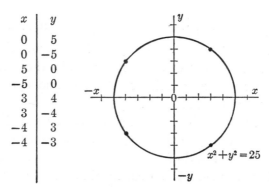

x	y
0	5
0	-5
5	0
-5	0
3	4
3	-4
-4	3
-4	-3

If we graph the relation $x - y = 4$ on the same axes,

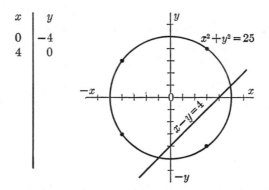

x	y
0	-4
4	0

we may obtain the approximate solution of the algebraic problem by determining the coordinates of the points of intersection of the two geometric figures. Since the coordinates of each point on the circle satisfy its equation and the coordinates of each point on the line satisfy *its* equation, the points common to both must satisfy both equations.

Furthermore, every real (x, y) pair which satisfies $x^2 + y^2 = 25$ defines a point on the circle, and every real (x, y) pair which satisfies $x - y = 4$ defines a point on the line (extended beyond the bounds of its graph if necessary). Then we may conclude that the two points of intersection represent the *only* real solutions of the system.

The correspondence between real number pairs and points of the plane also makes it possible to attack geometric problems algebraically.

"Point" and "line" are usually undefined elements of geometry. We can, however, define both in terms of number.

Definition 1   A point is an ordered pair of real numbers, (x, y).

Definition 2   A line is an ordered ratio of three real numbers, $a : b : c$, where a, b are not both zero.

By Definition 2, the ratio $2 : 3 : 5$ defines a line. But $4 : 6 : 10$ is the same line because $2 : 3 = 4 : 6$ and $3 : 5 = 6 : 10$. We may say, in general, that the triple $(a : b : c)$ and the triple $(ka : kb : kc)$, where k is an arbitrary nonzero constant, define the same line.

These definitions do not relieve us of the necessity of undefined elements; we have merely shifted to the undefined elements in the construction of the real number system.

Axiom   Point (x, y) lies on line $(a : b : c)$ if and only if $ax + by + c = 0$.

The equation $ax + by + c = 0$ is called the equation of the line or, simply, the line.

It can be shown that the above interpretation of points and lines is consistent with all the axioms of plane geometry. We shall demonstrate the idea by showing that (1) two distinct points determine one and only one line, and (2) two distinct lines determine at most one point.

To show that "two distinct points determine a line" it is sufficient to show that the points (x_1, y_1) and (x_2, y_2) lie on the line:

$$(y_1 - y_2)x + (x_2 - x_1)y + (x_1y_2 - x_2y_1) = 0$$

By the axiom, (x_1, y_1) lies on the line because

$$(y_1 - y_2)x_1 + (x_2 - x_1)y_1 + (x_1y_2 - x_2y_1)$$
$$= y_1x_1 - y_2x_1 + x_2y_1 - x_1y_1 + x_1y_2 - x_2y_1$$
$$= 0$$

Similarly, (x_2, y_2) lies on the line:

$$(y_1 - y_2)x_2 + (x_2 - x_1)y_2 + (x_1y_2 - x_2y_1)$$
$$= y_1x_2 - y_2x_2 + x_2y_2 - x_1y_2 + x_1y_2 - x_2y_1$$
$$= 0$$

The coordinates of the points determine the coefficients a, b, c which define the line

$$(a = y_1 - y_2) : (b = x_2 - x_1) : (c = x_1y_2 - x_2y_1)$$

To show that two distinct points determine only one line, we may use an indirect argument. Assume that (x_1, y_1) and (x_2, y_2) determine two distinct lines:

$$ax + by + c = 0$$
$$dx + ey + f = 0$$

Since both lines lie on (x_1, y_1), the following systems must be satisfied.

Equations 1: $\qquad \begin{cases} ax_1 + by_1 + c = 0 \\ dx_1 + ey_1 + f = 0 \end{cases}$

Since both lines lie on (x_2, y_2) the following must be satisfied.

Equations 2: $\qquad \begin{cases} ax_2 + by_2 + c = 0 \\ dx_2 + ey_2 + f = 0 \end{cases}$

If we solve Equations 1 and 2 we find that $x_1 = x_2$ and $y_1 = y_2$. Therefore the points (x_1, y_1) and (x_2, y_2) are the same point, contrary to the assumption that they are distinct.

We found, page 172, that two equations

$$a_1x + b_1y = c_1$$
$$a_2x + b_2y = c_2$$

have the unique solution

$$x = \frac{c_1b_2 - c_2b_1}{a_1b_2 - a_2b_1}; \quad y = \frac{a_1c_2 - a_2c_1}{a_1b_2 - a_2b_1}$$

if and only if $a_1b_2 \neq a_2b_1$.

If $a_1b_2 = a_2b_1$, there are two cases to consider: $c_1b_2 = c_2b_1$ and $c_1b_2 \neq c_2b_1$. In the first instance, $a_1b_2 = a_2b_1$ implies $a_1/a_2 = b_1/b_2$ and $c_1b_2 = c_2b_1$ implies $c_1/c_2 = b_1/b_2$. We may conclude that the ratios $a_1 : b_1 : c_1$ and $a_2 : b_2 : c_2$ define the same line. On the other hand, if $c_1b_2 \neq c_2b_1$, the two lines are distinct and have no points in common.

We may conclude from the above that two distinct lines have one point or no points in common.

The determination of a line requires only a ratio $a : b : c$ and not three independent numbers a, b, c.

Example Find the equation for the line through the points $(3, 4)$ and $(-2, 1)$.

Divide both sides of $ax + by + c = 0$ by c.

$$(a/c)x + (b/c)y + 1 = 0$$

Substitute $x = 3$, $y = 4$:

Equation 1: $a/c \cdot 3 + b/c \cdot 4 + 1 = 0$

Substitute $x = -2$, $y = 1$:

Equation 2: $a/c(-2) + b/c(1) + 1 = 0$

We may now solve Equations 1 and 2 simultaneously for the variables a/c and b/c:

Multiply Equation 2 by $\frac{3}{2}$ and add to Equation 1:

$$\tfrac{11}{2} \cdot b/c + \tfrac{5}{2} = 0$$
$$b/c = -\tfrac{5}{11}$$

Substitute $b/c = -\tfrac{5}{11}$ in Equation 1:

$$3 \cdot a/c - \tfrac{20}{11} + 1 = 0$$
$$a/c = \tfrac{3}{11}$$

The desired equation is

$$\tfrac{3}{11} x - \tfrac{5}{11} y + 1 = 0$$
$$3x - 5y + 11 = 0$$

In case $c = 0$, the above method fails.   But in this case it is only necessary to satisfy one equation in a and b.   In the equation for the line through $(2, 1)$ and $(4, 2)$, $c = 0$.   The requirements, $2a + b = 0$ and $4a + 2b = 0$, are one and the same.   We may assign any values to a and b as long as $b = -2a$.

———————   E   X   E   R   C   I   S   E   S   ———————

1.   Estimate the coordinates of the points of intersection on the graph, page 348.   Substitute these values in each of the two equations.

2.   Construct a graph of the system
$$\begin{cases} x^2 + y^2 = 16 \\ x - y = 10 \end{cases}$$

3.   From the graph of Exercise 2, what can we infer with regard to the real solutions of the system of equations?

4.   Construct a graph of the following system and determine the points common to the graphs of each equation.
$$\begin{cases} x^2 + y^2 = 25 \\ 3x - 4y + 25 = 0 \end{cases}$$

5.   How many points may a straight line and a circle have in common, if points of tangency are considered double points of intersection?

6.   The following system of equations can have how many real solutions?
$$x^2 + y^2 = r^2$$
$$ax + by = c, \text{ where } a, b, c, r \text{ are real}$$

7. Determine whether the following points are collinear: $(3, 5)$, $(7, 9)$, and $(9, 12)$.

8. Find the value of k in $3x + 4y + k = 0$, a line passing through the point $(1, 2)$.

9. Find the line determined by the points of intersection of lines $x + y - 1 = 0$ and $2x - y + 7 = 0$ and of lines $x - y = 0$ and $3x + y + 4 = 0$.

10. Prove that the point $(6, 7)$ is on the line $5x - 6y + 12 = 0$ and that the point $(1, -1)$ is not on the line.

11. The line $2x + 4y - 12 = 0$ crosses the x-axis at what point? The y-axis at what point?

12. For what value of c does the line $ax + by + c = 0$ pass through the origin?

13. Find the point of intersection of the line through $(3, 4)$ and $(5, 6)$ and the line through $(-1, 1)$ and $(2, -5)$.

14. Find the line through the origin $(0, 0)$ and the point $(-4, 5)$.

THE STRAIGHT LINE

11.2   In Section 11.1 we indicated the possibility of constructing the whole of plane geometry algebraically, by defining a point as a number pair (x, y) and a line as a ratio $a : b : c$.   However, in the usual development of analytic geometry number pairs are used to identify, to represent, points.   Analytic geometry provides new and powerful techniques for attacking geometric problems.   A considerable amount of geometric theory, developed in the usual synthetic manner, is the logical basis on which analytic geometry is built.

For example, the formula for the distance between two points is *proved*.   The proof is based on the Pythagorean Theorem.

The distance AB between two points $A = (x_1, y_1)$ and $B = (x_2, y_2)$ is

$$d = \sqrt{(x_1 - x_2)^2 + (y_1 - y_2)^2}$$

Proof:

In Figure 11.1, triangle ABC is a right triangle with legs $BC = x_2 - x_1$ and $AC = y_1 - y_2$.   Then by the Pythagorean Theorem

$$\overline{AB}^2 = \overline{BC}^2 + \overline{AC}^2$$

or

$$\overline{AB} = \sqrt{\overline{BC}^2 + \overline{AC}^2}$$

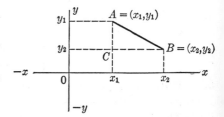

Figure 11.1   Distance between two points.

Substituting for BC and AC:

$$AB = d = \sqrt{(x_2 - x_1)^2 + (y_1 - y_2)^2} = \sqrt{(x_1 - x_2)^2 + (y_1 - y_2)^2}$$

In the figure, we have chosen the two points in the first quadrant: since $(x_1 - x_2) = -(x_2 - x_1)$, then $(x_1 - x_2)^2 = (x_2 - x_1)^2$.

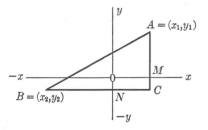

Since the coordinates x and y are directed segments (see page 149) the formula is applicable regardless of the relative location of the points. If x_1 and x_2 have opposite signs we find $(x_1 - x_2)$ by adding their undirected lengths. For example, in Figure 11.2, $AC = AM + MC$ but, since y_2 is negative, $AC = y_1$ minus the negative number y_2, or the sum of their absolute values. Similarly for BC.

Figure 11.2   The distance formula applies to any position of the points.

In contrast to the above proof of the distance formula, an abstract geometric system can include as a definition the *distance function*

$$d(A, B) = \sqrt{(x_1 - x_2)^2 + (y_1 - y_2)^2}$$

where $A = (x_1, y_1)$, $B = (x_2, y_2)$.

If we have defined a point as a number pair (x, y), we can picture points by means of two lines of reference whether they are mutually perpendicular or not. The two segments OA and OB in Figure 11.3 are equal if we accept the above definition of distance.

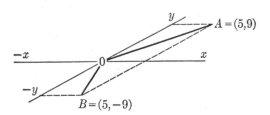

Figure 11.3   Segments OA and OB are equal.

The equation for the line through two points follows easily from the concept of the *slope of a line*.

Definition   The slope of a line is the ratio of its vertical change, $y_2 - y_1$, to its horizontal change, $x_2 - x_1$, where (x_1, y_1) and (x_2, y_2) are two points on the line.

A line parallel to the x-axis, through (x_1, y_1) and (x_2, y_1), has a zero slope.   A line parallel to the y-axis, through (x_1, y_1) and (x_1, y_2), has no slope, since the definition would require division by zero.

Slope is aptly characterized as the ratio of "the rise to the run." The straight line has the property of a constant slope.   That is, the ratio of rise to run is the same between any two points of the line. (This is further explained in Chapter XII; see page 400.)

For example, in Figure 11.4 we have the graph of the line $x - 2y + 1 = 0$.

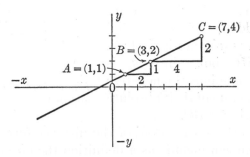

Figure 11.4   The slope of a straight line is constant.

The points $A = (1, 1)$ and $B = (3, 2)$ and $C = (7, 4)$ all lie on the line. From A to B, y increases from 1 to 2 and x increases from 1 to 3.   The ratio of the change in y to the change in x is $\frac{1}{2}$.   From B to C, y increases from 2 to 4 and x increases from 3 to 7.   The ratio of the y increase to the x increase is $\frac{2}{4}$, or $\frac{1}{2}$.

We can find the equation of the line through two points $A = (3, 5)$ and $B = (6, 7)$ by equating the slope between A and B with the slope between either A or B and a third point (x, y).   Here (x, y) merely stands for the coordinates of any other point on the line.

The slope from A to B is $(7 - 5)/(6 - 3) = \frac{2}{3}$.   The slope from A to (x, y) is $(y - 5)/(x - 3)$.   Setting these two slopes equal, we have the equation for the required line:

$$\frac{y - 5}{x - 3} = \tfrac{2}{3}$$

$$3y - 15 = 2x - 6$$

$$2x - 3y + 9 = 0$$

In general, two points (x_1, y_1) and (x_2, y_2) of a line are sufficient for determining the slope $(y_2 - y_1)/(x_2 - x_1)$.   The slope of the same line may be determined from (x_1, y_1) and any other point (x, y) of the line as $(y - y_1)/(x - x_1)$.

Equating these two results, we have the equation for a line through two points:

The Two-Point Form: $\dfrac{y - y_1}{x - x_1} = \dfrac{y_2 - y_1}{x_2 - x_1}$

The two-point form cannot be applied when the line is parallel to the y-axis. In such a case one point is sufficient for determining the equation. A line parallel to the y-axis passing through (x_1, y_1) has the equation $x - x_1 = 0$.

A line is determined by two points, but it may also be determined by a point and a direction. Suppose we wish to find the equation of a line which passes through $(3, 4)$ and has a slope $-\frac{2}{3}$. If (x, y) is any point of the line other than $(3, 4)$, we may express its slope as

$$(y - 4)/(x - 3)$$

Setting this equal to $-\frac{2}{3}$ we have

$$\frac{y - 4}{x - 3} = -\tfrac{2}{3}$$

$$(y - 4) = -\tfrac{2}{3}(x - 3)$$

If the slope of the line is m and the line passes through (x_1, y_1) the above result becomes

The Point-Slope Form: $(y - y_1) = m(x - x_1)$

If we know the point where the line cuts the y-axis $(0, b)$ the point-slope form reduces to

The Slope-Intercept Form: $(y - b) = m(x - 0)$, or
$$y = mx + b$$

If we know both the x-intercept $(a, 0)$ and the y-intercept $(0, b)$ we have, from the two-point form,

The Two-Intercept Form: $\dfrac{y - 0}{x - a} = \dfrac{b - 0}{0 - a}$

$$\frac{y}{x - a} = -\frac{b}{a}$$

$$\frac{y}{b} = -\frac{x - a}{a} = -\frac{x}{a} + 1$$

$$\frac{x}{a} + \frac{y}{b} = 1$$

We shall now examine two theorems concerning parallel lines and perpendicular lines.

Theorem   Two lines are parallel if and only if they have the same slope.

Consider the two lines l_1 and l_2 in Figure 11.5.   Here $A_1B_1 = A_2B_2$, B_1C_1 is perpendicular to A_1C_1, and B_2C_2 is perpendicular to A_2C_2.   If l_1 is parallel to l_2, then angle $B_1A_1C_1$ equals angle $B_2A_2C_2$ and the right

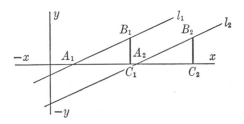

Figure 11.5   Parallel lines have the same slope.

triangles $A_1B_1C_1$ and $A_2B_2C_2$ are congruent.   Then $A_1C_1 = A_2C_2$ and $B_1C_1 = B_2C_2$.   But $(A_1C_1)/(B_1C_1)$ is the slope of l_1 and $(A_2C_2)/(B_2C_2)$ is the slope of l_2.   Therefore the parallel lines have equal slopes.

On the other hand, if l_1 and l_2 have equal slopes, then $(A_1C_1)/(B_1C_1) = (A_2C_2)/(B_2C_2)$ and the right triangles $A_1B_1C_1$ and $A_2B_2C_2$ are congruent.   Then $\angle B_1A_1C_1 = \angle B_2A_2C_2$.   Therefore the lines l_1 and l_2 are parallel.

Theorem   Two lines are perpendicular if the product of their slopes is -1.*

Consider the two lines $y = mx + b_1$

$$y = -\frac{1}{m}x + b_2$$

In Figure 11.6, $m = \dfrac{BD}{AD}$; $-\dfrac{1}{m} = \dfrac{BD}{CD}$.

(The directed segment CD equals $-DC$.)

Therefore $\dfrac{BD}{AD} \cdot \dfrac{BD}{DC} = m \cdot \dfrac{1}{m} = 1$

$$\frac{BD}{AD} = \frac{DC}{BD}$$

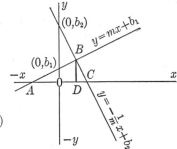

Figure 11.6   If the product of the slopes is -1 the lines are perpendicular.

---

* The converse holds also, provided both lines have a slope.   Vertical lines of the form $x = a$ do not have a slope.   They are perpendicular to lines whose slope is zero, $y = c$.

Since BD is perpendicular to AC, it follows that triangles ADB and BDC are similar right triangles and $\angle DAB = \angle DBC$. But $\angle DAB + \angle ABD =$ a right angle. Therefore $\angle DBC + \angle ABD$ makes a right angle and line AB is perpendicular to line BC.

The slope of a line may be found from the general equation for a straight line, $Ax + By + C = 0$, by solving for y:

$$y = -\frac{A}{B}x - \frac{C}{B}$$

The slope, $-\dfrac{A}{B}$, relative to the general equation, is the negative of the coefficient of x divided by the coefficient of y.

Two lines whose equations are in general form are perpendicular if the coefficients of x and y are interchanged and made to differ in sign with respect to one coefficient. These two lines are perpendicular:

$$Ax + By + C_1 = 0$$
$$Bx - Ay + C_2 = 0$$

Example   Find the equation of the line through $(3, 4)$ and perpendicular to $5x - 3y + 7 = 0$.

Any line perpendicular to $5x - 3y + 7 = 0$ will have the equation $3x + 5y + C = 0$. Since the required line must pass through $(3, 4)$,

$$3 \cdot 3 + 5 \cdot 4 + C = 0$$
$$C = -29$$

The required equation is $3x + 5y - 29 = 0$.

———————   E   X   E   R   C   I   S   E   S   ———————

1. Determine whether the triangle ABC is a right triangle if $A = (3, 4)$, $B = (5, 6)$, $C = (3, 8)$. If so, at which vertex is the right angle?

2. Determine whether triangle ABC is isosceles if $A = (1, 1)$, $B = (-2, 6)$, and $C = (0, 7)$.

3. Find the mid-point C of the segment AB where $A = (1, 7)$ and $B = (-5, -9)$.

4. Find the distance from the origin to each of the points $(-3, -4)$, $(4, -3)$, $(0, 5)$, $(-1, 2\sqrt{6})$.

5. Find the slope of the lines determined by the following pairs of points.
   (a) $(3, 4)$, $(-4, -3)$ (c) $(7, 0)$, $(0, 0)$
   (b) $(0, 2)$, $(3, 0)$ (d) $(-2, -3)$, $(4, 4)$

6. Prove that the perpendicular bisector of the segment from $A = (1, 3)$ to $B = (-5, -3)$ passes through $C = (3, -5)$.

7. Prove that the triangle whose vertices are $(2, 7)$, $(5, -2)$, and $(-4, -5)$ is a right triangle.

8. Prove that the length of the segment from the mid-point of the hypotenuse of the triangle in Exercise 7 to the vertex of the right angle is equal to $\frac{1}{2}$ the length of the hypotenuse.

9. Three consecutive vertices of a parallelogram are $(1, 1)$, $(7, 5)$, $(-1, 10)$. Find the fourth vertex.

10. The vertices of a triangle are $(2, 3)$, $(1, 0)$, and $(-3, 2)$. Find the equations for its altitudes. Show that the altitudes are concurrent (have one point in common).

11. Show that $(3, 4)$, $(-3, 2)$, $(6, 9)$, and $(3, 12)$ are the vertices of a trapezoid.

12. Show that the mid-points of the sides of the quadrilateral $(0, 0)$, $(3, 0)$, $(5, 7)$, $(2, 10)$ are the vertices of a parallelogram.

13. A line whose x-intercept is twice its y-intercept forms with the x and y axes a triangle whose area is 20. Find its equation.

14. Find the equation of the line whose y-intercept is 5 and which is perpendicular to the line through $(2, -3)$ and $(4, 6)$.

15. Find the equation of the line through $(3, 4)$ parallel to $3x + 5y + 6 = 0$.

16. Find the equation of the line through $(1, 1)$ perpendicular to $x - 3y - 4 = 0$.

17. Prove that the lines $3x + 4y - 6 = 0$, $4x - 3y - 1 = 0$, $6x + 8y + 1 = 0$, and $12x - 9y + 5 = 0$ form a rectangle.

18. Find the equation of a line with slope $-\frac{3}{2}$ and passing through $(2, 1)$.

DISTANCE FROM A POINT TO A LINE

11.3 If the general equation for a straight line, $Ax + By + C = 0$, is expressed in the slope-intercept form we have

$$By = -Ax - C$$

$$y = -\frac{A}{B}x - \frac{C}{B}$$

The slope m is $-\dfrac{A}{B}$; the y intercept, b, is $-\dfrac{C}{B}$.

We wish to find the distance from a line l, whose equation is $y - mx - b = 0$, to a point (x_1, y_1). See Figure 11.7.

The line l' parallel to l has the equation $y - mx - b_1 = 0$.   Since (x_1, y_1) also lies on l' we know that

$$y_1 - mx_1 - b_1 = 0$$

or $$b_1 = y_1 - mx_1$$

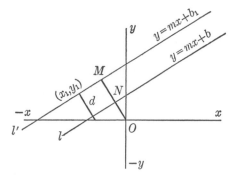

Figure 11.7   Distance d from l to (x_1, y_1).

   If we draw the line OM perpendicular to l and l', the required distance $d = MN$.   The equation for OM is

$$y + \frac{1}{m}\, x = 0$$

We must find the coordinates of M and N, the intersections of OM with l' and l respectively.   We may then apply the formula for the distance between two points to obtain the required distance.

Solving $y + \dfrac{1}{m} x = 0$ and $y - mx - b_1 = 0$ simultaneously, we find that the coordinates of M are

$$\left(-\frac{mb_1}{m^2 + 1},\ \frac{b_1}{m^2 + 1}\right)$$

Solving $y + \dfrac{1}{m} x = 0$ and $y - mx - b = 0$ simultaneously, we obtain the coordinates of N:

$$\left(\frac{-mb}{m^2 + 1},\ \frac{b}{m^2 + 1}\right)$$

The distance MN is

$$d = \sqrt{\left(\frac{-mb_1}{m^2 + 1} - \frac{-mb}{m^2 + 1}\right)^2 + \left(\frac{b_1}{m^2 + 1} - \frac{b}{m^2 + 1}\right)^2}$$

$$= \sqrt{\frac{(-mb_1 + mb)^2 + (b_1 - b)^2}{(m^2 + 1)^2}}$$

$$= \sqrt{\frac{(m^2 + 1)(b_1 - b)^2}{(m^2 + 1)^2}}$$

$$= \frac{b_1 - b}{\sqrt{m^2 + 1}}$$

Substituting the value $b_1 = y_1 - mx_1$, we get

$$d = \frac{y_1 - mx_1 - b}{\sqrt{m^2 + 1}}$$

The numerator $y_1 - mx_1 - b$ is the left member of the equation for l with the variables (x, y) replaced by the coordinates of the point (x_1, y_1).

If we replace m by $-\dfrac{A}{B}$ and b by $-\dfrac{C}{B}$ the distance will be expressed in terms of the equation for the line in general form:

$$d = \frac{y_1 + \dfrac{A}{B} x_1 + \dfrac{C}{B}}{\sqrt{\dfrac{A^2}{B^2} + 1}}$$

$$= \frac{Ax_1 + By_1 + C}{\sqrt{A^2 + B^2}}$$

If the equation $Ax + By + C = 0$ is written in the form

$$\frac{Ax + By + C}{\sqrt{A^2 + B^2}} = 0$$

we have what is known as the *normal form* for a straight line.

Example   Find the distance between the line $12x + 5y - 9 = 0$ and the point $(3, 5)$.

We write the equation in normal form

$$\frac{12x + 5y - 9}{13} = 0$$

and replace x, y with the coordinates $(3, 5)$.   Then the left member becomes the distance between the point and the line:

$$d = \frac{12(3) + 5(5) - 9}{13} = 4$$

———————   E   X   E   R   C   I   S   E   S   ———————

1.   Find the perpendicular distance from $4x - 3y = 15$ to each of the following points.
  (a)   (1, 1)   (b)   (3, 4)   (c)   (0, 0)   (d)   (−2, −4)

2.   Prove that the following pairs of lines are parallel and find their distance apart.
  (a) $6x - 8y + 7 = 0$, $3x - 4y + 12 = 0$
  (b) $x + 3y - 5 = 0$, $2x + 6y + 7 = 0$

3. Find the equation of a line that is parallel to $2x + y + 6 = 0$ and
    (a) Has (-3) as its y intercept
    (b) Passes through $(2, 3)$
    (c) Passes through the intersection of $x - y = 10$ and $3x + 2y + 5 = 0$

4. Find the equation for a set of points whose distance from $5x - 12y + 24 = 0$ is 3.

5. Find the equation for a set of points whose distance from $x - y - 2 = 0$ is equal to its distance from $(4, -2)$.

6. Verify that the points $(3, -1)$, $(6, 0)$, and $(2, -4)$ satisfy the equation found in Exercise 5. Draw the graph of the line $x - y - 2 = 0$. Locate the point $(4, -2)$ and the above points. Sketch the curve satisfying Exercise 5.

7. Find the equation for a set of points that are half as far from $4x + 3y = 0$ as from the point $(1, 1)$.

8. Find the equation for a line perpendicular to the line $3x - 5y + 8 = 0$ and passing through the intersection of $4x + y - 6 = 0$ and $2x - y + 12 = 0$.

THE CONIC SECTIONS

11.4   The conic sections were first studied systematically by the Greeks of Euclid's day. Apollonius, a contemporary of Euclid, is credited with much of their development.

The name "conic section" is derived from the fact that the curves are obtained from the intersection of a plane and a double-napped right circular conical surface, Figure 11.8. The axis of the surface is MON. The surface is generated by rotating AB about O at a constant

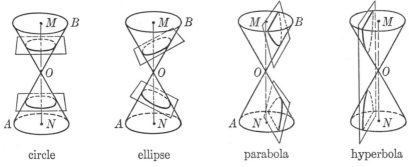

circle   ellipse   parabola   hyperbola

Figure 11.8   The conic sections.

angle with the axis MON. We picture only a portion of the surface since AB is a line, not just the line segment. We shall take up the conic sections in the order shown in Figure 11.8. The intersection of the surface and any plane perpendicular to the axis is a *circle*. The intersection of the surface and any plane parallel to any position of the line AB is a *parabola*. The intersection of the surface and a plane at any angle to the axis between that of a circle and that of a parabola is an *ellipse*. If the plane is parallel to the axis or intersects it at any angle less than that of the parabola, the intersection is a *hyperbola*. The hyperbola will cut both naps of the cone. The other three conic sections cut only one nap. The hyperbola and parabola are open curves, the circle and ellipse are closed. The plane can cut at only one angle to the axis in making a circle, and only one in making a parabola. Thus the circle and parabola may be thought of as limiting cases, separating the ellipses from the hyperbolas, both of which are obtained when a plane rotates in a line perpendicular to the axis.

The conic sections can be defined analytically in a variety of ways. We shall begin by defining the circle.

Definition A circle is a set of points in a plane a given distance from a given point.

If the given point is the origin $(0, 0)$ and the given distance is r, the circle thus defined is the set of points (x, y) such that the distance from $(0, 0)$ to (x, y) equals r.

$$\sqrt{(x - 0)^2 + (y - 0)^2} = r$$
$$x^2 + y^2 = r^2$$

is the equation for a circle with center at the origin and radius r.

The equation for any circle with center (a, b) and radius r is obtained similarly:

$$\sqrt{(x - a)^2 + (y - b)^2} = r$$
$$(x - a)^2 + (y - b)^2 = r^2$$

This form of the equation for the circle identifies immediately the center (a, b) and the radius r. We may expand it and obtain the *general form* for the circle:

$$x^2 - 2ax + a^2 + y^2 - 2by + b^2 = r^2$$
$$x^2 + y^2 - 2ax - 2by + a^2 + b^2 - r^2 = 0$$

If we set $-2a = A$, and $-2b = B$, and $a^2 + b^2 - r^2 = C$ we have the general form

$$x^2 + y^2 + Ax + By + C = 0$$

Since three noncollinear points determine a circle we may find its equation by substituting the coordinates of each point in the general equation and obtaining three equations in A, B, and C.

Example   Find the circle through $(1, -7)$, $(4, 2)$, and $(1, 3)$.

Substituting $(1, -7)$ for (x, y) we get
$$1 + 49 + A - 7B + C = 0$$
Equation 1: $A - 7B + C = -50$

Substituting $(4, 2)$ we get
$$16 + 4 + 4A + 2B + C = 0$$
Equation 2: $4A + 2B + C = -20$

Substituting $(1, 3)$ we get
$$1 + 9 + A + 3B + C = 0$$
Equation 3: $A + 3B + C = -10$

If we solve Equations 1, 2, and 3 simultaneously we get $A = -2$, $B = 4$, and $C = -20$.   The required circle is $x^2 + y^2 - 2x + 4y - 20 = 0$.

The parabola is defined in terms of a fixed point, called its *focus*, and a fixed line, called its *directrix:*

Definition   A parabola is a set of points each of which is the same distance from a fixed line as from a fixed point not on the line.

Let the distance from the focus to the directrix be p.   One of the points of the parabola will then be $p/2$ distant from the focus and from the directrix; this will be the mid-point of the segment perpendicular to the directrix.   This point is known as the *vertex* of the parabola. We let the focus be the point $(0, p/2)$ on the y-axis and the directrix be the line $y + p/2 = 0$; see Figure 11.9.   The vertex is the origin.   The

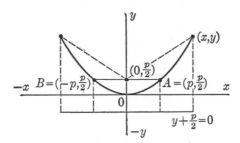

Figure 11.9   Parabola; vertex at the origin, axis of symmetry the y-axis.

perpendicular to the directrix through the focus is the *axis of symmetry*; in Figure 11.9 this is the y-axis.   The line perpendicular to the axis through the focus determines a chord of length $2p$.   This chord is called the *latus rectum*; it is AB in Figure 11.9.

We may determine the equation for the parabola by equating the distance between a general point (x, y) and the focus with the distance between (x, y) and the directrix. The distance to the point is

$$\sqrt{(x - 0)^2 + \left(y - \frac{p}{2}\right)^2}$$

The distance to the directrix is $y + \frac{p}{2}$.

The equation for the parabola is

$$y + \frac{p}{2} = \sqrt{x^2 + \left(y - \frac{p}{2}\right)^2}$$

$$y^2 + py + \frac{p^2}{4} = x^2 + y^2 - py + \frac{p^2}{4}$$

Equation 4: $x^2 = 2py$, where p is positive

Equation 5 has for its graph the reflection of the curve through the x-axis in Figure 11.9:

Equation 5: $x^2 = -2py$, where p is positive

If the axis of symmetry of a parabola through the origin is the x-axis, its equation is obtained by interchanging x with y in Equation 4 and Equation 5. If the parabola opens to the right, the equation is $y^2 = 2px$ (p positive). If the parabola opens to the left, the equation is $y^2 = -2px$ (p positive).

Definition   An ellipse is a set of points the sum of whose distances from two fixed points, the foci, is constant.

The equation for the ellipse will be in simplest form if we select foci on one axis and equidistant from the other axis. In Figure 11.10 we choose for foci $A = (c, 0)$ and $B = (-c, 0)$. The segment cut off on

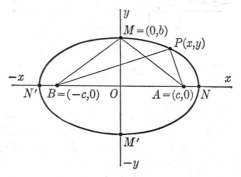

Figure 11.10   Ellipse; x-axis the major axis and y-axis the minor axis.

the line on which the foci lie, the x-axis in the figure, is the *major axis*. The segment that perpendicularly bisects the segment determined by the foci is called the *minor axis*. The intersection of the major and minor axis is the *center* of the ellipse. The constant sum of the distances from a point $P = (x, y)$ on the ellipse to the foci we designate as $2a$. Then

$$PA + PB = 2a$$

$$\sqrt{(x - c)^2 + (y - 0)^2} + \sqrt{(x + c)^2 + (y - 0)^2} = 2a$$

Subtracting the first radical from both sides and squaring, we get

$$(x + c)^2 + y^2 = 4a^2 - 4a\sqrt{(x - c)^2 + y^2} + (x - c)^2 + y^2$$

This simplifies to $a\sqrt{(x - c)^2 + y^2} = a^2 - cx$

Squaring again,

$$a^2x^2 - 2a^2cx + a^2c^2 + a^2y^2 = a^4 - 2a^2cx + c^2x^2$$

$$x^2(a^2 - c^2) + a^2y^2 = a^2(a^2 - c^2)$$

We now introduce $b^2 = a^2 - c^2$. How do we know that $a^2 > c^2$?

$$x^2b^2 + a^2y^2 = a^2b^2$$

Dividing by a^2b^2 we have

Equation 6: $$\frac{x^2}{a^2} + \frac{y^2}{b^2} = 1$$

If the curve crosses the y-axis at M we have $MA = MB$. But $MA + MB = 2a$; therefore $MA = a$. We see from the right triangle MOA that $OM = b$. Then b is the *semiminor axis*.

If the curve crosses the x-axis at N and N', we have

$$NA + NB = NA + AN' = 2a$$

or $$ON = a$$

Then a is the *semimajor axis*.

If the foci are on the y-axis the equation becomes

Equation 7: $$\frac{x^2}{b^2} + \frac{y^2}{a^2} = 1$$

In both Equation 6 and Equation 7, $a^2 > b^2$. The ellipse $x^2/25 + y^2/36 = 1$ has foci on the y-axis, since $36 > 25$. We can determine the foci from the relationship

$$b^2 = a^2 - c^2$$

or $$c^2 = a^2 - b^2$$

$$c^2 = 36 - 25 = 11$$

Therefore the foci are $(0, \sqrt{11})$ and $(0, -\sqrt{11})$.

Definition　A hyperbola is a set of points the difference of whose distances from two fixed points, the foci, is constant.

We use a method analogous to that followed with the ellipse.　Let the foci be $(c, 0)$ and $(-c, 0)$, Figure 11.11.　The segment cut off on

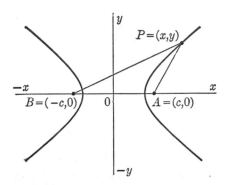

Figure 11.11　Hyperbola;　transverse axis on the x-axis.

the line determined by the foci is the *transverse axis* of the hyperbola. The *conjugate axis* is on the perpendicular bisector of the trans-verse axis.

If we designate the constant difference $PB - PA$ as $2a$ we have

$$\sqrt{(x + c)^2 + y^2} - \sqrt{(x - c)^2 + y^2} = 2a$$

$$\sqrt{(x + c)^2 + y^2} = 2a + \sqrt{(x - c)^2 + y^2}$$

Squaring, we get

$$x^2 + 2cx + c^2 + y^2 = 4a^2 + 4a\sqrt{(x - c)^2 + y^2} + x^2 - 2cx + c^2 + y^2$$

This simplifies to　　　$cx - a^2 = a\sqrt{(x - c)^2 + y^2}$

Squaring again,

$$c^2x^2 - 2a^2cx + a^4 = a^2x^2 - 2a^2cx + a^2c^2 + a^2y^2$$
$$(c^2 - a^2)x^2 - a^2y^2 = a^2(c^2 - a^2)$$

If we let $b^2 = c^2 - a^2$, the equation for the hyperbola becomes

$$b^2x^2 - a^2y^2 = a^2b^2$$

or　　　　　　　　　　$$\frac{x^2}{a^2} - \frac{y^2}{b^2} = 1$$

The distance $2b$ from $(0, b)$ to $(0, -b)$ is the conjugate axis of the hyperbola.   Figure 11.12 shows the significance of the conjugate axis as well as the relationship between a, b, and c.

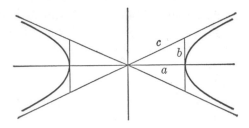

Figure 11.12

If the foci are $(0, c)$ and $(0, -c)$ the equation for the hyperbola becomes $y^2/a^2 - x^2/b^2 = 1$.

There is an alternate way of defining both the ellipse and the hyperbola, one which points up the earlier observation that the circle and parabola may be considered limiting cases separating the ellipses from the hyperbolas.

First we restate some definitions, and slightly modify them.

A parabola is a set of points such that the distance of each from a fixed point divided by its distance from a fixed line is 1.

An ellipse is a set of points such that the distance of each from a fixed point divided by its distance from a fixed line is a constant less than 1.

A hyperbola is a set of points such that the distance of each from a fixed point divided by its distance from a fixed line is a constant greater than 1.

The constant ratio, 1 for the parabola, <1 for the ellipse, and >1 for the hyperbola, is called the *eccentricity* of the conic.   As the eccentricity of the ellipse approaches zero, the ellipse becomes more nearly circular.   A circle is the limiting case for the ellipse and is said to have eccentricity zero.

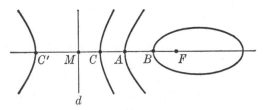

Figure 11.13   The family of conics with a fixed focus and directrix.

Consider Figure 11.13. The fixed point F is focus and the fixed line d is directrix. FM is perpendicular to d. The point A midway between F and d is the vertex of the parabola defined by F and d. Any point B between A and F is one vertex of an ellipse, with F as focus and d as directrix. Any point C between A and M is the vertex of one branch of a hyperbola, with F as focus and d as directrix. The other branch, through C', is on the other side of d, so located that $C'M/C'F = CM/CF$.

Thus we may think of a variable point moving from M to F. When the point is at M the two branches of the hyperbola coincide with the line d. When the variable point reaches F the ellipse degenerates into the single point F. Between these extremes we have a family of hyperbolas and ellipses separated by the parabola at A. Compare this description with that on page 362, where the conic is described in terms of the angle at which the cutting plane intersects the axis of the cone.

We may also consider the conic in terms of two fixed points and a variable line. In Figure 11.14, F is the fixed focus and A a fixed vertex:

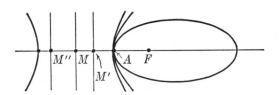

Figure 11.14 The family of conics with a fixed focus and variable directrix.

the directrix will be a line perpendicular to AF. If $AM' < AF$ we have the directrix of a hyperbola. If $AM = AF$ we have the directrix of the parabola. If $AM'' > AF$ we have the directrix of an ellipse. Here again, we see the parabola as the limiting case, separating a family of ellipses and hyperbolas, as the directrix moves to the left from A. As AM'' becomes larger the ellipse approaches more nearly a circle. When M'' "recedes to infinity" (a very loose reference to the limit process) the ellipse becomes a circle, with F as center and AF as radius. When the directrix is between A and F we have a hyperbola, but A is then the "far" vertex from F. How might one interpret the situation when the directrix passes through F?

———————— E X E R C I S E S ————————

Exercises with circles:

1. Find the equations for the following circles:
    (a) Center at the origin, radius 9
    (b) Center at $(2, -3)$, radius 2
    (c) Center at $(3, 4)$, passing through $(1, -1)$
    (d) Passing through $(2, 3)$, $(4, 5)$, and $(-1, 2)$
    (e) Center at $(3, 1)$ and tangent to the line $3x - y = 4$
    (f) Diameter is the segment from $(-5, -3)$ to $(4, 7)$
    (g) Concentric with $(x - 4)^2 + (y + 3)^2 = 16$ and tangent to $x - y - 3 = 0$

2. Find a third point on the circle found in Exercise 1(f).

3. Prove that the chords from the point found in Exercise 2 to the end of the diameter given in Exercise 1(f) are perpendicular.

4. Find the circle tangent to $3x + 4y + 7 = 0$ and $6x + 8y - 10 = 0$, and whose center is on line $4x - 3y = 0$.

5. Find the circle circumscribed about a triangle whose vertices are $(3, 5)$, $(-2, 4)$, $(-6, -2)$.

6. Prove that the vertices of the quadrilateral $(1, 1)$, $(7, -1)$, $(8, 2)$, and $(5, 5)$ are cyclic (lie on a circle).

Exercises with parabolas:

7. Find the coordinates of the focus, the equation of the directrix, and the length of the latus rectum of the following parabolas.
    (a) $y = x^2$ (c) $y^2 = 5x$ (e) $3y^2 = 4x$
    (b) $2x = y^2$ (d) $x^2 = 8y$

8. Find the equation of the parabola whose vertex is at the origin, axis vertical, and which satisfies the following additional condition:
    (a) Focus at $(0, 2)$
    (b) Directrix $y = 8$
    (c) Latus rectum 4 units long and above the origin
    (d) Passes through $(3, -2)$

9. Find the equation of the set of points equidistant from the point $(0, 4)$ and the line $y = -4$.

10. Find the equation of the set of points equidistant from the point $(5, 6)$ and the line $3x - 4y + 1 = 0$.

Exercises with ellipses:

11. Find the equation of the ellipse whose foci are $(-3, 0)$ and $(3, 0)$ and whose major axis is 8 units long.

12. Find the equation of the ellipse the ends of whose axes are $(0, 6)$, $(0, -6)$ and $(4, 0)$, $(-4, 0)$.

13. Find the equation of the set of points the sum of whose distances from $(1, 0)$ and from $(9, 0)$ is 10 units.

14. Show that $(0, 0)$, $(10, 0)$, $(5, 3)$, and $(5, -3)$ are members of the set of points whose equation was found in Exercise 13.

15. Find the equation of the set of points such that the distance of each point from $(2, 0)$ is $1/2$ of its distance from $x - 8 = 0$.

16. Show that $(4, 0)$, $(-4, 0)$, $(0, 2\sqrt{3})$, and $(0, -2\sqrt{3})$ are members of the set of points whose equation was found in Exercise 15. Sketch the curve.

17. Sketch the graph of $4x^2 + y^2 = 16$.

18. Find the equation of an ellipse whose foci are $(0, 0)$ and $(8, 0)$ and which goes through $(4, 3)$.

19. Find the ends of the axes and the foci of the ellipse $9x^2 + 25y^2 = 225$. Sketch the curve.

Exercises with hyperbolas:

20. Sketch the following curves.
    (a) $x^2 - y^2 = 4$ (b) $x^2 + y^2 = 4$ (c) $y^2 - x^2 = 4$

21. Determine the equations for the following hyperbolas.
    (a) Center at origin, transverse axis on y-axis, $a = 3$ and $b = 4$
    (b) Center at origin, transverse axis on x-axis, $a = b$, $c = 5\sqrt{2}$
    (c) Center at origin, transverse axis on y-axis, $a = 8$ and $b = 4$

22. Find the equation for the set of points such that the difference of the distances of each point from $(1, 3)$ and from $(1, -3)$ is 4 units.

23 Find the equation for the set of points such that the difference of the distances of each from $(2\sqrt{2}, 2\sqrt{2})$ and from $(-2\sqrt{2}, -2\sqrt{2})$ is always $4\sqrt{2}$. Sketch the curve.

24. Find the equation for the set of points such that the difference of the distances of each from $(4, -4)$ and from $(-4, 4)$ is always 8 units.

Further exercises with conics:

25. Find the equations for the following conics.
    (a) Focus $(2, 0)$, directrix $x = -2$, vertex $(0, 0)$
    (b) Focus $(4, 0)$, directrix $x = 6\frac{1}{4}$, vertex $(5, 0)$
    (c) Focus $(5, 0)$, directrix $x = 3\frac{1}{5}$, vertex $(4, 0)$

26. Sketch the curves of the equations found in Exercise 25.

27. The major axis of an ellipse is fixed and the foci approach the center of the ellipse. Describe the curve which the ellipse will approach.

28. Describe the conics formed in Figure 11.14, as the directrix "moves in from infinity" from the right toward the position of A. May we properly think of the circle as separating the entire family of ellipses?

29.   What does the conic degenerate into when the directrix passes through the focus?

30.   Describe the nature of the conics in Figure 11.13, as the variable vertex moves to.the right of F and to the left of M.

NON-EUCLIDEAN GEOMETRY

11.5   In terms of today's mathematical standards, Euclid's *Elements*, the first systematic treatment of geometry, contains several flaws. Many of the definitions are not really definitions at all.   Euclid seemed not to realize that some terms must be undefined.   He was, however, aware of the necessity of axioms.   But some of his proofs are not sound unless assumptions are made in addition to those he stated.

One of the axioms, known as the "parallel postulate," is one of the most famous statements in the history of mathematics:

The Parallel Postulate   If a straight line falling on two straight lines makes the interior angles on the one side together less than two right angles, the two straight lines, if produced indefinitely, meet on that side on which the angles together are less than two right angles.

A set of axioms must be *consistent* if any confidence is to be placed in the conclusions drawn from them.   They are consistent if they neither lead to nor contain a contradiction.

It is desirable that a set of axioms be *independent*.   A set of axioms is independent if each axiom of the set is independent.   An axiom is independent if it cannot be proved from the other axioms.   Aside from the esthetic quality of an independent set of axioms, the fewer axioms there are the less is the likelihood that they contain a hidden contradiction.   If the set contains an axiom which is not independent it can be eliminated and be proved as a theorem.

The parallel postulate was, for approximately two thousand years, thought not to be independent.   All attempts to prove it were either logically unacceptable or based on an assumption equivalent to it. Although there may be ample reason for using an equivalent assumption, the process can, of course, throw no light on the question of independence.

There are many theorems that are equivalent to Euclid's postulate, any one of which could be substituted for it, thereby making it possible to prove the postulate.   A few such equivalent statements are:

(1)   The sum of the angles of every triangle is two right angles.

(2)　There exist two lines that are everywhere the same distance apart.

(3)　There exists a pair of similar (but not congruent) triangles.

(4)　Through a point not on a line there can be drawn only one line parallel to the given line.

(5)　Three noncollinear points determine a circle.

The fourth of these, which is usually worded "one and only one line" rather than "only one line," is known as Playfair's Axiom. It is in this form that the parallel axiom is usually stated in high school geometry books.

The "parallel" problem was finally solved in the first half of the nineteenth century. For many years attempts were made to prove the parallel postulate by an indirect argument. If the assumption that through a point more than one parallel to a line exists leads to a contradiction, and if the assumption that no parallels exist also leads to a contradiction, Playfair's Axiom is established.

But when these assumptions were made no contradiction could be found!

The assumption of many parallels through a point leads to *hyperbolic geometry*. The assumption that there are no parallels requires the denial of another property of Euclidean geometry, the assumption that a line is infinite in length. Otherwise, it can be proved that one parallel exists. The denial of the existence of parallels is equivalent to the assumption that any two lines meet. If we assume they meet in one point we get *single elliptic geometry*, and if we assume they meet in two points we get *double elliptic geometry*. All four geometries — the Euclidean (also called "parabolic"), the hyperbolic, and the two elliptic — contradict each other. But no contradiction has been found *within* any of them. In fact, it has been shown that if any one of them contains a contradiction all four must contain it.

Although any geometric system which contradicts any of Euclid's axioms could properly be called non-Euclidean, the term is applied only to those geometries which contradict the parallel postulate.

───────── E X E R C I S E S ─────────

1.　Show that Playfair's Axiom is equivalent to the theorem, "If neither line *a* nor line *b* intersects line *c*, they do not intersect each other," by proving each, using the other as an axiom.

2.　State the converse of Euclid's parallel postulate.

3.   Does Euclid's parallel postulate imply that parallel lines cutting a third line make the interior angles equal two right angles?

4.   Does Euclid's parallel postulate imply that if two lines cut a third line making interior angles equal two right angles then the two lines are parallel?

5.   In the figure, if $\triangle ABC \sim \triangle DAC \sim \triangle DBA$, prove that the sum of the angles of $\triangle ABC$ equals two right angles.

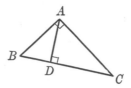

HYPERBOLIC GEOMETRY

11.6   In this section we shall make no attempt to describe more than a few of the most striking results of hyperbolic geometry.

In Figure 11.15, PM is perpendicular to l.   According to Euclid's parallel postulate, any line PN through P making an acute angle with PM will intersect l.   The only line through P which does not intersect l is the line PR perpendicular to PM.

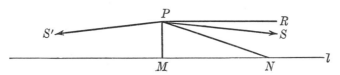

Figure 11.15   PS parallel to l, MPS acute.

As PM rotates about P the line will cut l for a time and then cease to cut l.   Since there is no last cutting line there must be a first non-cutting line.   The assumption is made in hyperbolic geometry that the first noncutting line PS will make an acute angle with PM.   This line is defined as parallel to l.   The line making the same angle on the left, PS', is also parallel to l.

None of the lines within the angle RPS will cut l but they bear a basically different relationship to l than PS does.   Each of these lines constitutes with l a pair of *nonintersecting* lines.

All the other axioms of Euclid are accepted.   With this one change, some seemingly strange results are obtained.

Before we decide that all this is unreal and unrelated to physical space, we should note that nothing has been said about how large the acute angle MPS is to be. It is obviously grossly distorted in Figure 11.15. The size of the angle depends on the length of PM. The angle MPS, called the *angle of parallelism*, is inversely related to the distance PM, called the *distance of parallelism*. As PM approaches zero the angle approaches a right angle. As the distance increases the angle approaches zero. For relatively short distances — a few million miles or so — the corresponding angle is so nearly a right angle that it is well within the margin of error for the most refined measurement.

After all, we can never verify that Euclidean parallels never meet.

The following are a few of the more striking results in hyperbolic geometry. Parallel lines approach each other closer and closer in one direction and diverge in the other. Any two pair of parallel lines are congruent.

Two lines have a common perpendicular if and only if they are non-intersecting. They diverge in both directions from the common perpendicular. Thus we see, Figure 11.16, that no two lines are everywhere the same distance apart.

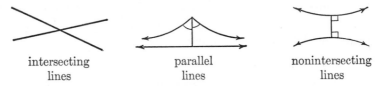

intersecting   parallel   nonintersecting
   lines   lines   lines

Figure 11.16   No two lines are everywhere equally distant.

The locus of points a fixed distance from a straight line is an *equidistant curve*. It has two branches, one on each side of the line.

If three angles of a quadrilateral are right angles the fourth angle is acute. This figure is known as a *Lambert quadrilateral*. Another important quadrilateral is the *Saccheri quadrilateral*. It has two right angles at its base and equal sides adjacent to the base.

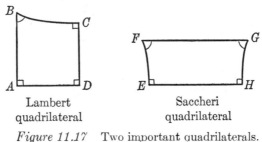

Lambert   Saccheri
quadrilateral   quadrilateral

Figure 11.17   Two important quadrilaterals.

The side opposite the base is called the *summit*, and the angles at its extremities, *summit angles*.   The base and summit are nonintersecting lines.   The summit angles are acute.

The sum of the angles of a triangle is always less than two right angles.   For that matter, the sum is a variable.   The difference between two right angles and the angle sum is known as the *defect* of a triangle.   The area of a triangle is directly proportional to its defect.

If three lines are parallel in pairs (Figure 11.18), we have what is known as the *ideal triangle*. Although the sides are infinite in length, a finite area is enclosed.   The area is constant since any two such figures are congruent.   It is greater than the area of any triangle.   In fact, we may think of the ideal triangle as a triangle with a defect of two right angles.   Its area is the limit

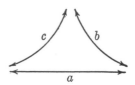

Figure 11.18   The ideal triangle.

which the area of a triangle approaches as the angle sum of the triangle approaches zero.

We know that in the Euclidean plane the only regular polygons which can be used to cover the plane are equilateral triangles, squares, and regular hexagons.   In the hyperbolic plane any regular polygon can cover the plane if the polygon is of the correct size.

Consider a sheaf of lines all perpendicular to the same line.   If a point not on the common perpendicular moves so that its locus is perpendicular to all lines of the given sheaf, the locus is one branch of an equidistant curve.   If the lines of the sheaf are all parallel in the same direction, the locus is a curve, called a *limiting curve*.   If the lines are concurrent in a point the locus is a circle (Figure 11.19).

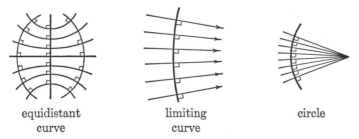

equidistant   limiting   circle
curve   curve

Figure 11.19   Three noncollinear points do not necessarily determine a circle.

The vertices of a triangle are equidistant from the line joining the mid-points of two of its sides.   Thus the vertices of a triangle always lie on three different equidistant curves — two on one branch and one on the other. In addition to this, the vertices will be on a circle, on a limiting curve, or on one branch of an equidistant curve.

——————   E X E R C I S E S   ——————

1.   Are the pairs of opposite sides of a Lambert quadrilateral $ABCD$, Figure 11.17, intersecting, parallel, or nonintersecting?

2.   In Figure 11.17, which is the longer, BC or AD? Which is the longer, AB or CD?

3.   In the figure below, $BA = AD$. If angles C and D are right angles, is it possible for the quadrilateral to be equilateral?

4.   In the Lambert quadrilateral below, $AB = BC$. Does $AD = DC$? Does AC bisect angles A and C?

5.   On the assumption that the angle sum of any triangle is less than two right angles prove that, in the figure of Exercise 4, $\angle BCA$ is greater than $\angle ACD$.

6.   If both pairs of opposite sides of a quadrilateral are parallel, are the opposite sides equal? Are the opposite angles equal?

7.   If the diagonals of a quadrilateral are perpendicular diameters of a circle, are all sides equal? Are all angles equal? Why is it not a square?

8.   What is the smallest number of quadrilaterals like the one described in Exercise 7 that is required for exactly filling the space around a point?

9.   If the area of the ideal triangle is α, what are the areas of the following?
      (a)   A right triangle whose acute angles are 20° and 25°
      (b)   An equilateral triangle whose angles measure each 30°
      (c)   A Lambert quadrilateral whose acute angle is 60°
      (d)   A Saccheri quadrilateral whose summit angles are each 60°

10. Determine the size of each of the equal angles of an equiangular quadri-
     lateral whose area is equal to that of the ideal triangle.

11. Is the Pythagorean Theorem valid in hyperbolic geometry?   *Hint:* In
     Euclidean geometry, one of the simplest proofs of the theorem is based
     on similar triangles.

12. If the vertices of a triangle lie on a limiting curve, what is the nature of
     the perpendicular bisectors of the sides?

13. If two lines cut a third line and form equal alternate interior angles,
     what kind of lines are they?

A NON-EUCLIDEAN FINITE GEOMETRY

11.7   When we realize that all measurements are approximate,
physical space serves as a model for the non-Euclidean geometries
just as well as for Euclidean geometry. We can never determine
through measurement whether the angle sum of a triangle is less than
180°, exactly 180°, or more than 180°. Whether a given geometry
perfectly describes space is beside the point when one is appraising the
"correctness" of the conclusions. Since the elements "point" and
"line" are undefined, it is possible for a geometry to have a number of
interpretations unrelated to physical points and lines.

In this section we shall develop a geometry in which we can show
there are only a finite number of points. We begin with a set of
undefined elements which we call *points*. Subsets of elements we call
lines. This does not imply that all subsets of the set of points are lines.
Whether or not a given subset of points is a line is determined
by the axioms. A line is not merely several points; there is a difference in kind between points and lines. To illustrate this idea: the
student body is a set of persons, the mathematics class is a subset of
this set of persons, but the class and the members of the student body
are different kinds of entities.

The only properties the undefined points and the subsets of points —
lines — possess are those prescribed by the axioms. When and if we
give them an interpretation which is consistent with the abstract
system we shall have provided a model for the geometry.

We have seven axioms (called N, for non-Euclidean):

N_1 There is at least one line on any two points.

N_2 There is at most one line on any two points.

N_3 There is at least one line.

N_4 Not all points are on the same line.

N_5 At least three points are on each line.

N_6 At most three points are on each line.

N_7 There is at least one point on any two lines.

The terminology, "point on line" and "line on point," should not imply a physical position. "One line on any two points" simply means that any two points are identified with some specific line. Two points selected at random must be elements of some subset of points which constitute a line. If point a is on line l then line l is on point a. Both assertions merely require that point a be an element of the subset of points l.

If we interchange "point" with "line" in N_1, the result is N_7. These two axioms are dual with respect to "point" and "line." Recall (page 238) that, if the dual of each axiom is an axiom or can be proved as a theorem and the dual of each definition is a definition, then we have a dual system. In such a system every theorem which is established can be dualized, giving a valid theorem.

Dualizing N_2 we get:

Theorem 1   There is at most one point on any two lines.

Let us assume, contrary to the theorem, that there are two points on each of two lines. Then, in violation of N_2, we have two points which have more than one line on them.

N_3 is an existence axiom. Without it we have no assurance that there are any points or lines. The set of undefined points could be the null set. The dual of N_3 gives:

Theorem 2   There is at least one point.

N_3 guarantees the existence of one line. Then, since by N_5 there are at least three points, we have shown there is at least one.

Since a set is considered a subset of itself, we have no assurance but that we have the one set of points, all on the same line. N_4 prevents this situation. The dual of N_4 is:

Theorem 3   Not all lines are on the same point.

There is a line l, by N_3. There is a point P not on l, by N_4. On line l there are three points — P_1, P_2, and P_3 — by N_5, and only these by N_6. If, contrary to the theorem, all lines are on one point, that point must be P_1, P_2, or P_3.   By N_1 there is a line on P and P_1, which by N_6 is not the line l.   By Theorem 1, neither P_2 nor P_3 can lie on this line.   Similarly, there is a line on P and P_2 such that neither P_1 nor P_3 can lie on it, and there is a line on P and P_3 such that neither P_1 nor P_2 can lie on it.

The dual of N_5 is:

Theorem 4   At least three lines are on each point.

From Theorem 3 we know there is a line l not on point P.   From N_5 there are at least three points — P_1, P_2, and P_3 — on line l.   From N_1, lines lie on P and P_1, on P and P_2, and on P and P_3.   By N_2 the three lines on point P are distinct.

Finally, if we dualize N_6 the result is:

Theorem 5   At most three lines are on each point.

From Theorem 3 there is a line l and a point P not on it.   From Theorem 4 there are three lines on P, one on each of the three points P_1, P_2, P_3 on line l.   Assume there is a fourth line on point P.   By N_7 there is a point on this line and line l.   But by N_2 this point is distinct from P_1, P_2, or P_3.   But this contradicts N_6.

Since the dual of each axiom is either an axiom or a theorem, we can dualize the proof of any subsequent theorem step by step and thus produce the proof of the dual of the theorem.   It is for this reason that we accept the dual of a valid theorem without further proof.

It should now be evident that we could just as well have started with a set of undefined elements called lines.   Accordingly, a point would then be a subset of lines.

All our axioms except N_6 and N_7 are consistent with Euclidean geometry.   Our geometry is finite by virtue of N_6.   As we shall see, this axiom limits the number of both points and lines that are possible.

We call the geometry non-Euclidean by virtue of N_7.   It precludes the possibility of parallel lines, that is, lines which have no point in common.

Theorem 6   Two points determine one and only one line.

If we recall that a line is a subset of points, the theorem asserts that any two points will be elements of one and only one such subset.   That they are elements of one such subset follows from N_1.   That they are elements of not more than one such subset follows from N_2.

By duality we have immediately:

Theorem 6-D   Two lines determine one and only one point.

We note that Theorem 6-D could be established by virtue of N_7 and Theorem 1.

Theorem 7   Each line contains exactly three points.

This theorem asserts that the subset of points which defines a line contains three elements.   The theorem follows from N_5 and N_6.

Theorem 7-D   Each point is common to exactly three lines.

Note in this instance the chance of connectives.   It would not be appropriate to say that each point "contains" three subsets of points. Each point is an element of exactly three subsets of points which define lines.

Theorem 8   There are at least seven points.

There is a line l_1 by N_3.   By Theorem 7 it contains exactly the three points P_1, P_2, and P_3.   There is a point P_4 not on l_1, by N_4.   By Theorem 6, P_1 and P_4 determine a line l_2, and P_2 and P_4 determine a line l_3, and P_3 and P_4 determine a line l_4.   By Theorem 7, l_2 contains a third point P_5, and l_3 a third point P_6, and l_4 a third point P_7.

Theorem 8-D   There are at least seven lines.

Theorem 9   There are at most seven points.

Using the notation of Theorem 8, assume there is another point, P_8. It cannot be on l_1, or Theorem 7 is violated.   Then by Theorem 6 it must determine a line with each of the points P_1, P_2, P_3.   None of these lines can contain P_4, for otherwise l_2, l_3, or l_4 would contain four points.   Yet P_8 and P_4 must determine a line.   Thus there must be four lines on P_8.   But this contradicts Theorem 7-D.

Theorem 9-D   There are at most seven lines.

A model for this abstract geometry is not difficult to find. Let us interpret the set of undefined points as the set of letters {a, b, e, o, r, t, y}, and the subsets of these which define lines as the set of English words {boy, bar, try, bet, oat, yea, ore}.   See Exercises 1 to 3 at the end of this section.

It would be interesting to try your hand at finding another model similar to the one above.   The letters {D, E, O, R, T, U, Y} and the words {DOT, DRY, DUE, YOU, YET, ORE, RUT} serve as a model just as well as the first set (we use capital letters to distinguish the two sets).   However, the two models are isomorphic.   The following correspondence of points will demonstrate this:

$$y \longleftrightarrow Y; \quad 0 \longleftrightarrow R; \quad b \longleftrightarrow D; \quad a \longleftrightarrow U; \quad r \longleftrightarrow E; \quad t \longleftrightarrow T; \quad e \longleftrightarrow O.$$

Now do Exercise 4, at the end of this section.

If a set of axioms is *categorical,* any two models for it are isomorphic. The set N_1 through N_7 is categorical.   If we eliminate N_5 the resulting set is not categorical.   Our model will still satisfy the remaining six axioms.   But so will the triangle ABC if we take the set of points $\{A, B, C\}$ as elements and define a line as a pair of such points; $\{AB, BC, CA\}$ is the resulting set of lines.   This is just as good a model for the set of axioms with N_5 deleted as is the original model, but the elements of the two models cannot be placed in one-to-one correspondence and hence cannot be isomorphic.

Returning to the first model, we may picture the situation in more conventional geometric terms, as in Figure 11.20.   The physical lines in the figure are merely an aid in visualizing the subsets of points (letters) which constitute the lines (words).   The fact that the line (oat) does not appear as a straight line in the figure should cause no concern; nothing has been said about straight lines.   Nor should the ordering of the points on the line (try) be of any concern, since nothing has been said about the ordering of points.   (See Exercise 5 at the end of this section.)

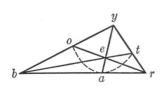

Figure 11.20 Seven points and seven lines.

The duality of the system is brought sharply into focus by means of an analytic representation.

Rather than a number pair to represent a point, we propose a triple, just as we use in representing a line.

The necessary and sufficient condition that point (x_1, x_2, x_3) lie on line (u_1, u_2, u_3) is that the following equation is satisfied:

$$u_1x_1 + u_2x_2 + u_3x_3 = 0$$

This gives meaning to the expression "point on line."   It also tells us what "line on point" means, for we may dualize the definition.

There are eight possible triples which can be obtained by using the numbers 0 and 1.   Of these, we exclude $(0, 0, 0)$.   If we did not exclude it, all points would be on line $(0, 0, 0)$ and all lines would be on point $(0, 0, 0)$.   (Parenthetically, number triples are used to define points and line in *projective geometry.*   In projective geometry the triple $(0, 0, 0)$ is also excluded as meaningless.)   The following triples are now left: $(0, 0, 1)$, $(0, 1, 0)$, $(1, 0, 0)$, $(0, 1, 1)$, $(1, 1, 0)$, $(1, 0, 1)$, $(1, 1, 1)$.   We further propose that the elements of the triples are elements of the field $(0, 1)$.   In other words, $1 + 1$ does not equal 2; it equals 0.

Each triple defines a point (x_1, x_2, x_3) and a line (u_1, u_2, u_3).   Thus $(0, 0, 1)$ are the point coordinates of a point A and the line coordinate of a line a.   We identify the seven points and lines as follows:

Point	Coordinates	Line
A	$(0, 0, 1)$	a
B	$(0, 1, 0)$	b
C	$(1, 0, 0)$	c
D	$(0, 1, 1)$	d
E	$(1, 1, 0)$	e
F	$(1, 0, 1)$	f
G	$(1, 1, 1)$	g

According to Theorem 6, two points determine one line.   Specifically, we wish to find the line (u_1, u_2, u_3) determined by points A and B.   The general equation

$$u_1 x_1 + u_2 x_2 + u_3 x_3 = 0$$

becomes, upon replacing (x_1, x_2, x_3) by $(0, 0, 1)$,

$$u_1 \cdot 0 + u_2 \cdot 0 + u_3 \cdot 1 = 0$$

or

$$u_3 = 0$$

If we replace (x_1, x_2, x_3) by $(0, 1, 0)$, the coordinates of B, we have

$$u_1 \cdot 0 + u_2 \cdot 1 + u_3 \cdot 0 = 0$$

or

$$u_2 = 0$$

Since $u_3 = u_2 = 0$ for any line through points A and B, the equation for the required line becomes

$$u_1 x_1 = 0$$

or, dividing by u_1,

$$x_1 = 0, \text{ the } \textit{point} \text{ equation for a } \textit{line}$$

This gives the necessary and sufficient condition that a point lie on the line; all those points and only those points whose first coordinate is 0 lie on the line.   Examination of the above point coordinates shows that there are three and only three points, A, B, and D, on the line, in accordance with Theorem 7.   Furthermore, we know the coordinates of the line.   Since both u_2 and u_3 must be 0, the line is c, or $(1, 0, 0)$.

We may verify that A lies on c by replacing the coordinates of each in the general equation

$$1 \cdot 0 + 0 \cdot 0 + 0 \cdot 1 = 0$$

Similarly, B lies on c since

$$1 \cdot 0 + 0 \cdot 1 + 0 \cdot 0 = 0$$

and D lies on c since

$$1 \cdot 0 + 0 \cdot 1 + 0 \cdot 1 = 0$$

It should be evident that lines a, b, and d lie on point C, because exactly the same coordinates are involved. We merely interchange the roles of u and x. The *line* equation of the *point* C is $u_1 = 0$. This means that the necessary and sufficient condition for a line (u_1, u_2, u_3) to lie on point C is $u_1 = 0$.

According to Theorem 6-D, two lines determine one point. If line $c = (1, 0, 0)$ lies on a point, substitution of its coordinates in the general equation yields

$$1 \cdot x_1 + 0 \cdot x_2 + 0 \cdot x_3 = 0$$

or

$$x_1 = 0$$

If line $d = (0, 1, 1)$ lies on a point we get

$$0 \cdot x_1 + 1 \cdot x_2 + 1 \cdot x_3 = 0$$

or

$$x_2 + x_3 = 0$$

Thus a point on both lines c and d must have the coordinate $x_1 = 0$ *and* the sum of coordinates $x_2 + x_3 = 0$. For example, point C is not on both lines, although $x_2 = x_3 = 0$, because $x_1 \neq 0$. Nor is point B on both lines, although $x_1 = 0$, since $x_2 + x_3 = 1$. If we recall that $1 + 1 = 0$, we may verify that point D does lie on both lines since $x_1 = 0$ and $x_2 + x_3 = 0$. Furthermore, no other point satisfies both conditions. The line equation for point D is obtained from

$$u_1 x_1 + u_2 x_2 + u_3 x_3 = 0$$

by requiring $x_1 = 0$ and $x_2 = x_3 = 1$. The equation for point D is

$$u_2 + u_3 = 0$$

The third line on point D is line g, since substituting the coordinates of g in the equation for D yields $1 + 1 = 0$.

By duality we have established that points C, D, and G lie on line d whose equation is $x_2 + x_3 = 0$.

E X E R C I S E S

1. Verify the fact that the interpretation of "point" and "line", page 380, is consistent with all seven axioms (page 377). "Line on point" should be interpreted "word contains letter." "Point on line" should be interpreted "letter in word."

2. Verify that Theorems 1 through 5 are satisfied.

3. Is "boat" a "line" in the model for abstract geometry given on page 380? Is "rat" a "line"? Is "rip" a "line"? Justify each answer.

4. Begin with the seven words in the first model on page 380 and make the letter replacements indicated there. Compare the result with the words in the second model.

5. Determine all three-man committees which are possible if a department consists of Adams, Ball, Evans, Owen, Ross, Tye, and Yates and the rules require that each man serves on exactly one committee with each other man.

6. Prove that points A, C, and F and no others lie on line b.

7. Prove that lines b, c, and e and no others lie on point A.

8. Prove that points A, E, and G and no others lie on line e.

9. Prove that lines b, g, and f and no others lie on point F.

10. Prove that points D, E, and F and no others lie on line g.

11. Dualize Exercises 6 through 10.

12. Find the equation for line g.

13. Find the equation for point G.

14. Label the following figure so as to show the correct relationship of points on lines and lines on points.

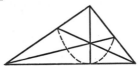

A EUCLIDEAN FINITE GEOMETRY

11.8 We called the geometry of Section 11.7 "non-Euclidean" because there were no parallel lines. By N_7 there is always a point common to two lines. It is also possible to build a finite geometry which is Euclidean, that is, in which there are pairs of lines having no points in common. This can be done without losing the property of duality. But it must follow that we also have pairs of parallel points, that is, pairs of points that have no line in common.   The axioms we shall use are identical with the previous set except that we must change N_7 and, because of duality, N_1.

E_1 Given a point P and a line l not on it, there is exactly one point on l which is on no line through P.

E_2 There is at most one line on any two points.

E_3 There is at least one line.

E_4 Not all points are on the same line.

E_5 At least three points are on each line.

E_6 At most three points are on each line.

E_7 Given a line l and a point P not on it, there is exactly one line on P which is on no point of l.

E_1 and E_7 are duals of each other.
The dual of E_2 follows immediately from E_2:

Theorem 1   There is at most one point on any two lines.

If we assume there is more than one point common to two lines, then there will be more than one line on two such points.   But this contradicts E_2.

The dual of E_3 follows from E_3 and E_5:

Theorem 2   There is at least one point.

The dual of E_4 is:

Theorem 3   Not all lines are on the same point.

There is a line l by E_3.   There is a point P not on line l, by E_4.   There is a line l' on point P and on no point of l.   But if all lines are on the same point they must be on one of the points on l.

The dual of E_5 is:

Theorem 4   At least three lines are on each point.

There is a point P by Theorem 2, and a line l not on P by Theorem 3. By E_3, there are at least three points on l.   By E_1 there are at least two points on l which are on lines through P.   By E_7 there is exactly one line on P which is on no point on l.

The dual of E_6 is:

Theorem 5   At most three lines are on each point.

If P is a point not on l assume there are four lines on P.   By E_7, three of these lines are on points on l.   And by E_1, there is one point on l which is on no line on P.   This requires that there be four points on l, contrary to E_6.

This establishes the duality of the system.

Theorem 6 follows immediately from E_5 and E_6:

Theorem 6   There are exactly three points on each line.

By duality, we have:

Theorem 6-D   There are exactly three lines on each point.

As an aid in establishing the next theorem we adopt the notation

$$
\begin{matrix}
A \\
B \\
C
\end{matrix}
$$

to indicate the line on which are the three points A, B, and C.

Theorem 7   There are at least nine lines.

By E_3 there is a line on which, by Theorem 6, there are three points:

$$
\begin{matrix}
A \\
B \\
C
\end{matrix}
$$

By E_4 there is a point D not on this line:

$$
\begin{matrix}
A & \quad D \\
B \\
C
\end{matrix}
$$

By E_1 there is a line on D which is not on A, B, or C, but on which there are two more points, E and F:

$$
\begin{matrix}
A & \quad D \\
B & \quad E \\
C & \quad F
\end{matrix}
$$

By E_1, exactly one of the points A, B, C is not on a line through D. Therefore exactly two of the points are on lines through D.   Similarly, exactly two of the points A, B, C are on lines through E, and two of the points A, B, C are on lines through F.   By the same reasoning, exactly two of the points D, E, F are on lines through A, two of them are on lines through B, and two of them are on lines through C.

$$
\begin{matrix}
A & D & D & D & E & E & F & F \\
B & E & B & C & C & A & A & B \\
C & F & & & & & &
\end{matrix}
$$

By Theorem 6 each of these six lines must have a third point which, by E_1 and E_2, must be different from the six points A through F and, in the case of $\begin{smallmatrix} D \\ B \end{smallmatrix}$ $\begin{smallmatrix} D \\ C \end{smallmatrix}$, different from each other:

A	D	D	D	E	E	F	F
B	E	B	C	C	A	A	B
C	F	G	H				

By E_7 there must be a line which is on E and on no point of

$$\begin{matrix} D \\ B \\ G \end{matrix}$$

and a line which is on E and on no point of

$$\begin{matrix} D \\ C \\ H \end{matrix}$$

This may be expressed by the following:

A	D	D	D	E	E	F	F
B	E	B	C	C	A	A	B
C	F	G	H	I	G		

By E_7 there must be a line which is on F and on no point of

$$\begin{matrix} D \\ B \\ G \end{matrix} \quad \text{or} \quad \begin{matrix} D \\ C \\ H \end{matrix}$$

and there must be a line which is on F and on no point of

$$\begin{matrix} E \\ C \\ I \end{matrix} \quad \text{or} \quad \begin{matrix} E \\ A \\ G \end{matrix}$$

This may be expressed by the following:

A	D	D	D	E	E	F	F
B	E	B	C	C	A	A	B
C	F	G	H	I	G	H	I

By Theorem 6-D there must be a third line on H, a third on I, and a third on G. This is accomplished by the line $H\,I\,G$.

A	D	D	D	E	E	F	F	H
B	E	B	C	C	A	A	B	I
C	F	G	H	I	G	H	I	G

By duality, we have:

Theorem 7-D   There are at least nine points.

To show that there are exactly nine points and nine lines, we may prove either and get the other by duality.

Theorem 8   There are at most nine points.

Assume there is a tenth point K. If K were on any of the known nine lines Theorem 6 would be violated. But K must lie on lines which are on two of the three points on each line by E_1. Such is impossible, for each of these points would then lie on four different lines, contrary to Theorem 6-D.

Dualizing this result, we get:

Theorem 8-D   There are at most nine lines.

A model for this geometry is pictured in Figure 11.21.

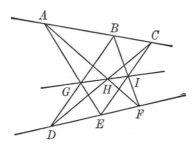

Figure 11.21   Nine points and nine lines.

E   X   E   R   C   I   S   E   S

1.   In Figure 11.21 each line is parallel to two others. List the three sets of parallel lines.

2.   In Figure 11.21 each point is parallel to two others. List the three sets of parallel points.

3.   Draw a figure which is the dual of Figure 11.21.

4.   If the set of letters {a, e, n, o, p, s, t, w, y} is interpreted as points and the set of words {top, pen, sap, yet, nay, soy, taw, won, sew} interpreted as lines, show that these elements satisfy the axioms of this section.

5.   Show that the interpretation in Exercise 4 is consistent with Theorems 1 through 6-D.

6.   Verify that the configuration in Figure 11.21 satisfies all of the axioms of this section.

7.   Which of the axioms, pages 377 and 378, are satisfied by the configuration in Figure 11.21?

8.   Construct another model similar to the one given in Exercise 4, using bona fide English words as lines.

CHAPTER XII

MATHEMATICAL FUNCTIONS

Most of the functional relationships studied in Chapter VI are such that it would be difficult to state algebraically what the relationship is. Consider the continuous temperature chart of Figure 6.7. Obviously, a functional relationship between time and temperature does exist. Corresponding to each instant of time in the interval there exists a specific temperature. We may read the temperature corresponding to any specified time directly from the chart. However, if we attempted to state how to compute the temperature corresponding to an arbitrarily chosen time, we would have a difficult task. There are ways of determining a mathematical function whose graph will very closely approximate our temperature chart. But this is beyond our present scope. In this particular illustration the mathematical function would be quite involved. However, nature is filled with functional relationships which are much less complicated. The behavior of falling bodies and that of gases under pressure are two illustrations which were discussed in Chapter VI.

We noted that the observed time required for a body to fall a fixed distance conformed very closely to the function $f(x) = 16x^2$. The function $f(x) = 16x^2$ is an abstract mathematical function. We do not attempt to define either $f(x)$ or x; we merely define f, the relationship between them. When we assign to x and $f(x)$ a concrete interpretation, our function becomes a formula. The formula for falling bodies being $d = 16t^2$, we have given to $f(x)$ the interpretation, distance (in feet) fallen, and to x, time (in seconds) of fall. This is by no means the only formula which might be derived from the function $f(x) = 16x^2$. The cost, c, of carpeting a square floor whose side is s with carpet which costs \$16 per square yard is given by $c = 16s^2$. Here we have interpreted $f(x)$ to mean cost of carpeting a square floor and x to mean the length of the side of the floor. If we interpret $f(x)$ to mean cost of gasoline and x as gallons of gasoline, $c = 16g^2$ is an incorrect interpretation of the function $f(x) = 16x^2$. Unless you have studied physics you may not have any opinion regarding the first formula, but we all should agree that the middle one is correct. What about $f(x) = 16x^2$? Is it true or false? Until we give x and $f(x)$ a meaning it is pointless to talk about whether the function is true or false. We can, however, study the behavior of the two undefined variables, x and $f(x)$, which are related in the manner indicated by the functional notation $f(x) = 16x^2$, with the assurance that our conclusions are applicable to all physical formulas which display this same functional relationship.

We may choose the domain of x in the function $f(x) = 16x^2$ in any way we please. But we do not have such liberty with regard to concrete interpretations. The domain of t in the function $d = 16t^2$ must be restricted to nonnegative values. In the function $c = 16s^2$, the domain of s must be restricted to positive values. For that matter, extremely small positive values would make things rather stuffy.

LINEAR FUNCTIONS

12.1 Possibly the simplest way in which two variables may be related is by the *more than* relationship. John is eleven years old and Betty is six. John's age is five years more than Betty's. Ten years

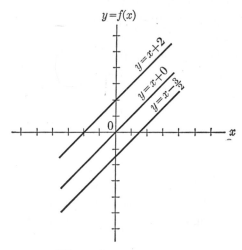

Figure 12.1 $y = x + b.$

from now, or forty years from now, the relationship will still be the same, John will be five years older.   The two variables differ by a constant.   A relationship of this type is expressed as $y = f(x) = x + b$, where b is a constant.

Figure 12.1 shows the graph of the function $f(x) = x + b$ for various values of b.

Note that the graphs are all parallel.   Note further that the two variables, x and y, increase at the same rate; y increases one unit for each increase of one unit in x.   A change of the value of the constant b causes a corresponding vertical shift of the graph.

Another very simple and quite common way in which two variables may be related is by the *times as much* relationship.   The distance, d, traveled at 60 miles per hour, is a function of the number of hours, t, traveled.

$$d = f(t) = 60t$$

The number of miles traveled is 60 "times as much" as the number of hours.   In this case one variable is a constant multiple of the other. This is expressed as $y = f(x) = ax$.   Figure 12.2 shows the graph of the function $f(x) = ax$ for various values of a.

When $a = 0$ we have $f(x) = 0$.   Its graph is the x-axis, the y-ordinate of each point on the x-axis being zero.   When $a = 1$ the function

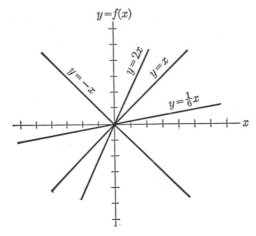

Figure 12.2 $y = ax$.

becomes $y = x$.   Here the two variables increase at the same rate; corresponding to a given change in x we have exactly the same change in y.   When $a = \frac{1}{6}$, x is increasing six times as fast as y.   For all values of a greater than one, the graph will lie between the line $y = x$ and the y-axis. As a continues to increase the graph gets steeper. It is impossible for a to be large enough for the graph to be the y axis. All points on the y-axis have the x value zero. We may consider the y-axis as representing no function of x, but a function of y, namely $f(y) = 0$. In effect, this states that, corresponding to all values of y, the value of x is zero.

If we imagine a line starting at the x-axis and rotating counter-clockwise about the origin, then the values of a start at zero at the x-axis and increase without limit as we approach the y-axis. If we rotate the line in a clockwise direction, the values of a are negative and increase in absolute value without limit as we approach the y-axis from this direction. For every positive a the graph rises as it moves to the right and for the negative values of a it falls as it moves to the right.

If we combine the "more than" relationship and the "times as many" relationship, we have what is known as the general *linear function*, $y = f(x) = ax + b$. In the function $ax + b$ the value of a indicates the *slope* of the graph, that is, the ratio of its *rise*, or vertical change, to its *run*, or horizontal change. The variable y is always b more than a times as large as x. Then b gives the value of y when x is zero. In terms of the graph, the value of b indicates where the graph crosses the y-axis.

The formula which relates Fahrenheit and centigrade temperature readings illustrates the general linear function.

$$F = \tfrac{9}{5} C + 32$$

Here $a = \tfrac{9}{5}$ and $b = 32$. Each Fahrenheit reading is 32 more than $\tfrac{9}{5}$ times as large as the corresponding centigrade reading. This situation is characteristic of a change from one scale to another. A scale must have a zero point and some size unit. The relationship between two different scales both of which measure the same kind of magnitude, such as length or weight, is a linear relationship. The constant b is the difference in location of the zero points, and the constant a reflects the difference in size of the units.

Since the value of a indicates the slope of the graph, any two linear functions of the form $f(x) = ax + b$ will have parallel graphs if they have the same value for a.

We omit the proof, but it can be shown that all ordered pairs (x, y) which are elements of the function defined by $y = ax + b$ correspond

to points which are collinear.   Conversely, the points of any line in the
coordinate plane, with the exception of those parallel to the y-axis,
whose equations are $x = c$, have coordinates which are elements of
some function of the form $y = ax + b$.   For this reason the function
defined by $y = ax + b$ is called a linear function.

Since two points determine a line we may determine the graph of
the linear function by finding the points corresponding to two (x, y)
pairs and connecting them with a straight line.

Definition   The zeros of a function are those values of the independent
variable which are paired with the function value zero.

Those values of x for which $(x, 0)$ is an element of the function are
the zeros of the function.   The points where the graph of a function
crosses the x-axis indicate the zeros of the function.   A linear function
has one and only one zero if its graph is not parallel to the x-axis.
When the graph is parallel to the x-axis the function is of the form
$y = c$, a constant.   Unless the constant is zero, y can never be zero;
otherwise, it is always zero.

---------------------   E   X   E   R   C   I   S   E   S   ----------------

1.   If a is always 10 more than 3 times as large as b, write a as a function
     of b.   Find three number pairs which are elements of this function.
     Graph the function.

2.   Find the slope and the zeros of the following functions.   Sketch their
     graphs.
     (a) $3x - 6$ (c) $2x - 4$ (e) $3x - 4$
     (b) $2x + 5$ (d) $-3x + 6$

3.   Explain what the slope of a linear function means in terms of its graph;
     in terms of the variables.

4.   If a line passes through $(0, 4)$ and $(-4, 0)$ it is the graph of what
     function?

5.   If $f(x) = ax + 5$, the coefficient a is called the *parameter* of a family of
     functions, each assignable value of a yielding a member of the family.
     On one pair of axes, graph the functions obtained when $a = \frac{1}{2}$, $a = 1$,
     $a = 2$, $a = -\frac{1}{2}$, $a = -1$, $a = -2$.

6.   It costs a manufacturer \$500 per day to maintain his plant and \$10 per
     unit to manufacture his product.   Express the daily operating cost as a
     function of the number of units produced.

7.   In Exercise 6, if the plant capacity is 1000 units per day, what are the
     domain and the range of this function?

8.   If, Exercise 6, on a given day 700 units are produced, what is the cost per unit?

9.   If, Exercise 6, the product is sold for $12 per unit, how many per day must be produced for the operation to show a profit?

10.   Convert to the Fahrenheit scale:
(a)   30° C   (b)   0° C   (c)   100° C

11.   What are the zeros of the function $F = \frac{9}{5} C + 32$?

12.   Express centigrade temperature as a function of Fahrenheit temperature.

13.   Convert to the centigrade scale:
(a) $-10°$ F   (b)   200° F   (c)   32° F

AN EQUATION IS A PROPOSAL THAT TWO FUNCTIONS HAVE EQUAL VALUES

12.2   Consider the linear equation $2x + 3 = x - 5$. When we solve the equation we find the value of x which makes the right and left members equal. The variable x is sometimes referred to as the *unknown*. When we consider the *equation*, x is actually the unknown quantity; it is a constant. There is just one value, namely -8, which makes the proposed equality true. Any other value of x makes the proposition that $2x + 3 = x - 5$ false. In what sense, then, is x a

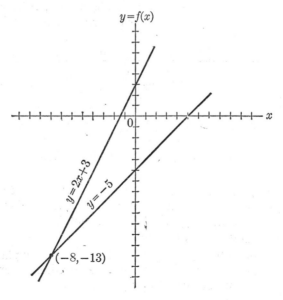

Figure 12.3 For what value of x do the two functions have the same value?

variable?   Actually, the left member of the equation is a function of x, it is $f(x) = 2x + 3$; and the right member is an entirely different function, $F(x) = x - 5$.   With respect to these functions, x is a variable; it may take any value.   Corresponding to each value it takes there is a value for each of the functions.   The two values of the functions corresponding to a particular value of x are in general different.   When $x = 3$, then $f(x) = 9$ but $F(x) = -2$.   We have solved the equation when we find that value of x which causes the two functions to have the same value.   Figure 12.3 shows the graphs of the two functions of the above equation, $2x + 3 = x - 5$.   The two graphs cross at the point $(-8, -13)$.

This indicates that both functions take the value -13 when x takes the value -8.   The solution of the equation is -8, since we seek the value of x which gives both functions the same value.   It is just incidental that they happen to equal -13.

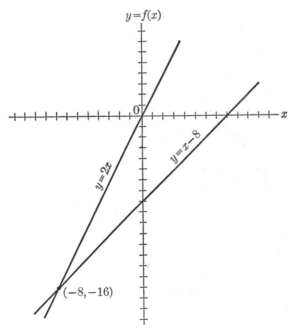

Figure 12.4 For what value of x do the two functions have the same value?

Suppose we proceed to solve the equation by subtracting 3 from both members, getting $2x = x - 8$.   Both of the original functions obviously are gone.   The subtraction axiom does not assert that if equals are subtracted from equals *the* equality is preserved but, rather, *an* equality is preserved. What we really assume is that whatever value of x gives the functions $2x + 3$ and $x - 5$ equal values will also make the functions $2x$ and $x - 8$ take equal values. The two functions, $f(x) = 2x$ and $F(x) = x - 8$, are pictured in Figure 12.4. We see that these two graphs do not intersect at the point that the former ones did. They intersect at $(-8, -16)$. These functions happen to equal -16 when they have the same value. However, in both cases the pairs of functions have equal values when $x = -8$.

The next step in the solution after $2x = x - 8$ is taken by subtracting x from each function, obtaining $x = -8$. Once again we graph the two functions $f(x) = x$ and $F(x) = -8$; we see the result in

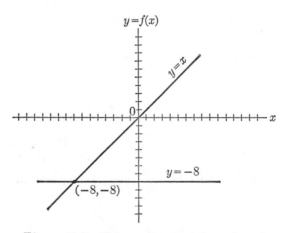

Figure 12.5 The x-ordinate of the point of intersection is still -8.

Figure 12.5. The graph of $F(x) = -8$ is the horizontal line 8 units below the x-axis. It crosses the graph of $f(x) = x$ at the point $(-8, -8)$. These graphs also intersect at a point whose x value is -8.

You will recall that in solving an equation we actually construct a chain of logical inferences which lead to a recognizable condition. In the above example, when we solve the equation $2x + 3 = x - 5$ our logic is:

(1) *If* there is a number x which satisfies the proposed equality $2x + 3 = x - 5$, *then* it will satisfy $2x = x - 8$.

(2) *If* there is a number x which satisfies the proposed equality $2x = x - 8$, *then* it will satisfy $x = -8$.

We know by inspection what value of x will satisfy the last equality. You will further recall that to be logically certain that -8 satisfies the original equality we must either verify the fact by substitution or establish the converse argument. Actually, we have merely concluded that the only value of x which can satisfy the equation is -8, and are not certain that it will.

If we solve the equation $5(x - \frac{1}{15}) = 5x - 3$ we get $5x - \frac{1}{3} = 5x - 3$ and then $-\frac{1}{3} = -3$. This means that the only condition under which $5(x - \frac{1}{15})$ can equal $5x - 3$ is that $-\frac{1}{3} = -3$. But, regardless of x, this condition cannot be met. If we graph the two functions $f(x) = 5(x - \frac{1}{15})$ and $F(x) = 5x - 3$, the above conclusion

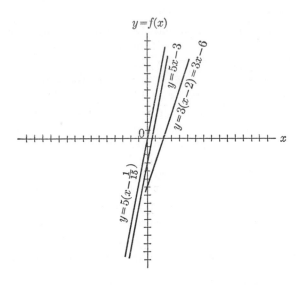

Figure 12.6   Two functions may have all elements in common or no elements in common.

is verified. Figure 12.6 shows the graphs of the two functions to be parallel, and we can find no value of x which makes the two functions have equal values. When we attempt to solve $3(x - 2) = 3x - 6$ we reach the conclusion $-6 = -6$. In the previous example the condition $-\frac{1}{3} = -3$ could never be met, regardless of x. But in this case the condition $-6 = -6$ is always met, regardless of x. The equation is an *identity*; it is satisfied by any value of x. If we graph the two functions $3(x - 2)$ and $3x - 6$, we find that we get the same line both times. In the previous case the two lines had no point in common. In this case they have every point in common. The two functions are equal, they consist of the same set of ordered pairs.

—————————   E X E R C I S E S   —————————

1. Graph the two functions $3x - 5$ and $3x + 6$ on the same coordinate axes. For what value of x do the two functions have the same value? What is the solution of the equation $3x - 5 = 3x + 6$?

2. Graph the function $5x + \frac{1}{2}$. From the graph determine the solution of the following equations.
(a) $5x + \frac{1}{2} = 7$ (b) $5x + \frac{1}{2} = -6\frac{1}{2}$ (c) $5x + \frac{1}{2} = 0$

3. On the same coordinate axes graph $4x + 3$, $2x + 3$, and $-6x + 3$. If two linear functions $a_1 x + b$ and $a_2 x + b$ are equated, what bearing, if any, will the values of a_1 and a_2 have on the solution of the equation?

4. Graph the functions $2x - 3$ and $3x + 5$ on the same coordinate axes. For what value of x do the two functions take the same value? Solve the equation $2x - 3 = 3x + 5$.

5. Graph the functions $x - \frac{2}{3}$ and $3x - 4$ on the same axes. For what value of x does $x - \frac{2}{3}$ equal $3x - 4$?

6. If $f(x) = 4x + 6$, then $f(2) = 4(2) + 6$ and $f(3) = 4(3) + 6$. In general, if we replace the x in the notation $f(x)$ by any other symbol, this implies that x is to be replaced by that symbol throughout the function. Accordingly, $f(-x) = 4(-x) + 6$. However, $-f(x)$ means $-(4x + 6)$ $= -4x - 6$. Construct the graphs of $f(x) = 4x + 6$, of $f(-x) = 4(-x) + 6$, and of $-f(x) = -4x - 6$, using one set of axes for all three.

7. If $f(x) = 4x + 6$, what does $-f(-x)$ equal? Construct the graph of $-f(-x)$ on the same axes that were used in Exercise 6.

8. On the basis of Exercises 6 and 7, how are any two functions $f(x)$ and $-f(x)$ related? How are any two functions $f(x)$ and $f(-x)$ related?

SECOND DEGREE FUNCTIONS

12.3   The function $f(x) = ax^2 + bx + c$, where $a \neq 0$, is a quadratic, or second degree, function of x.

If in the linear function $ax + b$ we increase x by an amount ϵ, it becomes $a(x + \epsilon) + b = ax + a\epsilon + b$. The function increases by an amount $(ax + a\epsilon + b) - (ax + b) = a\epsilon$ while x increases by the amount ϵ. Thus the ratio between the change in x and in $f(x)$ is the constant a. This supports the assertion, given without proof in Section 12.1, that the graph of the function $ax = b$ is a straight line. Accordingly, we actually have to know only two pairs of values in order to construct its graph. This is not true of higher degree functions. If we wish to obtain the graph of a quadratic function, we must find enough points (pairs of values of the dependent and independent variable) to get a fairly accurate picture of the shape of the curve, then join these points with a smooth curve. Table 12.1 (page 402) gives values for the functions $f(x) = x^2 + x$, and $f_1(x) = x^2 + x + 1$, and $f_2(x) = x^2 + x - 1$ corresponding to chosen values of x. We remark that the table of values does not define the function; it merely gives some of the infinitely many ordered pairs which comprise the function. The domain of each function is the real number system. The range is the real numbers $\geq -\frac{1}{4}$ in the case of $f(x)$, $\geq \frac{3}{4}$ in the case of $f_1(x)$, and $\geq -\frac{5}{4}$ in the case of $f_2(x)$.

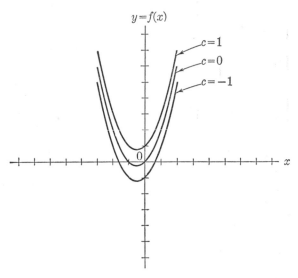

Figure 12.7   The quadratic function $ax^2 + bx + c$.
A change in c shifts the graph vertically.

Note that, corresponding to each value of x in the table, $f_1(x)$ is one greater and $f_2(x)$ is one less than $f(x)$. Figure 12.7 shows how the graphs of the three functions compare.

The complete graph of $f(x)$ is shifted up one unit when c is changed from 0 in $f(x)$ to 1 in $f_1(x)$. It is shifted down one unit when the change is from 0 in $f(x)$ to -1 in $f_2(x)$. The zeros of $f(x)$ are $x = 0$ and $x = -1$, for it is at these values of x that the function becomes zero. The graph of $f_1(x)$ indicates that it has no zeros since the graph does not cut the x-axis. No value of x can make $f_1(x)$ take the value zero. The zeros of $f_2(x)$ lie between $x = 0$ and $x = 1$ and between $x = -1$ and $x = -2$. Had the domain of definition been the complex

Table 12.1 $f(x) = x^2 + x$; $f_1(x) = x^2 + x + 1$; $f_2(x) = x^2 + x - 1$.

x	0	1	2	-2	3	-3	4	-4	5	-5	6	-6	7	-7	8	-8	9	-9	10	-10
$f(x)$	0	2	6	2	12	6	20	12	30	20	42	30	56	42	72	56	90	72	110	90
$f_1(x)$	1	3	7	3	13	7	21	13	31	21	43	31	57	43	73	57	91	73	111	91
$f_2(x)$	-1	1	5	1	11	5	19	11	29	19	41	29	55	41	71	55	89	71	109	89

Table 12.2 $F(x) = -x^2 - x$; $F_1(x) = -x^2 - x - 1$; $F_2(x) = -x^2 - x + 1$.

x	0	1	-1	2	-2	3	-3	4	-4	5	-5	6	-6	7	-7	8	-8	9	-9	10	-10
$F(x)$	0	-2	0	-6	-2	-12	-6	-20	-12	-30	-20	-42	-30	-56	-42	-72	-56	-90	-72	-110	-90
$F_1(x)$	-1	-3	-1	-7	-3	-13	-7	-21	-13	-31	-21	-43	-31	-57	-43	-73	-57	-91	-73	-111	-91
$F_2(x)$	1	-1	1	-5	-1	-11	-5	-19	-11	-29	-19	-41	-29	-55	-41	-71	-55	-89	-71	-109	-89

number system, f_1 would have had zeros.   We may verify this by evaluating $f(-\frac{1}{2} + \sqrt{3}/2i)$.   It is not correct to say that *no* value of x will make $f_1(x)$ become zero.   What the graph shows is that no *real* number will make $f_1(x)$ become zero.   We have plotted on the graph only real values of x and only real values of $f(x)$.   You will recall that there is a one-to-one correspondence between the real numbers and the points on a line.   In Section 7.9 we displayed the complex numbers as points in a plane; we had a real axis and an imaginary axis.   But here, since we must use one axis for the independent variable and one axis for the dependent variable, we can plot only the real number pairs.   A complex number is defined as a real number pair, but if we wished to include complex values in our graph we would have to be able to plot a *pair* of real number pairs as a point in the plane.

Suppose we change the sign of each of the above functions and get $F(x) = -f(x) = x^2 - x$, and $F_1(x) = -f_1(x) = -x^2 - x - 1$, and $F_2(x) = -f_2(x) = -x^2 - x + 1$.   How are these three functions related to the original three?   Table 12.2 shows the values of the functions corresponding to the same values of x that were used in Table 12.1.

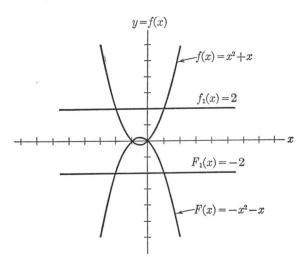

Figure 12.8 Multiplying a function by -1 rotates its graph about the x-axis through $180°$.

Every value of the first three functions is identical with the corresponding value of the latter three, except that the signs are changed in every case.   The only number that is unaffected by a change of signs is zero.   Then the only value common to these pairs of functions is the value zero.   Figure 12.8 shows how $f(x) = x^2 + x$ compares with $F(x) = -x^2 - x$. Multiplying by -1 certainly changes the function, but it does not change its zeros. The graph of $F(x)$ can be obtained from that of $f(x)$ by rotating the latter through 180° about the x-axis.

When we solve the quadratic *equation*, $ax^2 + bx + c = 0$, graphically we do not graph the equation, we graph the *function* $ax^2 + bx + c$. When we find the zeros of the function we find those values of x which satisfy the condition of the equation, namely, that the function $ax^2 + bx + c$ take the value zero. Otherwise stated, the equation consists of the two functions of x, $f(x) = ax^2 + bx + c$ and $F(x) = 0$. But the graph of $F(x) = 0$ is the x-axis. The two functions have the same value, zero in this case, when their graphs have points in common. Then the solution of the equation $ax^2 + bx + c = 0$ consists of finding the value for x for which the two functions $f(x) = ax^2 + bx + c$ and $F(x) = 0$ have the same value, namely, the values of x at the point where the curve crosses the x-axis.

We may refer to Figure 12.8 and obtain the solution to the equation $x^2 + x = 2$ as follows: The graph of $f(x) = x^2 + x$ crosses the graph of $f_1(x) = 2$ when $x = -2$ and again when $x = 1$; hence $x = -2$ and $x = 1$ are the two values which satisfy the equation $x^2 + x = 2$.

We have learned that we may multiply both sides of an equality by -1 and still have an equality. The above equation becomes, upon multiplying both sides by -1, the equation $-x^2 - x = -2$. Referring to Figure 12.8 again, we now wish to find the points common to $F(x) = -x^2 - x$ and $F_1(x) = -2$. We do not get the same two points of intersection as before but the points do have the same x values, namely -2 and 1. The only thing common to the two equations $x^2 + x = 2$ and $-x^2 - x = -2$ is the fact that the same values of x satisfy both of them.

RATE OF CHANGE OF THE SECOND DEGREE FUNCTIONS

12.4   If $y = 4x + 3$ we know the slope of the graph is 4. This means that the change in y is always four times as great as the corresponding change in x. The rate of change is constant. This is not true of the second degree function. A glance at the entries in Table 12.1 will show this. When $x = 1$, then $f(x) = 2$; when $x = 2$, then $f(x) = 6$. While x was increasing by 1, $f(x)$ increased by 4. But if x increases by 1 more we get $x = 3$ and $f(x) = 12$ and, corresponding to this increase of 1 in x, $f(x)$ increases by 8. Here the ratio of the change in the independent variable to the change in the function is itself continuously changing. Figure 12.7 shows that, as x increases, $f(x)$ decreases very rapidly until we reach the neighborhood of $x = -\frac{1}{2}$. At this point the function begins to increase and it continues to increase more and more rapidly as x increases.

It is shown in more advanced mathematics that this *changing rate of change* is a function of x. For the function $f(x) = ax^2 + bx + c$, the ratio of the change in the function to the change in x is $2ax + b$. Thus the rate of change is not constant, as in the linear function; it changes as x does. Suppose we let the independent variable change from x to $x + \epsilon$. The dependent variable will change from $ax^2 + bx + c$ to $a(x + \epsilon)^2 + b(x + \epsilon) + c = ax^2 + 2ax\epsilon + a\epsilon^2 + bx + b\epsilon + c$. The increase in the independent variable is $x + \epsilon - x = \epsilon$. The corresponding increase in the dependent variable is $(ax^2 + 2ax\epsilon + a\epsilon^2 + bx + b\epsilon + c) - (ax^2 + bx + c) = 2ax\epsilon + a\epsilon^2 + b\epsilon = (2ax + a\epsilon + b)\epsilon$. The ratio between these changes is

$$(2ax + b + a\epsilon)\epsilon/\epsilon = 2ax + b + a\epsilon$$

In calculus we define the instantaneous rate of change — that is, the instantaneous ratio of change in the function to change in the independent variable — as the limit the above ratio approaches as ϵ approaches zero. The only term in $2ax + b + a\epsilon$ that is affected by a change in ϵ is the term $a\epsilon$. As ϵ approaches zero so does $a\epsilon$. Then

$$\lim_{\epsilon \to 0} (2ax + b + a\epsilon) = 2ax + b$$

In $f(x) = x^2 + x$, Figure 12.7, the instantaneous rate of change $2ax + b$ is $2x + 1$. If we set this function equal to zero and solve the equation $2x + 1 = 0$ we find that value of x for which the rate of change is zero. We observe from its graph that the function $x^2 + x$ is decreasing as x increases and approaches $x = -\frac{1}{2}$. The ratio of the change in y, a negative change, to the change in x, a positive change, is negative. As x increases beyond $x = -\frac{1}{2}$ the function also increases and the ratio is positive. Since the ratio changes from negative to positive at $x = -\frac{1}{2}$ we conclude that it must be zero at that point.

We summarize these observations and state without formal proof the following: The rate at which the quadratic function $ax^2 + bx + c$ is changing is the function $2ax + b$. To find the value of x which yields the lowest (or highest) value of the function, set $2ax + b = 0$ and solve.

──────────   E   X   E   R   C   I   S   E   S   ──────────

1.   Find the value of x for which each of the following functions is the minimum.   Find the minimum values.
     (a) $f_1(x) = 3x^2 - 5x + 6$ (c) $f_3(x) = x^2 - 3x - 1$
     (b) $f_2(x) = 2x^2 + 4x - 6$

2.   Plot the following functions on the same coordinate axes.   What is the role of c in the function $ax^2 + bx + c$?
     (a) $f_1(x) = 3x^2 + 2x + 6$ (c) $f_3(x) = 3x^2 + 2x - 6$
     (b) $f_2(x) = 3x^2 + 2x + 1$

3.   Plot the following functions on the same coordinate axes.
     (a) $f_1(x) = 2x^2 - x + 4$ (c) $f_3(x) = 2x^2 + 4$
     (b) $f_2(x) = 2x^2 + 4x + 4$

4.   Plot the following functions on the same coordinate axes.
     (a) $f_1(x) = x^2 - 4$ (b) $f_2(x) = 2x^2 - 4$ (c) $f_3(x) = 4x^2 - 4$

5.   If $f(x) = 3x^2 - 4x + 2$, find $-f(x)$; find $f(-x)$.

6.   On the same axes, graph $f(x)$, $-f(x)$, $f(-x)$ from Exercise 5.

7.   If $f(x) = 2x^2 - 4x + 5$ complete the following table.

x	1	0	2	−1	3	−2	4	−3	5	−4	6	−5	7	−6	8	−7
$f(x)$																

8.   Use the pairs of values obtained in Exercise 7 to plot the graph of $f(x) = 2x^2 - 4x + 5$.   What can you conclude from the graph concerning the roots of the equation $2x^2 - 4x + 5 = 0$?

9.   Use the graph of Exercise 8 to determine the roots of the equation $2x^2 - 4x + 5 = 4$.   Also solve from this graph $2x^2 - 4x + 5 = x + 3$ by plotting $F(x) = x + 3$ on the same axes.

10. What is the rate of change of the function $2x^2 - 4x + 5$ when $x = 3$? $x = -1$? $x = 0$?

11. For what value of x is the function $2x^2 - 4x + 5$ the smallest?   What is its value corresponding to this value of x?

IMPLICIT FUNCTIONS

12.5   The functions which we have studied so far in this chapter are explicit functions; $y = f(x)$ states explicitly how y is determined from x. The two relationships $y = \frac{2}{3}x - 6$ and $2x - 2 = 3y + 16$ actually are equivalent statements of the relationship between x and y.   This can be shown by solving the latter equation for y.   We may also demonstrate the fact that any pair of values for x and y which satisfy one of the relationships will also satisfy the other.   In the latter equation it is only by implication that we can say y is a function of x.   There certainly is a relationship between them, but we have not stated explicitly how to find the value of y which corresponds to an arbitrarily assigned x.   In the relationship $2x - 2 = 3y + 16$, y is an *implicit* function of x, and x is an implicit function of y.

INVERSE VARIATION

12.6   Quite frequently two variables are so related that their product is always a constant.   If we express this as an implicit function we have $xy = c$.   We may express y as an explicit function of x by dividing by x; we get $y = c/x$.   In this form, it is more obvious that the relationship is such that when one variable increases the other decreases.

As a simple example of inverse variation, suppose we have a 100-mile trip to make.   The faster we go, the less time is required.   The more time consumed, the slower we must travel.   The relationship between rate and time is

$$100 = r \cdot t$$

or, if r is a function of t,

$$r = \frac{100}{t}$$

or, if t is a function of r,

$$t = \frac{100}{r}$$

Table 12.3 gives values for $f(x) = 10/x$ and $F(x) = -10/x$, for various values of x.

Table 12.3 $f(x) = 10/x$; $F(x) = -10/x$.

x	1	2	5	10	20	$\frac{1}{2}$	-1	-2	-5	-10	-20	$-\frac{1}{2}$
$f(x)$	10	5	2	1	$\frac{1}{2}$	20	-10	-5	-2	-1	$-\frac{1}{2}$	-20
$F(x)$	-10	-5	-2	-1	$-\frac{1}{2}$	-20	10	5	2	1	$\frac{1}{2}$	20

Note that x and $f(x)$ always agree in sign, and x and $F(x)$ always disagree.   This means that the graph of $f(x)$ will always be in the first and third quadrants and that of $F(x)$ in the second and fourth quadrants.   Figure 12.9 shows the graphs of these two functions.   The graph of each function consists of two branches neither of which touches either axis.   Since they do not touch the x-axis, the implication is that neither function possesses a zero.   If $f(x)$ took the value zero, we would have $0 = 10/x$ which implies $0 \cdot x = 10$, and this violates the rule which requires that a zero factor always produce the

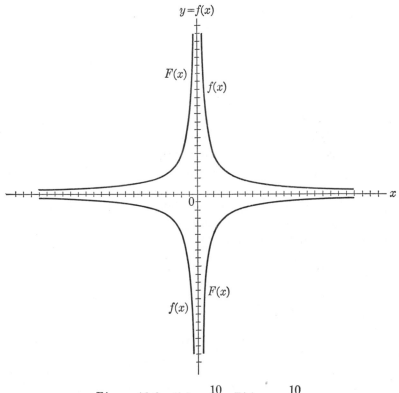

Figure 12.9 $f(x) = \dfrac{10}{x} \; ; F(x) = -\dfrac{10}{x} .$

product zero.   If the graph touched the y-axis we would then be able to find the value of the function corresponding to $x = 0$.   But since the function is defined as $f(x) = 10/x$, we cannot assign the value zero to x since division by zero is meaningless.   The function is undefined, it does not exist, when $x = 0$.

INVERSE FUNCTIONS

12.7   The definition of a function permits a value of the dependent variable to be paired with more than one value of the independent

variable.   However, many functions are one-to-one; that is, exactly
one value of x is paired with each value of $f(x)$ and exactly one value
of $f(x)$ is paired with each value of x.   If the roles of the variables in a
function of this kind are interchanged, the resulting function is called
the inverse of $f(x)$.   It is sometimes written as $f^{-1}(x)$.   The superscript
-1 attached to the symbol for the function should not be confused
with the exponent -1.   It was adopted because the exponent -1
attached to a number gives its inverse under multiplication.   We
should not confuse $f^{-1}(x)$ with $[f(x)]^{-1} = 1/f(x)$.

An interchange of the variables of a function is equivalent to a
reversal of the order of the numbers making up the number pairs of the
function.   If $(3, 4)$, $(-12, 15)$, $(2, -2)$ are elements of $f(x)$ then
$(4, 3)$, $(15, -12)$, $(-2, 2)$ are elements of $f^{-1}(x)$.   Then any table of
values for $f(x)$ can serve equally well as a table of values for $f^{-1}(x)$,
provided $f(x)$ is one-to-one.

We can determine the algebraic description of $f^{-1}(x)$ from $f(x)$ by
interchanging x and y, then solving the resulting equation for y.

Example   Given $y = f(x) = 2x - 14$, find $f^{-1}(x)$.

Interchange x and y and we get $x = 2y - 14$ which, solved for y, is $y = (x + 14)/2$.   Then $f^{-1}(x) = (x + 14)/2$.   The   pairs $(0, -14)$, $(7, 0)$,
$(4, -6)$ are some of the elements of $f(x)$, and $(-14, 0)$, $(0, 7)$, $(-6, 4)$
are elements of $f^{-1}(x)$.

Any function that is unchanged by interchanging x and y is its own
inverse.   This is true of the function described in Section 12.6.   However, this is not synonymous with its being an example of inverse variation.   The implicit function $x + y = 1$ is unchanged by an interchange of variables, it is its own inverse, but this is not an example of
inverse variation.   Here the *sum* of the x and y values of any pair is
constant.   But in the function $xy = c$ it is the *product* of the x and y
values of any pair that is constant.

The expression $x^2 + y^2 = 1$ does not define an implicit function, it
defines a relation.   It is unchanged by an interchange of x and y, and
is its own inverse.

The graph of any function, or relation, which is its own inverse is
symmetric to the line $y = x$.   If (a, b) defines a point of its graph,
(b, a) must also be a point of its graph.   Intuitively, this means that
if we fold the graph along the line $y = x$ the points (a, b) and (b, a)
will coincide.

In a similar fashion, if (a, b) defines a point on the graph of $f(x)$,
then (b, a) must define a point on the graph of $f^{-1}(x)$.   The graphs of
two inverse functions are symmetric to the line $y = x$.

────────────   E   X   E   R   C   I   S   E   S   ────────────

1.   Find $f^{-1}(x)$ if $f(x) = 3x + 5$. If the domain of f is the set of real numbers ≥ 0, what is its range?

2.   What is the inverse of $\frac{1}{2}x - 6$? $ax + b$?   Graph the function $\frac{1}{2}x - 6$ and its inverse on the same axes.

3.   If $f(x) = \sqrt{9 - x^2}$ what part of the real numbers can be chosen for domain? What is the range? Find $f^{-1}(x)$ and graph both $f(x)$ and $f^{-1}(x)$.

4.   Given the function $y = 4x + 6$, if we interchange x and y we get $x = 4y + 6$. Solving this for y we get $y = \frac{1}{4}x - \frac{3}{2}$. Graph the function $f^{-1}(x) = \frac{1}{4}x - \frac{3}{2}$. Place on the same axes the graph $f(x) = 4x + 6$.

5.   On the basis of the above exercises, what is the relationship between the graphs of two inverse functions?

6.   Show that the domain of $f(x)$ is the range of $f^{-1}(x)$ and the range of $f(x)$ is the domain of $f^{-1}(x)$.

7.   If $f(x) = x^2 + 3x - 2$, how must the domain be restricted if $f(x)$ is to have an inverse? Find $f^{-1}(x)$.

8.   Plot $f(x)$ and $f^{-1}(x)$, described in Exercise 7, on the same coordinate axes.

CLASSIFICATION OF FUNCTIONS

12.8   The linear and quadratic functions which we have studied in this chapter are special cases of *polynomial functions*. The polynomial function is obtained by adding, subtracting, and multiplying the independent variable and constants. If $y = a_0x^n + a_1x^{n-1} + a_2x^{n-2} + \ldots a_{n-1}x + a_n$ where n is a nonnegative integer and $a_0, a \ldots a_n$ are complex numbers, then y is a polynomial function of x. The domain of the function is the set of complex numbers. If $a_0 \neq 0$, then y is of degree n. The polynomial function equated to zero

$$a_0x^n + a_1x^{n-1} + a_2x^{n-2} + \ldots + a_{n-1}x + a_n = 0$$

is a polynomial equation. The fundamental theorem of algebra refers to this type of equation. It asserts that a polynomial equation has at least one root. The theorem does not require that the root be real; the equation must have a complex root. As a consequence of the fundamental theorem, it can be shown that the polynomial equation of degree n has exactly n complex roots. All n of these roots do not have to be real. In fact, sometimes they are all imaginary. We should keep this in mind when studying the graph of a polynomial function. We know that the graph of a function of degree n will cut the x-axis in not more than n places. It may not cut it at all, since the zeros of the function are the roots of the corresponding equation. The graph of the function crosses the x-axis in points which correspond to the *real roots* of the corresponding equation. In fact, the graph of a polynomial of degree n is such that no straight line can cut it in more than n points. See Figure 12.10.

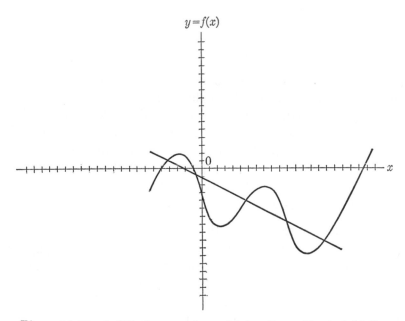

$y=f(x)$

Figure 12.10 A fifth degree polynomial function. No straight line can cross it in more than five points.

If we add division to the list of operations which generate the polynomial function we have a *rational function*. We may define the rational function $R(x)$ as the ratio of two polynomials, $f(x)/g(x)$. If $R(x) = f(x)/g(x)$, then $R(x)$ is undefined for those values of x which make $g(x) = 0$.

Example
$$R(x) = \frac{x^2 + 2}{x - 4}$$

Since division by zero must remain undefined, $R(x)$ is undefined when $x = 4$.

$$R_1(x) = \frac{x - 4}{x^2 + 2}$$

If the domain of definition is the set of real numbers, then $R_1(x)$ is defined for every real x.   If the domain is the largest possible subset of the set of complex numbers, $R_1(x)$ is undefined for $x = \pm\sqrt{2}i$.

If we permit, in addition to the four arithmetic operations, the extraction of roots, we can then generate *algebraic functions*.

If the domain of definition of an algebraic function is a subset of the real numbers, the function may be undefined for certain values of x for reasons other than the fact that division by zero is undefined.   For example, consider the function

$$\frac{\sqrt{x-2} - \sqrt[3]{2x}}{\sqrt[4]{x^2 - x - 2}}$$

whose domain of definition is the largest possible subset of the set of real numbers.   If $x = 2$ or -1 the denominator becomes zero and the function is not defined.   But if $2 > x > -1$ the denominator itself is undefined, since an even root of a negative number does not exist in the real number system.   The first term of the numerator, $\sqrt{x-2}$, is not a real number if $x < 2$.   Therefore this function is undefined in the field of real numbers for any $x < 2$.   The domain of definition of the function is $\infty > x > 2$.

Example   Sketch the graph of the function $y = \sqrt{x^2 - 9}$.

Since we are concerned only with real values in sketching a graph, $|x| < 3$ is ruled out because any value less than 3 will make y imaginary.   The

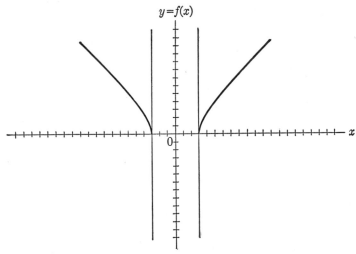

Figure 12.11 $y = \sqrt{x^2 - 9}$.

domain of the function is the set of real numbers except $|x| < 3$. Stated otherwise, the domain is $\infty > x \geq 3$; $-\infty < x \leq -3$. There is an empty band between 3 and -3. The total curve lies outside this strip. The range of the function is $0 \leq y < \infty$. As x gets large in absolute value the function gets large.

Table 12.4

x	± 3	± 4	± 5	± 6	± 7	± 8	± 9	± 10
y	0	2.65	4	5.20	6.32	7.42	8.49	9.54

The table of values, Table 12.4, may be helpful in sketching the graph, Figure 12.11, of the function $y = \sqrt{x^2 - 9}$.

TRANSCENDENTAL FUNCTIONS

*12.9   In Section 7.4 we defined a transcendental number as one that is not algebraic. We shall do the same for functions.

Definition   A transcendental function is a function which is not algebraic.

The polynomials and rational functions of Section 12.8 are special cases of algebraic functions just as the linear and quadratic functions are special cases of the polynomial function.

Two of the elementary transcendental functions are the logarithm function and its inverse, the exponential function. The definition of a logarithm (Section 9.12) defines a function. It states a rule for pairing the elements of the two sets. The independent variable is the set of numbers which have logarithms and the dependent variable is the set of logarithms. If we take as the domain of definition the set of real numbers greater than zero, the range is the set of real numbers. From the definition,

$$y = \log_e x$$

if and only if

$$e^y = x$$

If we interchange variables in $y = \log_e x$ we get $x = \log_e y$. Solve $x = \log_e y$ for y, and we will have the inverse of the logarithm function. But the definition requires that $\log_e y = x$ if and only if $e^x = y$. Then the *logarithm function*, $\log_e x$, and the *exponential function*, e^x, are inverse functions. Figure 12.12 shows the graphs of the two functions. Note that the two curves are symmetric to the line $x = y$. Domain and range are interchanged in the two functions; the domain of the exponential function is the set of real numbers and its range is the set of real numbers greater than zero.

One of the many interesting properties of the exponential function, e^x, is the fact that the rate at which it is increasing is always equal to its size. This is the typical growth phenomenon — the bigger it is the faster it grows, for a time at least.

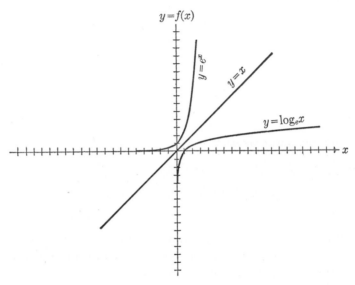

Figure 12.12 $\text{Log}_e x$ is the inverse of e^x. They are mirror images through the line $y = x$.

We referred to the exponential function as e^x since the logarithm function was expressed as $\log_e x$. You will recall that two logarithm bases are in wide use, 10 and e. We observed that 10 is the most useful base for logarithms when they are used as computing aids since 10 is also the base of our system of notation. The natural, base e, logarithm and its inverse are indispensable in advanced mathematics. Although the reason for their importance is beyond our scope it is inherent in the definition of the constant e, which is $\lim_{n \to \infty} (1 + 1/n)^n$.

Although we confine logarithms to base 10 and base e, any real number greater than 1 could be used. For each choice of base there is a corresponding inverse function. In fact, e^x is a special case of the more general exponential function a^x, where a is any constant.

The formula for compound interest

$$A = p(1 + r)^n$$

gives the amount, A, accumulated by p dollars in n interest periods at the rate of interest, r, per period.   If the number of periods, n, is the independent variable this formula illustrates the exponential function.

Example   If \$1,000 is deposited to John Smith's account the day he is born, and compounded annually at 4 per cent, find the amount on his eighteenth birthday.

$$A = 1,000(1 + .04)^n$$

gives the amount, A, as a function of the number of periods, n.   The solution to our problem consists in finding the A which corresponds to $n = 18$.   The answer can be read directly from a compound interest table. If we do not have such a table, logarithms are helpful in computing the result.   Since

$$A = 1,000(1 + .04)^{18}$$

we may take the logarithm of both sides of the equation,

$$\begin{aligned}
\log A &= \log 1,000(1 + .04)^{18} \\
&= \log 1,000 + \log (1.04)^{18} \\
&= \log 1,000 + 18 \log 1.04 \\
&= 3 + 18(.0170) = 3.3060
\end{aligned}$$

Then $A = $ antilog $3.3060 = \$2,023$

The method employed in the example may be used to solve the *exponential equation* $C = a^x$.   We cannot always determine by inspection the value of x required to satisfy this equation.   In that event we can take the logarithm of both sides of the equation, getting

$$\log C = \log a^x = x \log a$$

This we solve for x

$$x = \log C / \log a$$

(*Caution:* $\log C / \log a$ is not the same thing as $\log C/a$.)

Example   Solve the equation $51 = 3^x$.

$$\log 51 = \log 3^x = x \log 3$$

Then $x = \log 51 / \log 3 = 1.7076/.4771$

If we wish, we may do the indicated division by means of logarithms, but we are no longer concerned with the fact that 1.7076 and .4771 are logarithms.   They are just numbers and have logarithms.

$$\begin{aligned}
\log 1.7076 &= 10.2325 - 10 \\
\log .4771 &= 9.6786 - 10 \\
\log x &= .5539 \\
x &= 3.58
\end{aligned}$$

─────────── * E   X   E   R   C   I   S   E   S ───────────

1. Classify the following functions. If it is agreed that the domain of each function is the largest possible subset of the real numbers (maybe all of them), state the domain and range of each.

   (a) $2x$
   (b) x^2
   (c) 2^x
   (d) $\sqrt{x} - 5/(x^3 + 3)$
   (e) $(x - 1)/(x + 2)$
   (f) $\log_8 (5/x)$
   (g) $3x^7 - 2x^3 + 1$

2. Graph the following functions on one set of axes.

   (a) $y = 2x$, where $x > 0$
   (b) $y = x^2$, where $x > 0$
   (c) $y = 2^x$, where $x < 0$

3. Write the inverse of each of the following functions.

   (a) $3x + 5$
   (b) $-\sqrt{x^2 + 4}$, where $x \leq 0$
   (c) e^{2x-3}
   (d) $\log_e (5x - 1)$

4. Solve: (a) $5^{x-2} = 175$ (b) $3^{-x} = 9$

5. In how many years will \$500 amount to \$650 at simple interest at 4 per cent? How long will it take at compound interest at 4 per cent, compounded annually?

6. Use the definition of e to find its value to three significant figures.

7. If the number, N, of bacteria present in a certain culture after t hours is given by the formula $N = N_0 10^{1.6\,t}$, how many bacteria were present when the experiment began? In how many hours will there be ten times as many bacteria as there were to begin with? How many bacteria will there be in 5 hours?

8. Graph the function $y = \log_{10} x$ and its inverse $y = 10^x$ on the same axes.

9. Use the logarithm table to find x or y in the following.

   (a) $y = 10^{.537}$
   (b) $156 = 10^x$
   (c) $y = 10^{2.7463}$
   (d) $83720 = 10^{x+1}$

TRIGONOMETRIC FUNCTIONS

*12.10 The algebraic functions, logarithm and exponential functions, and the *trigonometric* and *inverse trigonometric functions* are called the elementary functions. There are many other mathematical functions which are studied in advanced work in mathematics. But the above functions constitute the bulk of those studied in elementary mathematics and through beginning calculus.

The trigonometric functions are usually first studied as functions of angles, in the sense that the size of the angle determines the value of

the function.   From this point of view the usefulness of the trigonometric functions is confined largely to the solution of triangles.   However, trigonometry has a tremendously greater scope.   Its use in
advanced mathematics has little resemblance to the solution of triangles.   In fact the trigonometric functions can be defined in terms of
number alone as convergent infinite series.   When this is done a relationship which is startlingly unexpected may be established between
them and the exponential functions.   We shall look into this in the
final section of this chapter.

We shall define the trigonometric functions in the same manner as
we have treated the other functions, namely as a set of ordered number
pairs.

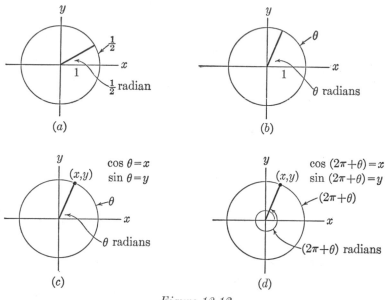

Figure 12.13

Recall (Section 8.8) the definition of a radian as a measure of angle.
In Figure 12.13(a), if angle α is $\frac{1}{2}$ radian, then its corresponding arc is
$\frac{1}{2}$ radius in length.   But if the radius of the circle is taken as unity,
then the length of the arc is $\frac{1}{2}$.   In general, with a unit radius the
angle of θ radians subtends an arc whose length is θ units.

If we start with the positive half of the x-axis and rotate counter-
clockwise through an angle of θ radians, the end of the radius moves
through a positive arc θ radii long.   We designate (x, y) as the coordinates of the end of the radius in its terminal position.   If we rotate
clockwise we generate a negative arc.   Corresponding to each arc

length θ there is a unique (x, y) pair. We define the sine (sin) and cosine (cos) functions as follows:

$$x = \cos \theta$$
$$y = \sin \theta$$

The length of arc θ is not confined to the first quadrant; in fact it is not confined to one revolution. We may see at once that as the arc continues to rotate through more than one revolution the same sequence of (x, y) coordinates repeats for each revolution. Although there is a unique x and a unique y corresponding to each arc length there are many arc lengths corresponding to each x or each y. We must, therefore, restrict the domain of the trigonometric functions if they are to have inverses.

The inverse of sin x is written $\sin^{-1} x$. It is read either "inverse sine of x" or "arc sine of x," and it means "that arc which has x for its sine." It does not mean the reciprocal of sine x; that is $1/\sin x$. Since the circumference of the circle is 2π times its radius, the unit circle has an arc length of 2π. The length of an arc of one quadrant is $\frac{1}{4}$ of this, or $\pi/2$ units; of two quadrants, π units; and of three quadrants, $3\pi/2$ units.

Since all (x, y) pairs which determine the sine and cosine functions lie on the unit circle, neither $|x|$ nor $|y|$ can ever exceed 1. The domain of both the sine and cosine is the set of real numbers. The range of each is the subset of real numbers equal to or less than 1 in absolute value. The following pairs are elements of the sine function; they can be obtained directly from Figure 12.13: $(0, 0)$, $(\pi/2, 1)$, $(\pi, 0)$, $(3\pi/2, -1)$. Likewise, the following are elements of the cosine function: $(0, 1)$, $(\pi/2, 0)$, $(\pi, -1)$, $(3\pi/2, 0)$. From these values we may verify that $\sin^2 0 + \cos^2 0 = 1$. $\sin^2 0$ is read "sine square zero" and simply means the sine of zero times itself. Since the sine of zero is 0, $\sin^2 0 = 0 \times 0 = 0$; and since $\cos 0 = 1$, $\cos^2 0 = 1 \times 1 = 1$. Therefore $\sin^2 0 + \cos^2 0 = 0 + 1 = 1$. In the same fashion we may show $\sin^2 \pi/2 + \cos^2 \pi/2 = 1$. Similarly for π and $3\pi/2$. The property holds for any other arc, regardless of the quadrant in which it terminates, since the Pythagorean Theorem gives $x^2 + y^2 = 1$ for any point on the unit circle. This relationship, $\sin^2 \theta + \cos^2 \theta = 1$, being true regardless of the value of θ, is an identity.

We observed that the same set of (x, y) coordinates recur over again once each revolution, or each arc of length 2π. However, the same set of x values recurs two times in one complete cycle. We may verify from Figure 12.13 that x varies from 1 to 0 in the first quadrant, 0 to -1 in the second, -1 to 0 in the third, and 0 to $+1$ in the fourth.

The basic set of values which occur in the first quadrant is repeated in reverse order with opposite sign in the second quadrant, the same order and opposite sign in the third quadrant, and reverse order and same sign in the fourth.

In a similar manner the sine repeats the same basic sequence four times. We see that y varies from 0 to 1 in the first quadrant, 1 to 0 in the second, 0 to -1 in the third, and -1 to 0 in the fourth. Its values in the second quadrant are those of the first quadrant in reverse order. In the third quadrant we have the same order as in the first but with opposite sign, and in the fourth quadrant both order and sign are changed.

The above facts make it possible to find a function of any arc when we know the functions of arcs between 0 and $\pi/2$. For this reason it is customary for tables to give the functions only through this range of values. As a matter of fact, the sine and cosine utilize the same set of values for dependent variable. In the first and third quadrants the values of the sine are those of the cosine in reverse order, and in the second and fourth quadrants both order and sign are reversed. These relationships are inherent in the identity $\sin^2 \theta + \cos^2 \theta = 1$.

The other trigonometric functions are defined in terms of sine and cosine. They are tangent (tan), cotangent (cot), secant (sec), and cosecant (csc). They are defined as follows:

$$\tan \theta = \sin \theta / \cos \theta = y/x$$
$$\cot \theta = \cos \theta / \sin \theta = x/y$$
$$\sec \theta = 1/\cos \theta = 1/x$$
$$\csc \theta = 1/\sin \theta = 1/y$$

Thus the six functions are three functions and their reciprocals (not inverses). Since these four functions are defined in terms of sine and cosine which are related by $\sin^2 \theta + \cos^2 \theta = 1$, any one of the six functions can be expressed in terms of any other.

Table 12.5 gives arcs and corresponding functions for arcs from 0 through $\pi/2$. Sine, cosine, and tangent are given. The other three functions are the reciprocals of these three. The table is actually three tables combined into one. Corresponding to each value of the independent variable, arc, in the table there is a value for each of the three dependent variables. For example, opposite the arc .75 we find, under sin, .6816; under cos, .7317; and under tan, .9316. This line of the table represents one element from each of the three functions. The number couple (.75, .6816) is an element of the sine function, the couple (.75, .7317) an element of the cosine function, and the couple (.75, .9316) an element of the tangent function.   Each function has an

Table 12.5   Trigonometric functions — sine, cosine, and tangent.

Arc	Sine	Cosine	Tangent
.00	.0000	1.000	.0000
.05	.0500	.9988	.0500
.10	.0998	.9950	.1003
.15	.1494	.9888	.1511
.20	.1987	.9801	.2027
.25	.2470	.9689	.2553
.30	.2955	.9553	.3093
.35	.3429	.9394	.3650
.40	.3894	.9211	.4228
.45	.4350	.9005	.4831
.50	.4794	.8776	.5463
.55	.5227	.8525	.6131
.60	.5646	.8253	.6841
.65	.6052	.7961	.7602
.70	.6442	.7648	.8423
.75	.6816	.7317	.9316
$\pi/4$	.7071	.7071	1.000
.80	.7174	.6967	1.030
.85	.7513	.6560	1.138
.90	.7833	.6216	1.260
.95	.8134	.5817	1.398
1.00	.8415	.5403	1.557
1.05	.8674	.4976	1.743
1.10	.8912	.4536	1.965
1.15	.9128	.4085	2.235
1.20	.9320	.3624	2.572
1.25	.9490	.3153	3.010
1.30	.9636	.2675	3.602
1.35	.9757	.2190	4.455
1.40	.9855	.1700	5.798
1.45	.9927	.1205	8.238
1.50	.9975	.0707	14.10
1.55	.9998	.0208	48.08
$\pi/2$	1.000	.0000	....

infinite number of elements.   The table does not define the function, it merely gives selected elements of the function.   For that matter, it only gives approximate values for most of those selected elements. The sine of the arc .75 is .6816 to four significant digits, not exactly

.6816.   The exact value is irrational, and thus an endless nonrepeating decimal.

By utilizing the manner in which the functions recur, as discussed above, we may find the function of any arc from this table.

Example 1   Find sin $(\pi + .2)$.

The arc $(\pi + .2)$ terminates in the third quadrant.   In the third quadrant the sine function goes through the same cycle of values that it does in the first, except that the sign is changed.   Then sin $(\pi + .2) = -\sin .2 = -.1987$.

Example 2   Find cos $(7\pi/2 + .35)$.

The arc $(7\pi/2 + .35)$ terminates in the fourth quadrant.   In the fourth quadrant the cosine goes through the same cycle of values as in the first but in reverse order.   Then cos $(7\pi/2 + .35) = \cos (\pi/2 - .35) = \cos 1.22 = .3436$.   Here we approximate π as 3.14 and we find cos 1.22 by interpolation.   We take for cos 1.22 the value which is four tenths of the way between cos 1.20 and cos 1.25.

Trigonometric functions other than the six we have discussed are used on occasion; they are useful in special types of problems.   Among them are the versed sine, coversed sine, and haversine.

THE EXPONENTIAL AND TRIGONOMETRIC FUNCTIONS RELATED

*12.11   Since by definition $e = \lim_{n \to \infty} (1 + 1/n)^n$, we can express e^x as a limit also:

$$e^x = [\lim_{n \to \infty} (1 + 1/n)^n]^x$$

It is developed in the theory of limits that this is equivalent to

$$e^x = \lim_{n \to \infty} (1 + 1/n)^{nx}$$

The expression $(1 + 1/n)^{nx}$ can be expanded by the binomial theorem (Section 10.12).

$$(1 + 1/n)^{nx} = 1^{nx} + nx \, 1^{nx-1} (1/n) + \frac{nx(nx - 1)}{1 \cdot 2} 1^{nx-2} (1/n)^2$$

$$+ \frac{nx(nx - 1)(nx - 2)}{1 \cdot 2 \cdot 3} 1^{nx-3} (1/n)^3 + \cdots$$

If we take the limit of each term as $n \to \infty$ . . . it is shown in the calculus that we get

$$e^x = 1 + x + x^2/(1 \cdot 2) + x^3/(1 \cdot 2 \cdot 3) + \cdots$$

We may also obtain from the calculus the values for sin x and cos x as infinite series:

$$\sin x = x - x^3/(1 \cdot 2 \cdot 3) + x^5/(1 \cdot 2 \cdot 3 \cdot 4 \cdot 5)$$
$$- x^7/(1 \cdot 2 \cdot 3 \cdot 4 \cdot 5 \cdot 6 \cdot 7) + \ldots$$
$$\cos x = 1 - x^2/(1 \cdot 2) + x^4/(1 \cdot 2 \cdot 3 \cdot 4)$$
$$- x^6/(1 \cdot 2 \cdot 3 \cdot 4 \cdot 5 \cdot 6) + \ldots$$

These functions, e^x, sin x, and cos x, have been defined for the domain of real numbers. The above series gives the same results as the definitions. If we wish to extend the domain of definition to the complex numbers we will have to find new definitions. Sin $5i$ is meaningless under our definition of the sine function because there is no arc $5i$ units long. This is the same kind of situation we were faced with when we wished to extend the notion of an exponent beyond natural numbers as exponents. Since the above infinite series give correct results for real values of x we can let the series *define* the functions in the complex domain. When the trigonometric functions are defined in this way we are dealing with number couples only; angles and arcs are superfluous.

Let us replace x with ix in the series which defines e^x.

$$e^{ix} = 1 + ix + (ix)^2/(1 \cdot 2) + (ix)^3/(1 \cdot 2 \cdot 3)$$
$$+ (ix)^4/(1 \cdot 2 \cdot 3 \cdot 4) + (ix)^5/(1 \cdot 2 \cdot 3 \cdot 4 \cdot 5)$$
$$+ (ix)^6/(1 \cdot 2 \cdot 3 \cdot 4 \cdot 5 \cdot 6)$$
$$+ (ix)^7/(1 \cdot 2 \cdot 3 \cdot 4 \cdot 5 \cdot 6 \cdot 7) + \ldots$$
$$= 1 + ix + i^2x^2/(1 \cdot 2) + i^3x^3/(1 \cdot 2 \cdot 3)$$
$$+ i^4x^4/(1 \cdot 2 \cdot 3 \cdot 4) + i^5x^5/(1 \cdot 2 \cdot 3 \cdot 4 \cdot 5)$$
$$+ i^6x^6/(1 \cdot 2 \cdot 3 \quad 4 \cdot 5 \cdot 6)$$
$$+ i^7x^7/(1 \cdot 2 \cdot 3 \cdot 4 \cdot 5 \cdot 6 \cdot 7) + \ldots$$
$$= 1 + ix - x^2/(1 \cdot 2) - ix^3/(1 \cdot 2 \cdot 3)$$
$$+ x^4/(1 \cdot 2 \cdot 3 \cdot 4) + ix^5/(1 \cdot 2 \cdot 3 \cdot 4 \cdot 5)$$
$$- x^6/(1 \cdot 2 \cdot 3 \cdot 4 \cdot 5 \cdot 6)$$
$$- ix^7/(1 \cdot 2 \cdot 3 \cdot 4 \cdot 5 \cdot 6 \cdot 7) + \ldots$$
$$= [1 - x^2/(1 \cdot 2) + x^4/(1 \cdot 2 \cdot 3 \cdot 4)$$
$$- x^6/(1 \cdot 2 \cdot 3 \cdot 4 \cdot 5 \cdot 6) + \ldots]$$
$$+ i[x - x^3/(1 \cdot 2 \cdot 3) + x^5/(1 \cdot 2 \cdot 3 \cdot 4 \cdot 5)$$
$$- x^7/(1 \cdot 2 \cdot 3 \cdot 4 \cdot 5 \cdot 6 \cdot 7) + \ldots]$$

But the real component is the series definition of cos x, and the imaginary component is sin x. Therefore we have

$$e^{ix} = \cos x + i \sin x$$

thus relating the exponential and the trigonometric functions.   Finally, if we let $x = \pi$ we get

$$e^{i\pi} = -1 \text{ or } e^{i\pi} + 1 = 0$$

which brings together five most important constants, two transcendental and one imaginary, in an unbelievably simple relationship.

──────────── * E   X   E   R   C   I   S   E   S ────────────

1. For what values of x, between 0 and 2π, is sin x positive? Cos x? Tan x?

2. What is the range of sec x? Tan x?

3. For what values of x is tan x undefined? Cot x? Sec x? Csc x?

4. Find the following.
    (a) sin $(\pi/2 + .40)$ (b) tan 6.38   (c) cos (-1.30)

5. Distinguish between $\cos^{-1} x$, $(\cos x)^{-1}$, and $\cos x^{-1}$.

6. Find three values for x if
    (a) sin $x = .6052$ (b) cos $x = .9950$ (c) tan $x = 1.187$

7. Find the value of e to three significant figures by replacing x with 1 in the infinite series which defines e^x.   Compare this with Exercise 6, Section 12.9.

8. Use the infinite series definition of sin x to find sin .25.   Compare this with the value in Table 12.5.

9. Find e^2 to three significant figures.

10. Find e^i to three significant figures in the form $a + bi$.

BIBLIOGRAPHY

Allendoerfer, C. B., and C. O. Oakley. *Principles of Mathematics.* New York: McGraw-Hill Book Co., 1955.

Andrews, F. E. *New Numbers.* New York: Essential Books, 1944.

Ball, W. W. R. *A Short Account of the History of Mathematics.* Boston: Houghton Mifflin Co., 1930.

_____. *Mathematical Recreations and Essays* (11th ed.). New York: Macmillan Co., 1939.

Bell, E. T. *Men of Mathematics.* New York: Simon and Schuster, 1937.

_____. *Numerology.* Baltimore: Williams & Wilkins Co., 1933.

Boyer, L. E. *Mathematics, A Historical Development.* New York: Henry Holt & Co., 1946.

Cajorie, Florian. *A History of Mathematical Notations,* Vol. I. Chicago: Open Court, 1928.

Courant, Richard, and Herbert Robbins. *What Is Mathematics?* New York: Oxford University Press, 1941.

Dantzig, Tobias. *Number: The Language of Science* (2nd ed.). New York: Macmillan Co., 1933.

Dresden, Arnold. *An Invitation to Mathematics.* New York: Henry Holt & Co., 1936.

Dudeney, H. E. *Amusements in Mathematics.* London: Thomas Nelson and Sons, 1917.

Eves, Howard, and Carroll V. Newson. *An Introduction to the Foundations and Fundamental Concepts of Mathematics.* New York: Rinehart & Co., 1958.

Harkin, Duncan. *Fundamental Mathematics.* New York: Prentice Hall, 1941.

Hogben, Lancelot. *Mathematics for the Millions.* New York: W. W. Norton & Company, 1937.

Hooper, Alfred. *Makers of Mathematics.* New York: Random House, 1948.

Jones, Burton W. *Elementary Concepts of Mathematics.* New York: Macmillan Co., 1947.

Karpinski, Louis Charles. *The History of Arithmetic.* New York: Rand McNally & Co., 1925.

Kasner, Edward, and James Newman. *Mathematics and the Imagination.* New York: Simon and Schuster, 1940.

Kemeny, John G., J. Lauris Snell, and Gerold L. Thompson. *Introduction to Finite Mathematics.* Englewood Cliffs, N. J.: Prentice Hall, 1957.

Kraitchik, Maurice. *Mathematical Recreations.* New York: W. W. Norton & Co., 1942.

Lieber, Lillian R., and Hugh G. Lieber. *The Education of T. C. Mits.* New York: W. W. Norton & Co., 1941.

Merriman, G. M. *To Discover Mathematics.* New York: John Wiley & Sons, 1942.

Meserve, Bruce E. *Fundamental Concepts of Algebra.* Cambridge, Mass.: Addison-Wesley Publishing Co., 1953.

———. *Fundamental Concepts of Geometry.* Cambridge, Mass: Addison-Wesley Publishing Co., 1955.

Moore, John T. *Fundamental Principles of Mathematics.* New York: Rinehart & Co., 1960.

National Council of Teachers of Mathematics, The. *Insights into Modern Mathematics.* Washington: The National Council of Teachers of Mathematics, 1957.

National Council of Teachers of Mathematics, The. *The Metric System of Weights and Measures.* New York: Bureau of Publications, Teachers College, Columbia University, 1948.

Richards, R. K. *Arithmetic Operations in Digital Computers.* New York: D. Van Nostrand Co., 1955.

Richardson, M. *Fundamentals of Mathematics.* New York: Macmillan Co., 1958.

Sanford, Vera. *A Short History of Mathematics.* Boston: Houghton Mifflin Co., 1930.

Schaaf, William L. *Basic Concepts of Elementary Mathematics.* New York: John Wiley & Sons, 1960.

Smith, D. E. *History of Mathematics,* Vol. I and II. Boston: Ginn & Co., 1925.

Smith, D. E., and Jekuthiel Ginsburg. *Numbers and Numerals.* New York: Teachers College, Columbia University, 1937.

Stabler, E. R. *An Introduction to Mathematical Thought.* Cambridge, Mass.: Addison-Wesley Publishing Co., 1953.

Steinhaus, H. *Mathematical Snapshots.* New York: Oxford University Press, 1950.

ANSWERS

SECTION 1.6   *page 7*

1. "We do not know what we are talking about" means we use undefined terms; "Whether what we say about it is so" means our conclusions are based on unproved assumptions.

3. We probably would not accept either the axiom or the definition because of the possibility of parallel lines.   But if we did accept them we would be forced to accept the theorem.

5. We could define perpendicular lines as lines which form equal adjacent angles.

SECTION 2.2   *page 12*

1. (a) p: The Dodgers won the pennant.   (f) p: Sue likes cats.
          q: The White Sox won the pennant. q: Sue likes dogs.
                        $p \wedge q$ $p \wedge \sim (\sim q)$

2. (a) $\sim p \wedge q$ (e) $p \underline{\vee} \sim q$

4. (a)   Sam is rich and Tom is not handsome, or Jim is lucky.
    (f)   Sam is rich, or it is not true that Tom is handsome and Jim is lucky.

5. (a)   (d), (f), (g), (h)

7. (a)

$\sim$	p	$\vee$	q
F	T	T	T
F	T	F	F
T	F	T	T
T	F	T	F

p: This polygon is a square.

q: This polygon is a rectangle.

SECTION 2.3   *page 16*

1. (a) $p \rightarrow q$ (d) $q \rightarrow p$
    (c) $q \rightarrow p$ (e) $p \rightarrow q, q \rightarrow p$

3.

(~	p	∨	q)	↔	(p	→	q)
F	T	T	T	T	T	T	T
F	T	F	F	T	T	F	F
T	F	T	T	T	F	T	T
T	F	T	F	T	F	T	F

6. "It is false that p is true and q is false" is equivalent to "p is false **or** q is true."

9.

(p	→	q)	∧	p
T	T	T	T	T
T	F	F	F	T
F	T	T	F	F
F	T	F	F	F

We must concede that q is true.

10. That p is false.

12. Nothing.

SECTION 2.4   *page 20*

1. $[(m \to p) \land (p \to a)] \to (m \to a)$

5. False.

6.

all cats are animals   some animals are cats

all tigers are cats   some cats are tigers

all tigers are animals   some animals are tigers

8. (a)   *Hypothesis:* Mr. Jones goes to church.
               Churchgoers are good.
        Conclusion: Mr. Jones is a good man.   (Valid)

    (c)   *Hypothesis:* Kind people are honest.
               Mr. Jones is unkind.
        Conclusion: Mr. Jones is not honest.   (Not valid)

    (e)   *Hypothesis:* Beautiful movie actresses smoke X brand cigarettes.
               You smoke X brand cigarettes.
        Conclusion: You are beautiful.   (Not valid)

    (g)   *Hypothesis:* Anyone who does not study cannot pass this course.
               Mary does study.
        Conclusion: Mary will pass this course.   (Not valid)

SECTION 2.5 *page 24*

1. (a) *Converse:* If my feet hurt today it will rain tomorrow.
         Inverse: If it does not rain tomorrow my feet will not hurt today.
         Contrapositive: If my feet do not hurt today it will not rain tomorrow.
    (h) *Converse:* If a number is odd it ends in 7.
         Inverse: If a number does not end in 7 it is not odd.
         Contrapositive: If a number is not odd it does not end in 7.
3. (a) *Converse:* $(q \vee \sim r) \to \sim p$
         Inverse: $p \to \sim(q \vee \sim r)$
         Contrapositive: $\sim(q \vee \sim r) \to p$
    (c) *Converse:* $\sim p \to \sim q$
         Inverse: $q \to p$
         Contrapositive: $p \to q$
6. (c), (d)

SECTION 2.7 *page 27*

1. (a) Necessary but not sufficient
    (c) Necessary and sufficient
    (e) Neither necessary nor sufficient
    (g) Neither necessary nor sufficient
2. (a) An inductive conclusion is not certain.
    (c) Reasoning in a circle
    (e) A converse of a valid proposition is not necessarily valid.
4. (a) $\sim p \to \sim q$ (c) $p \to q$
    (b) $p \to q$ (f) $p \leftrightarrow q$
5. (c) Rain today is a sufficient condition for postponement of the base-ball game, and it is not true that no rain today is a sufficient condition not to postpone the baseball game.   In other words: in case of rain, no game; but there may not be one anyway.
7. (b)
10. Necessary but not sufficient.   Product is odd if, and only if, *all* factors are odd.

SECTION 2.8 *page 34*

1. (a) $x = 0$ (f) Any value of x
    (b) None   (g) $x = 8$
    (c) $x = 8$ (h) No condition
    (d) $x = 14$ (i) $x = 6$
    (e) $x = 1$ or 3 (j) $x = 3$

SECTION 2.9   *page 37*

2. If a natural number has at least one odd factor, the number is odd. (False)

4. Four is a perfect square.

6.

$[(H$	$\wedge$	$\sim$	$C)$	$\rightarrow$	$C]$	$\leftrightarrow$	$(H$	$\rightarrow$	$C)$
T	F	F	T	T	T	T	T	T	T
T	T	T	F	F	F	T	T	F	F
F	F	F	T	T	T	T	F	T	T
F	F	T	F	T	F	T	F	T	F

8. They are contradictions.

10. $[(r \rightarrow p) \wedge \sim p] \rightarrow \sim r$ is a tautology.

12. Show that the assumption $a/b = \sqrt{3}$ requires that both a and b have the factor 3.

SECTION 2.10   *page 40*

1. The nth odd integer is $2n - 1$.

3. $2^{64} - 1$

5. $\dfrac{n(n+1)}{2}$

SECTION 2.11   *page 43*

1. (b) Lower   (d) No   (f) 2π feet

5. $1^3 + 2^3 + \ldots + n^3 = (1 + 2 + \ldots + n)^2$

7. No. It is independent of your assumptions.

8. There is no parallel, etc. There is more than one parallel, etc.

10. Quite likely it is an induction.

SECTION 3.1   *page 50*

1. 1898

3. MCCCLXXXIV

4. MMMMMCCCLXX

7. CCLXXXVIII

9. MMLIV

11. DLXXXVIII

SECTION 3.2   *page 52*

1. (a) DXLVI, ℂℂℂℂℂ ∩∩∩∩ ׀׀׀׀׀

    (c) MCXI, 𝄃ℂ∩׀

3. (b) MCXCIII

4. (a) 𝄃ℂ∩∩∩ ׀׀׀

5. (b) CCLII

6. (c) ℂℂℂ׀׀׀

8. MMMCDXXXII

9. ׀𝄃ℂℂℂℂℂ ∩∩∩∩∩∩∩∩∩ ׀׀

SECTION 3.3   *page 53*

2. /CXOC

3. Eleven months, 29 days

5. Fox

6. (b) Ψ K H
    (c) /B Υ K E

7. (b) Υ N A

SECTION 3.6   *page 58*

1. 1758

6. 7694

7. 45 years, 3 months, 15 days

SECTION 3.9   *page 63*

1. (a) 4   (k) $\dfrac{1}{49}$
    (c) 1
    (e) b^2 (m) 81
    (g) a^3 (o) 729
    (i) 1

4. $1 \times 10^4 + 6 \times 10^3 + 5 \times 10^2 + 5 \times 10 + 3$

SECTION 3.11   *page 68*

1.   (a)   196   (c)   205   (f)   82
2.   (a) 110110000_2 7.   No, no, yes.
4.   131 cannot, 31 can.   9.   (b)   101
5.   Eight   11. 111011110_2

SECTION 3.12   *page 71*

2.

+	0	1	2	3
0	0	1	2	3
1	1	2	3	10
2	2	3	10	11
3	3	10	11	12

×	0	1	2	3
0	0	0	0	0
1	0	1	2	3
2	0	2	10	12
3	0	3	12	21

4.   33300

6.   2212

10.   Express in base 3.   Replace each coefficient 2 with $(3 - 1)$.

11.   1690

13. $3t3_{11}$

16.   Factors of 36_{10} are 2, 3, 4, 6, 9, 12, 18.   Factors of 36_{12} are 2, 3, 6, 7, 14, 21.

SECTION 3.13   *page 75*

1. 357_{12} 499_{10} 6.   (a) $\sim \square \square \sim$
3. $175.7 - .5$ 8.   (a) $\square \triangle \square \sim$
5.   (a) $\square \triangle \triangle \triangle \sim \sim \sim \checkmark$

SECTION 4.4   *page 84*

2.   They can be paired in 24 different ways.

4.   The names of the months with the first 12 number names.

6.   (b)   4, cardinal; 24, ordinal   (g)   14, cardinal; 156, ordinal

8. $1/1$ $1/2$ $1/3 \ldots 1/n \ldots$
     $\updownarrow$ $\updownarrow$ $\updownarrow$ $\updownarrow$
     1 2 $3 \ldots n \ldots$

SECTION 4.6   *page 89*

2.   (a), (d)

4.   Commutative and associative axioms

6.   The addends of a sum may be arranged in any order without changing the sum.

8. $[(a + b) + c] + d = (a + b) + (c + d)$ by A_1
     $(a + b) + (c + d) = (c + d) + (b + a)$ by A_2
     $(c + d) + (b + a) = c + [d + (b + a)]$ by A_1

12. Change $+$ in the proofs of Exercises 5 and 7 to $\times$ and you have proofs of Exercises 10 and 11 respectively.

SECTION 4.8   *page 93*

1.   (a), (c), (d)

2.   (a) A_2 (d) A_5
     (b) A_4 (e) A_1
     (c) A_5

3.   Try $a = 4$, $b = 5$, and $c = 6$.

5. $a = 2, b = 3, c = 4$
     $a = 3, b = 5, c = 6$
     $a = 4, b = 7, c = 8$

7. $a(b + c + d) = a[b + (c + d)] = ab + a(c + d) = ab + ac + ad$

11. No.   No.

SECTION 4.11   *page 98*

1.   (a), (d)

2.   No.

3.   Relationship holds if and only if $c = 0$.

5.   No.

7.   (a) $60 \div (4 \cdot 3) - 2$ (c) $60 \div 4 \cdot (3 - 2)$
     (b) $60 \div 4 \cdot 3 - 2$ (d) $60 \div (4 \cdot 3 - 2)$

9.   Why is the following undefined: $0^5 \div 0^5 = 0^0$?

11. No; otherwise $a + 1 = 1$ for any a.

13. Addition is associative.

SECTION 4.12   *page 104*

2.   We add $999 - 276$, then subtract 1000, and add 1.

4.
$$136 \times 73$$

272	36
544	18
1088	9
2176	4
4352	2
8704	1

9928

7.
```
       9
       5
      54
    7332
    6476
  113516
     538
   32777
     322
       3
```

9.

```
        6        3        5
     ┌────────┬────────┬────────┐
  1  │ 1    / │ 0    / │ 1    / │
     │    /4  │    /6  │    /2  │ 2
     ├────────┼────────┼────────┤
  6  │ 0    / │ 0    / │ 0    / │
     │    /6  │    /3  │    /5  │ 1
     ├────────┼────────┼────────┤
  0  │ 2    / │ 1    / │ 1    / │
     │    /2  │    /1  │    /7  │ 3
     └────────┴────────┴────────┘
        0        7        7
```

12.
$$234_5 \times 43_5$$

1023	21
2101	10
4202	2
13404	1

22322

SECTION 4.13   *page 107*

2.   (a) $4 + 3 + 3 + 6 = 16; 1 + 6 = 7.$
$1 + 7 + 0 + 2 = 10; 1 + 0 = 1.$
$7 - 1 = 6.$
$2 + 6 + 3 + 4 = 15; 1 + 5 = 6.$

   (b) $8 + 2 + 5 + 4 = 19; 1 + 9 = 10; 1 + 0 = 1.$
$7 + 6 + 4 + 1 = 18; 1 + 8 = 9 \equiv 0.$
$1 - 0 = 1.$
$6 + 1 + 3 = 10; 1 + 0 = 1.$

4. $4 + 3 + 5 = 12; 1 + 2 = 3. \quad 2 + 0 + 0 = 2. \quad 3 \times 2 = 6.$
$3 + 4 + 6 = 13; 1 + 3 = 4. \quad 6 + 4 = 10. \quad 1 + 0 = 1.$
$8 + 7 + 3 + 4 + 6 = 28; 2 + 8 = 10; 1 + 0 = 1.$

SECTION 4.14   *page 111*

2. $5 + 8 + 3 = 16; 1 + 6 = 7; 4 + 2 + 7 = 13; 1 + 3 = 4; 4 \times 7 = 28;$
$2 + 8 = 10, 1 + 0 = 1.$
$2 + 4 + 8 + 9 + 4 + 1 = 28, 2 + 8 = 10; 1 + 0 = 1.$

4. $8 + 3 + 1 = 10, \quad 1 + 0 = 1; \quad 1 + 7 + 3 = e \equiv 0; \quad 1 + 1 + 2 + e$
$+ 4 + 3 = 1t; 1 + t = e \equiv 0.$

6. $68 + 140 = 208 \equiv 0$, mod 13; $3 + 10 = 13 \equiv 0$, mod 13

8. (a) $8n + 2$ (b) $9n + 4$ (c) $5n + 4$ (d) $7n + 1$

10. To show the commutative property holds: If $A \equiv a$ and $B \equiv b$, then $AB \equiv ab$ and $BA \equiv ba$. But $AB \equiv BA$; therefore $ab \equiv ba$.

SECTION 4.16 *page 115*

1. (a) $2, 3, 4, 6$; remainder 2 upon division by 5, remainder 4 upon division by 8, and remainder 6 upon division by 9
    (c) Remainder 1 upon division by 2, remainder 0 upon division by 3, remainder 3 upon division by 4, remainder 1 upon division by 5, remainder 3 upon division by 8, and remainder 6 upon division by 9

4. Not necessarily; five is not a factor of 12.

6. The number is divisible by 4 if and only if the units digit plus two times the tens digit is divisible by 4.

SECTION 5.3 *page 123*

1. Construct modulo 5 addition table.
    (1) Content of cells gives closure.
    (2) Congruence is associative.
    (3) The identity 0 can be verified from the table.
    (4) Inverses are 1–4 and 2–3.

3. Do not have closure since $2 \times 2 = 0$.

4. Yes.

6. The correspondence of elements is $1 \leftrightarrow 360°$, $2 \leftrightarrow 90°$, $4 \leftrightarrow 180°$, $3 \leftrightarrow 270°$.

8. No.

9. Yes.

10. No.

SECTION 5.4 *page 128*

2. (a) $\begin{pmatrix} 123 \\ 321 \end{pmatrix} \cdot \begin{pmatrix} 123 \\ 213 \end{pmatrix} = \begin{pmatrix} 123 \\ 312 \end{pmatrix} = c$

    (b) $\begin{pmatrix} 123 \\ 312 \end{pmatrix} \cdot \begin{pmatrix} 123 \\ 132 \end{pmatrix} = \begin{pmatrix} 123 \\ 213 \end{pmatrix} = f$

    (c) $\begin{pmatrix} 123 \\ 213 \end{pmatrix} \cdot \begin{pmatrix} 123 \\ 321 \end{pmatrix} = \begin{pmatrix} 123 \\ 231 \end{pmatrix} = b$

4. $\begin{pmatrix}1234\\1234\end{pmatrix} = a,$ $\begin{pmatrix}1234\\2341\end{pmatrix} = b$

$\begin{pmatrix}1234\\3412\end{pmatrix} = c,$ $\begin{pmatrix}1234\\4123\end{pmatrix} = d$

	a	b	c	d
a	a	b	c	d
b	b	c	d	a
c	c	d	a	b
d	d	a	b	c

6. $\begin{pmatrix}1234\\1234\end{pmatrix} = a,$ $\begin{pmatrix}1234\\2143\end{pmatrix} = e$

$\begin{pmatrix}1234\\4321\end{pmatrix} = f,$ $\begin{pmatrix}1234\\3412\end{pmatrix} = c$

	a	e	f	c
a	a	e	f	c
e	e	a	c	f
f	f	c	a	e
c	c	f	e	a

8. No.

10. No, inverse property not satisfied.

SECTION 5.5   page 130

2. Yes. $E \leftrightarrow 0, 0 \leftrightarrow 1$.

4. No. Nonzero elements are not a multiplication group. Closure and inverse properties not satisfied.

6.

+	0	1	2	3
0	0	1	2	3
1	1	2	3	10
2	2	3	10	11
3	3	10	11	12

×	0	1	2	3
0	0	0	0	0
1	0	1	2	3
2	0	2	10	12
3	0	3	12	21

8. No. Divisors of zero must have a factor in common with the modulus.

10. The modulus must be a prime number.

SECTION 5.6   page 132

2. $3(4 + 2) = 3 \cdot 4 + 3 \cdot 2$
   $3 \cdot 1 = 2 + 1$
   $3 = 3$

5. If a number congruent to 3, modulo 5, is divisible by a number congruent to 4, modulo 5, the quotient is congruent to 2, modulo 5.

7. $2 + 2 \equiv 4, 3 + 4 \equiv 2$. The modulo 5 field is not ordered.

9. It is its own inverse. Element 4.

SECTION 5.9 *page 139*

1. (a) (6, 5)   (b) (7, 5)   (c) (9, 1)   (d) (5, 11)
3. (a) (8, 8)   (b) (23, 26)   (c) (18,24)   (d) (15, 12)
5. (a) (8, 2)   (b) (24, 6)   (c) (4, 6)   (d) (2, 5)
7. $(0, b) < (c, 0)$ because $0 + 0 < b + c$.
10. $(0, b) < (a, a)$ because $0 + a < b + a$.

SECTION 5.11 *page 144*

2. (a) $[(+1) + (-4)] + (+3) = (+1) + [(-4) + (+3)]$
    (b) $(-3) + (-2) = (-2) + (-3)$
    (c) $(-2) + 0 = (-2)$
    (d) $[(+5) + (-3)] + (+2) = +5 + [(-3) + (+2)]$
4. (a) $[(-3) \cdot (+6)] \cdot (+2) = (-3) \cdot [(+6) \cdot (+2)]$
    (b) $(+4) \cdot (+4) = (+4) \cdot (+4)$
    (c) $(+5) \cdot (-1) = -5$
    (d) $[(+5) \cdot (-3)] \cdot (-4) = +5 \cdot [(-3) \cdot (-4)]$
6. (a) $(+2) \cdot [(-3) + (-3)] = (+2) \cdot (-3) + (+2) \cdot (-3)$
    (b) $(-4) \cdot [(+3) + (-4)] = (-4) \cdot (+3) + (-4) \cdot (-4)$
    (c) $(+2) \cdot [(-3) + (+7)] = (+2) \cdot (-3) + (+2) \cdot (+7)$
8. (a) $(-4) - (+2)$
    (b) $(-5) - (+8)$
    (c) $(+4) - (+7)$
    (d) $(-7) - (-2)$
10. $2 \times 3 = 0 \times 3$ but $2 \neq 0$.

SECTION 5.12 *page 147*

1. (a) -6 (e) -3
    (b) $+45$ (f) $+9$
    (c) -60 (g) $+43$
    (d) $+1$ (h) $+12$
3. If b is a negative integer.
5. Nothing.   An even number of negative factors.
7. (a) For any positive values the last inequality will follow from the first two.
    (b) If a is positive and b, c, and d are negative the conclusion follows.
    (c) Any values that satisfy the first two inequalities will satisfy the third.

9.   If a, b are positive, we may write them $(a, 0)$, $(b, 0)$. The difference
        $(a, 0) - (b, 0) = a, b$. But (a, b) positive means the natural number
        $a >$ the natural number b. By D_3, $(a, 0) > (b, 0)$ if and only if $a > b$.
        If a is positive and b negative we may write them $(a, 0)$ and $(0, b)$. The
        difference $(a, 0) - (0, b) = [(a + b), 0]$ is always positive. Thus any
        positive integer is $>$ any negative integer.
        If a, b are negative we may write them $(0, a)$ and $(0, b)$. The difference
        $(0, a) - (0, b) = (b, a)$ is positive if and only if the natural number $b >$
        the natural number a. By D_3, $(0, a) > (0, b)$ if and only if $b > a$.

SECTION 5.13   *page 152*

2.   If we start at the left (or right) of zero and move to the right (or left), we
        must move a greater number of steps than we are from our starting
        position if we are to cross to the other side of zero.

4.   That $(-b) = (+b)$.

5.   (a) $(-5) - (-4) = (0, 5) - (0, 4)$ which by definition equals $(4, 5)$
              or -1. On the directed line "start at -5 and move to the *left
              minus* 4 steps means "start at -5 and move to the *right plus*
              4 steps" and this brings us to -1.

7.   965 years

9.   184 years nearer Thales

11.   4392 years when Columbus discovered America

13. $27°$ at foot; $-22°$ at top; $+7°$ at foot; $-27°$ at top; $37°$ at the foot; $-3°$
        at the foot; $3°$ at the top; $-37°$ at the top

15.   A $= -5.6$, B $= -3.4$, last reading 8.2

17. $-6[3 + (-5)] = -6(-2) = +12$
        $(-6) \cdot 3 + (-6)(-5) = -18 + 30 = +12$

18.   "Start at -6 and move to the right 3 steps." "Start at the opposite side
        of the origin, and the same distance from it, the position reached by start-
        ing at $+6$ and moving 3 steps to the left." They are the same in that
        we end up in the same place.

SECTION 5.16   *page 159*

1. $b = 9$

3.   (a) $(3, 5)$
        (b) $(-7, a)$ if a is positive, $(-9, a)$ if a is negative
        (c) $(-4, -6)$
        (d) $(-3, -3)$

5. (b) $(6, a) \cdot (2a, 4) = 3 = (2a, 4)(6, a)$

6. (d) $(2, -3) + (2, 3) = \{[3 \cdot 2 + (-3) \cdot 2], [(-3) \cdot 3]\} = (0, -9) = (0, 1)$

SECTION 5.17 *page 161*

2. $(a, b) \div (0, c) = (a \cdot c, b \cdot 0) = (ac, 0)$ but a second component zero is not permitted under the definition of rational numbers.

3. $(a, b) \cdot (c, d) = (ac, bd)$. If $(ac, bd) = (0, x)$ then $acx = 0$ but, since $x \neq 0$ and $a \neq 0$, then c must equal 0.

4. No.

SECTION 5.20 *page 165*

1. a/b is rational by definition of rational numbers; $a/b + c$ is rational because the rational numbers are closed under addition; $d - e$ is rational because the rational numbers are closed under subtraction. Therefore $\dfrac{(a/b) + c}{d - e}$ is rational because the rational numbers are closed under division.

3. If $a/b + c/d = (a + c)/(b + d)$, then $e/f(a/b + c/d) = \dfrac{e(a + c)}{f(b + d)} = \dfrac{ea + ec}{fb + fd}$. But if the distributive law holds, then $e/f(a/b + c/d) = e/f \cdot a/b + e/f \cdot c/d = ea/fb + ec/bd = \dfrac{ea + ec}{fb + bd}$, where the last equality results from our "definition" of addition.

5. Assume $1/a + 1/b = 2/(a + b)$. Then $(b + a)/ab = 2/(a + b)$, and $a^2 + 2ab + b^2 = 2ab$, and $a^2 + b^2 = 0$. But this is impossible since a^2 and b^2 are both positive.

8. To prove $a/b > a/c$ if $b < c$. If $b < c$ then $b^2ac < abc^2$, but this is the condition that $a/b > a/c$.

11. $10\frac{1}{2}$ oz. box is a better buy.

13. Show that $(ad + bc)/2bd$ is between a/b and c/d.

16. The integers and addition form a group, but the negative integers and addition do not. They lack the identity element and inverse elements.

18. Not under addition; they lack the identity element and inverse elements. They are a group under multiplication, the identity element being 1 and the inverse of a/b being b/a.

23. Yes.

1. (a) $\frac{1}{9}$ (f) $\frac{1}{32}$
    (b) 144   (g) 1
    (c) 25   (h) $x^{\frac{7}{6}}$
    (d) -2 (i) $\sqrt{a/b}$
    (e) 8

3. $(\sqrt[3]{64})^2 = 4^2 = 16; \sqrt[3]{64^2} = \sqrt[3]{4096} = 16$

5. $.346_8 = .5483_{12}$

7. .011 111 101
    Written in base 10, the above is
    $0 \times 2^{-1} + 1 \times 2^{-2} + 1 \times 2^{-3} + 1 \times 2^{-4} + 1 \times 2^{-5} + 1 \times 2^{-6}$
    $+ 1 \times 2^{-7} + 0 \times 2^{-8} + 1 \times 2^{-9}$
    $\quad = (0 \times 2^{-1} \times 2^3 + 1 \times 2^{-2} \times 2^3 + 1 \times 2^{-3} \times 2^3)2^{-3}$
    $\qquad + (1 \times 2^{-4} \times 2^6 + 1 \times 2^{-5} \times 2^6 + 1 \times 2^{-6} \times 2^6)2^{-6}$
    $\qquad + (1 \times 2^{-7} \times 2^9 + 0 \times 2^{-8} \times 2^9 + 1 \times 2^{-9} \times 2^9)2^{-9}$
    $\quad = 3 \times 8^{-1} + 7 \times 8^{-2} + 5 \times 8^{-3}$

8. 180.2_9

10. The required number of steps equals the exponent of the power of 2, or
    of 5, whichever is the greater, in the denominator.

1. (a) $-\frac{3}{4}$ (b) $-\frac{20}{3}$ (c) 1   (d) 8

3. (a) $\frac{3}{2}, -4$ (b) 3   (c) $0, -\frac{4}{3}$ (d) -1

4. (a) $x = 5$ (b) $x = 6$

5. (a) $a_0 = 2, a_1 = 2, a_2 = 6, a_3 = 5$
    (b) $a_0 = 1, a_1 = 3, a_2 = 5, a_3 = 4, a_4 = 1$

1. (a) -1 (d) 4
    (b) No solution   (e) Identity
    (c) Identity

3. (a) $x \equiv 2$
    (b) $x \equiv 2$
    (c) $x \equiv 2, \quad y \equiv 4$
    (d) $x \equiv 1, \quad y \equiv 3$
    (e) Inconsistent
    (f) Inconsistent

SECTION 6.5 *page 185*

1. (a) 4
   (b) 3
   (c) 6
   (d) $2a^2 - a + 3$
   (e) $2x^2 - x + 3$
   (f) $2x^2 + x + 3$

3. $(2, 1); (4, 1); (6, 3); (8, 3); (10, 5)$

5. $(1, 12)$ $(\frac{3}{4}, 12)$ $(-6, 12)$ $(12, 12)$ $(100, 12)$; in fact, (any rational number, 12) is an element.

7. Yes. The domain consists of the four countries. The range consists of the assigned populations.

10. Yes. Domain: natural numbers and zero. Range: natural numbers ≥ 5.

12. $f[g(x)] = (2x + 1)^2 - (2x + 1) + 3$
    $g[f(x)] = 2(x^2 - x + 3) + 1$

SECTION 6.9 *page 193*

1. (a) Circle graph is appropriate.
   (b) Broken-line graph
   (e) Broken-line graph

2. (b) Kind of unit used on vertical axis is not indicated. Bottom of graph is cut off, leaving impression 1932 and 1933 income was almost zero.

3.
Time	8:00	8:15	8:30 ...
Temperature	103	104	104.5 ...

SECTION 6.10 *page 199*

2. $\frac{1}{100} \cdot 15001 > 150$

3. First component is zero.

5. A straight line in Quadrants I and III, through the origin, making 45° angle with axes.

8. If the coefficient of x is unchanged the graphs are parallel. The constant indicates where the graph crosses the y-axis.

10. They should.

12. They should.

SECTION 6.11   *page 202*

1.   (1, 1000); (2, 500); (200, 5); (5, 200)

3. $f(x) = 3x + 5$.   Domain: the integers x such that $0 \leq x \leq 6$.   Range: integers $\equiv 2$, mod 3, such that $5 \leq f(x) \leq 23$.

5.   Graph is the set of discrete points in the table Exercise 4.

7.   (a) $-\frac{1}{4}$ (b) $-\frac{1}{4}$ (c) $2\frac{3}{4}$ (d) $2\frac{3}{4}$

9.   If the son's age S is a function of the father's age F, then $S = F - 24$; domain of F is $24 \leq F \leq 56$; range of S is $0 \leq S \leq 32$.

SECTION 7.1   *page 208*

1.
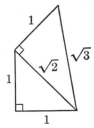

3.   If $4b^2 = a^2$ it does not follow that a must have 4 as a factor since $4 = 2 \times 2$.

5.   13 feet

7.   No.   Because an integer divided by $\sqrt{2}$ cannot be a rational number.
     If it could, $\sqrt{2}$ would be rational.

SECTION 7.3   *page 211*

2.   (a) $\dfrac{73}{445}$ (b) $\dfrac{611}{445}$ (c) $\dfrac{137}{111}$

4. $.26\overline{851} \ldots$

6. $.\overline{15} \ldots$

8. $.3762$ is one of infinitely many.

10. $\frac{1}{3}$ is $\frac{1}{3000}$ greater.

12. $\frac{1}{81} \times 9 = \frac{1}{9}$.   The decimal expansion of $\frac{1}{9}$ is $.111 \ldots$.   This times d gives $.ddd \ldots$

SECTION 7.4   *page 215*

2. $\frac{22}{7}$ is greater.   3.1416 is nearer π.

4.   (b) $500 \div 25 = 20$; $(20 + 25)/2 = 22.5$; $500 \div 22.5 = 22.2$; $(22.5 + 22.2)/2 = 22.35$; $500 \div 22.35 = 22.36$; $\sqrt{500} = 22.4$

6.   Because all rational numbers must be algebraic.

8. Any two different rational numbers can agree in only a finite number of digits. Consider the highest digit position in which they disagree. If the digits in this position are not consecutive integers select an integer between them. The required irrational number consists of the digits common to the rationals, a digit between the two in the position where the rationals disagree followed by an endless nonrepeating sequence.

Example: R .235793 ...
            I   235794010010001 ...
           R .235795

In case the first digit position where the rationals disagree is occupied by consecutive integers, let the irrational agree with the larger in this position and select a smaller value in the next lower position.

Example: R .23579595 ...
            I .235794010010001 ...
           R .23578999 ...

If the larger rational terminates in the position where they disagree, let the irrational agree with the smaller in this position and select a larger value in the next lower position.

Example: R .2357900 ...
            I .235788010010001 ...
           R .2357861 ...

11. No identity, not closed ($\sqrt{2} \cdot \sqrt{2} = 2$).

SECTION 7.6   *page 218*

2. No, $1/\sqrt{2}$ is a fraction but it is irrational.

4. Yes: $\sqrt{2} - (1 + \sqrt{2}) = -1$

6. Exercise 5(a): $x + 3 = 2; x = -1$
                 $x + 3 = -2; x = -5$
We get the two linear equations because a number has 2 square roots.

8. (a) $\frac{25}{48}$ (b) $\pm 4\sqrt{3}i$ (c) 0, or 1

10. $2(2)^2 - 3(2) - 2 = 0 \equiv 0$, mod 5.

12. (a) $x \equiv 2$ (b) $x \equiv 2$

14. $b^2 - 4 \cdot a \cdot c = 3$. It is not the square of any element. No elements satisfy the equation.

16. (a) $m = 1$ or -4 (d) $x = -2 \pm \sqrt{5}$
     (c) $a = \dfrac{1 \pm \sqrt{21}}{2}$

18. The graph is the set of points (0, 0), (1, 2), (2, 4) and (3, 6).

SECTION 7.7   *page 222*

2.   Real points on line from 0 to 1.

4.   1   2 ... n ...
     $\updownarrow$ $\updownarrow$ $\updownarrow$
     101 102 $n + 100$

6.   The real numbers consist of the rationals and irrationals. Since $\aleph_0 + \aleph_0 = \aleph_0$, if the cardinality of the irrationals were $\aleph_0$ so also would be the cardinality of the reals.

SECTION 7.9   *page 230*

2. $|b|$

4.   Yes.

	1	-1	i	$-i$
1	1	-1	i	$-i$
-1	-1	1	$-i$	i
i	i	$-i$	-1	1
$-i$	$-i$	i	1	-1

6.   (a) $\frac{3}{34} - \frac{5}{34}i$ (e) -16
     (b) $-\frac{1}{3}$ (f) 1
     (c) $5i$ (g) There is none.
     (d) $-5 + 4i$

8. $8 + 3i$

10. (a) $1 + 5i$ (b) $7 - 7i$ (c) $1 + 5i$

12. To prove $-i = 1/i$: $1/i \cdot i/i = i/i^2 = i/-1 = -i$.

SECTION 7.12   *page 235*

1. $A + B$ = Tom, Dick, Harry, and Jack
     $A \cdot B$ = Tom, Harry

3.   Yes. Yes.

5.   No. The set of real numbers and the set of rational numbers are not equivalent.

7. O, U.

9. $A + B$ = the real numbers from 3 through 10 except those >7 and <8. $A \cdot B = 0$.

13. A' consists of the elements of U not in A. $(A')'$ consists of the elements of U not in A', $\therefore$ $(A')'$ consists of the elements of U not not in A, that is, in A.

SECTION 7.15   *page 239*

2.   The set A plus the null set gives the set A.

4.   By B_{12} $0 + 0' = U$; by B_2 $0' + 0 = U$. But by B_4 $0' + 0 = 0'$ ∴ by substitution $0' = U$.

6. $A + A \cdot B = A \cdot B + A$ (by B_2) $= AB + AU$ (by B_{10}) $= A(B + U)$ (by B_{11}) $= A(B + U)U$ (by B_{10}) $= A(B + U)(B + B')$ (by B_{12}) $= A(B + UB')$ (by B_5) $= A(B + B'U)$ (by B_8) $= A(B + B')$ (by B_{10}) $= AU$ (by B_{12}) $= A$ (by B_{10}).

10.   (a)   All positive real numbers < 100 except the odd integers
      (b)   The positive rational numbers < 100 which are not integers
      (c)   The null set
      (d)   All positive rational numbers < 100 except the even integers
      (e)   The positive even integers
      (f)   The positive even integers

12. $(A + B)' = A' \cdot B'$

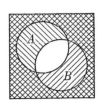

(A + B)' shaded   A' • B' cross hatch

SECTION 7.16   *page 243*

2.   (a) $(A' + B)(A + B')$ (c) $A(B + C)$
      (b) $AB' + C' + D'$ (d) $A(A + B)$

4.   It is false that A is false or B is false.

6.

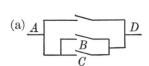

(a)

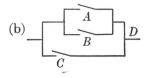

(b)

SECTION 8.4   *page 249*

1.   21,600 nautical miles; $21,600 \times \dfrac{6080}{5280}$ approximate statute miles

3.   8 pounds   7.   No.

5.   Troy   9.   Yes. The same.

SECTION 8.5 *page 252*

1. (a) 2000   (d) 5
   (b) .3   (e) 20
   (c) .0125   (f) 3.25
3. (a) 4.616   (b) 4616, 4616000
5. Approximately 378,000
7. 30.2¢   37.8¢

SECTION 8.6 *page 253*

2. (a) $2.18   (b) $2.18
4. (a) .71¢, .044¢   (b) 1.6¢, .0016¢
6. 155-mm.
8. $20\frac{5}{11}$
10. $\dfrac{281^3 \times 62.4}{125 \times 1728}, \dfrac{281^3}{125}, \dfrac{281^3}{125 \times 231}$
12. $49.05
14. 88
16. 1 m. 75 cm. 70 kg. 909 g.

SECTION 8.9 *page 259*

2. $37\frac{1}{2}°$
4. None.
6. (a) 60°   (b) 180°   (c) $56\frac{1}{4}°$ (d) 360°
   (e) $\dfrac{270°}{\pi}$ (f) .5625°   (g) 720°   (h) 180°
8. 600π
10. $\dfrac{2112}{\pi}, \dfrac{352}{5}, \dfrac{12672}{\pi}$
12. 1,018
14. 5,500 feet

SECTION 8.13 *page 263*

1. $\frac{1}{64}$ sq. ft.   4. 8 ft.
2. 5 m.   5. 6.3 ft.
3. 16 ft.

SECTION 8.15   *page 269*

2.   (a) $\frac{1}{2}, \frac{1}{6}, \frac{1}{12}, \frac{1}{20}$ (b)   2, 4, 8, 16   (c)   1, 4, 9, 16   (d) $\frac{2}{1}, \frac{3}{4}, \frac{4}{9}, \frac{5}{16}$

4.   Yes.

6.   Zero.   One.

8.   The sequence converges to the limit 1 because $|1 - a_n| = 0$ for any n.
     Hence $|1 - a_n| < \epsilon$ regardless of what positive number ϵ may be.   On
     the other hand, if the series converges, this implies that the sequence
     $1, 2, 3, \ldots n, \ldots$ converges.   But this cannot be true since we can find
     a term greater than any number we choose.

SECTION 8.18   *page 275*

2.   832

4. $\dfrac{104\pi}{81}$ cu. yd.

6. 54π sq. in., 54π cu. in.

8. $1000\pi/9$ dollars

10.   Show that each equals $4\pi r^2$.

12. $\dfrac{5300\pi}{3}$

14. 428π sq. ft.

16. $555.\overline{5} \ldots$ cu. yd.

18. $6/\pi$

20. 64000000π sq. mi.;
      $\dfrac{256000000000\pi}{3}$ cu. mi.

SECTION 9.1   *page 281*

2.   (a)   Possible; π is an exact number.
     (b)   Impossible.
     (c)   Possible; 3.1416 is an approximate number when used as π.
     (d)   Possible; any count which is subject to error.

SECTION 9.4   *page 285*

1. $12\frac{1}{2}$ represents a value within the range $12\frac{1}{4}$ to $12\frac{3}{4}$.
     12.5 represents a value within the range 12.45 to 12.55.
     12.50 represents a value within the range 12.495 to 12.505.

3.   .003 inches

5.   (a)   .0030 inch more precise; same accuracy
     (e)   1,100 feet more precise; 186,000 miles more accurate

7.   33 miles

9.   (a)   5 miles; $\frac{1}{432}$; .23%
     (d) $\frac{1}{2}$ acre; $\frac{1}{684}$; .15%

SECTION 9.10   *page 293*

2.   8 and 8,000

4.   Yes.

6.   (a) 48.2   (b) 19.2   (c) 1,400

14.   Exact, unless you are good at arguing with policemen.

8.   8.1

10.   3 qt.

12. $\frac{2}{3}$ per cent error

SECTION 9.11   *page 297*

2.   (a)   .00931
      (b)   800000
      (c)   80$\underline{0}$000

4. 5.87×10^{12}

6.   3

8.   .27

(d)   .00000006338821
(e)   333
(f)   .000000000001

SECTION 9.12   *page 298*

1.   (a)   2   (c)   1   (e)   0   (h)   1

2.   (a)   10   (c) a (e)   16

3.   (a)   2   (c)   100   (e) a

5.   1

7.   (a) $10^3 = 1000$ (b) $6^2 = 36$ (c) $a^y = x$ (d) $4^{\frac{1}{2}} = 2$

9.   (a) $x = \frac{4}{3}$ (b) $x = \frac{2}{9}$ (c) $x = \frac{17}{5}$

SECTION 9.13   *page 302*

1.   (a)   .8274   (c)   .1399   (e)   .8733   (g)   4

2.   (a)   8.15   (c)   5.77   (e)   3.90   (g)   1,000

SECTION 9.15   *page 304*

1.   (a) $6.8785 - 10$ (c)   0.2765   (c)   2.5877

2.   (a) $10^{1.8669} = 73.6$ (c) $10^6 = 1,000,000$

3.   (a)   1,520   (c)   .01   (e)   .754

4.   (a)   2.2539   (c)   3115

SECTION 9.17   *page 310*

1. (b) 14.09   (d) 11.67   (f) .3456
2. (a) $2,229   (c) 300 ft.
3. −1, −.699, −.5229, −.3979, −.3010, 0, .3010, .4771, .6021, .6990, 1
5. (a) $x = -.3979$ (b) $x = -2.231$

SECTION 9.18   *page 312*

1. The slowest absolute growth is the fastest growth in terms of current size.
3. Yes.   Population will be decreasing.

SECTION 10.5   *page 320*

2. The median is more favorable to the worker.
4. Mean.
5. Although the classes are of approximately equal standing, Section A had more exceptionally good students and Section B had more exceptionally poor ones.

SECTION 10.7   *page 324*

1. 40 m.p.h.; 38 m.p.h.   3.   (a) $9   (b) $8.14

SECTION 10.8   *page 326*

1. M = 113.8
3. Mode = 110, median = 114.9
4. (a) Ar.M = $9\frac{1}{3}$, H.M. = $8\frac{4}{7}$
    (b) Ar.M. = $5\frac{1}{2}$, H.M. = $2\frac{172}{229}$
    (c) Ar.M. = 4, H.M. = $3\frac{3}{4}$.

SECTION 10.9   *page 329*

1. $\sigma = 8.5$
2. 2.5; 4.0
3. If $\sigma = 0$, $\sum (x_i - \bar{x})^2 = 0$. But since $(x_i - \bar{x})^2 \geq 0$, each term in the summation must be zero, hence $x_i = \bar{x}$. If $x_i = \bar{x}$, then
$$\sigma = \sqrt{\frac{1}{n} \sum 0^2} = 0.$$

5. $M = 17.7, \sigma = 4.3.$

7. $M = 6.01, \sigma = .04.$

SECTION 10.11 *page 333*

2. $\frac{9}{47}$

4. $\frac{2}{3}; \frac{1}{3}; \frac{1}{6}$

6. A priori probability is determined theoretically before the event. Empirical probability is determined from experience, after the event. The statistician is concerned with both.

8. $\frac{1}{8}$

SECTION 10.13 *page 336*

1. $H^7 + 7H^6T + 21H^5T^2 + 35H^4T^3 + 35H^3T^4 + 21H^2T^5 + 7HT^6 + T^7$

3. $1,000,000 - 30,000 + 300 - 1 = 970299$

5. $1 + \frac{1}{2} - \frac{1}{8} + \frac{1}{16} - \frac{5}{128} + \frac{7}{256} - \frac{21}{1024} + \cdots$

7. $10^{-7} - 7 \cdot 10^{-8} + 28 \cdot 10^{-9} - 84 \cdot 10^{-10} + \cdots$

SECTION 10.15 *page 341*

1. No heads one time, 1 head six times, 2 heads fifteen times, 3 heads twenty times, 4 heads fifteen times, 5 heads six times, 6 heads one time.

4.
```
   1  6   15  20   15   6  1
  1 7  21   35   35  21   7 1
1 8 28   56   70   56   28 8 1
```

6. If $1 + 2 + 3 + \ldots + k = k\dfrac{(k+1)}{2}$

then $1 + 2 + 3 + \ldots + k + (k+1) = \dfrac{k(k+1)}{2} + (k+1)$

$$= \frac{k(k+1) + 2k + 2}{2}$$

$$= \frac{k(k+1) + 2(k+1)}{2}$$

$$= \frac{(k+1)(k+2)}{2}$$

But this is the $(k+1)$th case.

The statement is true when $n = 1$ because $1 = \dfrac{1(1+1)}{2}$.

8. Sum of numbers in nth row equals 2^{n-1}.

SECTION 10.18 *page 345*

2. $1.03; 2.06; .326$

4. No. Much nearer zero.

SECTION 11.1 *page 351*

2.

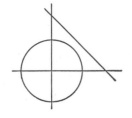

3. There are none.
5. Two or none.
7. No.
8. -11
9. $4x + y + 5 = 0$
11. $(6, 0); (0, 3)$
13. $\left(-\frac{2}{3}, \frac{1}{3}\right)$

SECTION 11.2 *page 357*

1. Yes. *B.*

2. No.

3. $(-2, -1)$

4. 5 in each case.

5. (a) 1   (b) $-\frac{2}{3}$ (c) 0   (d) $\frac{7}{6}$

7. Slope of line through $(2, 7)$ and $(5, -2)$ is -3. Slope of line through $(-4, -5)$ and $(5, -2)$ is $\frac{1}{3}$.

9. There are three possibilities: $(5, 14)$, $(9, -4)$, or $(-7, 6)$.

11. Line through $(3, 12)$ and $(-3, 2)$ has the same slope as line through $(6, 9)$ and $(3, 4)$.

13. $\dfrac{x}{4\sqrt{5}} + \dfrac{y}{2\sqrt{5}} = 1$

15. $3x + 5y - 29 = 0$

17. $3x + 4y - 6 = 0$ has slope $-\frac{3}{4}$; $4x - 3y - 1 = 0$ has slope $\frac{4}{3}$; $6x + 8y + 1 = 0$ has slope $-\frac{3}{4}$; $12x - 9y + 5 = 0$ has slope $\frac{4}{3}$.

SECTION 11.3 *page 360*

1. (a) $\frac{14}{5}$ (b) 3   (c) 3   (d) $\frac{11}{5}$

3. (a) $2x + y + 3 = 0$
    (b) $2x + y - 7 = 0$
    (c) $2x + y + 1 = 0$

5. $x^2 + 2xy + y^2 - 12x + 4y + 36 = 0$

7. $39x^2 + 96xy + 11y^2 + 50x + 50y - 50 = 0$

SECTION 11.4   *page 369*

1.   (a) $x^2 + y^2 = 81$
     (c) $x^2 - 6x + y^2 - 8y - 4 = 0$
     (f) $x^2 + x + y^2 - 4y - 41 = 0$
     (g) $x^2 - 8x + y^2 + 6y + 17 = 0$

2. $(6, 2 - \sqrt{3})$

3.   Slope of chord through $(-5, -3)$ and $(6, 2 - \sqrt{3})$ is $\dfrac{5 - \sqrt{3}}{11}$.   Slope of chord through $(4, 7)$ and $(6, 2 - \sqrt{3})$ is $\dfrac{5 + \sqrt{3}}{-2}$.   The product of these two slopes: $\dfrac{5 - \sqrt{3}}{11} \cdot \dfrac{5 + \sqrt{3}}{-2} = -1$.

6.   Find the circle determined by any three of the points and show that the fourth point is on it.

7.   (a) $(0, \frac{1}{4})$, $y + \frac{1}{4} = 0$, 1
     (c) $(\frac{5}{4}, 0)$, $x + \frac{5}{4} = 0$, 5
     (e) $(\frac{1}{3}, 0)$, $x + \frac{1}{3} = 0$, $\frac{4}{3}$

8.   (b) $x^2 = -32y$ (d) $x^2 = -\frac{9}{2}y$

10. $16x^2 + 24xy + 9y^2 - 256x - 292y + 1524 = 0$

11. $x^2/16 + y^2/7 = 1$

13. $9x^2 - 90x + 25y^2 = 0$

15. $3x^2 + 4y^2 - 48 = 0$

17. Center is at origin.   Ends of major axis are $(0, 4)$ and $(0, -4)$.   Ends of minor axis are $(2, 0)$ and $(-2, 0)$.

19. Ends of major axis are $(5, 0)$ and $(-5, 0)$.   Ends of minor axis are $(0, 3)$ and $(0, -3)$.   Foci are $(4, 0)$ and $(-4, 0)$.

20. (a) Hyperbola: transverse axis $(2, 0)$ to $(-2, 0)$; conjugate axis $(0, 2)$ to $(0, -2)$
     (b) Circle: center at origin, radius 2
     (c) Hyperbola: transverse axis $(0, 2)$ to $(0, -2)$; conjugate axis $(2, 0)$ to $(-2, 0)$

21. (b) $x^2/25 - y^2/25 = 1$

22. $4x^2 - 8x - 5y^2 + 24 = 0$

24. $xy = -8$

25. (a) $y^2 = 8x$ (c) $x^2/16 - y^2/9 = 1$

27. The ellipse approaches a circle.

29. In this case the line through the focus perpendicular to the directrix may be considered a degenerate parabola.   We may also consider two lines cutting through the focus and making equal angles with the directrix as a degenerate hyperbola.

SECTION 11.5   *page 372*

2.   If two straight lines meet, a third line falling on the two straight lines makes interior angles together less than two right angles on that side on which the two lines meet.

3.   Yes.

4.   No.

SECTION 11.6   *page 376*

1.   Both pairs are nonintersecting.

2. $BC > AD; AB > CD$

3.   No; $AB > CD$

4. $AD = DC$. No, if $\angle DAB$ and $\angle BCD$ were bisected $\triangle ADC$ would have an angle sum of two right angles.

5. $\angle BCA = \angle BAC$; $\angle DCA = \angle DAC$; $\angle DCA + \angle DAC <$ a   right angle $\therefore$ $\angle BCA + \angle BAC >$ a right angle $\therefore$ $\angle BCA > \angle ACD$

6.   No.   No.

7.   Yes.   Yes.   Angles are not right angles.

8.   Five.

9.   (a) $\alpha/4$ (b) $\alpha/2$ (c) $\alpha/6$ (d) $\alpha/3$

10. $45°$

11.   No.

12.   They are parallel.

13.   Nonintersecting.

SECTION 11.7   *page 384*

1. N_1; any two letters are found in at least one word: a, b are in bar; a, e in yea; a, o in oat; etc.
     N_2; any two letters are found in not more than one word: a and b are both in no word except bar; r and t are both in no word except try; etc.

3.   No, boat violates N_6.   No, if rat and bar are "lines", N_2 is violated. No, neither i nor p is a "point."

6. $A = 0, 0, 1; b = 0, 1, 0$
     Replace x_1, x_2, x_3 by 0, 0, 1, and u_1, u_2, u_3 by 0, 1, 0, in equation

$$u_1 x_1 + u_2 x_2 + u_3 x_3 = 0$$
$$0 \cdot 0 + 0 \cdot 1 + 1 \cdot 0 = 0$$

Therefore A lies on b. Similarly for C and D. On the other hand, replace x_1, x_2, x_3 by $B = 0, 1, 0$, and you get $0 \cdot 0 + 1 \cdot 1 + 0 \cdot 0 = 1 \neq 0$. Therefore B is not on b. Similarly for E, F, and G.

9.   Line b is on point F because $0 \cdot 1 + 1 \cdot 0 + 0 \cdot 1 = 0$.   Line g is on
      point F because $1 \cdot 1 + 1 \cdot 0 + 1 \cdot 1 = 0$.   Line f is on point F because
      $1 \cdot 1 + 0 \cdot 0 + 1 \cdot 1 = 0$.   Line a is not on point F because $0 \cdot 1 +$
      $0 \cdot 0 + 1 \cdot 1 = 1 \neq 0$.   Similarly for lines c, d, e.

12.   Replace $g = 1, 1, 1$ for u_1, u_2, u_3 in $u_1 x_1 + u_2 x_2 + u_3 x_3 = 0$; $x_1 + x_2 +$
      $x_3 = 0$ is the required equation.

13.   Replace $G = 1, 1, 1$ for x_1, x_2, x_3 in $u_1 x_1 + u_2 x_2 + u_3 x_3 = 0$; $u_1 + u_2 +$
      $u_3 = 0$ is the required equation.

SECTION 11.8   *page 388*

1. $\{ABC, GHI, DEF\}$, $\{AGE, DHC, BFI\}$, $\{AHF, DGB, EIC\}$

2. $\{A, I, D\}$, $\{B, H, E\}$, $\{C, G, F\}$

3.
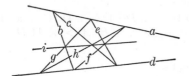

5.
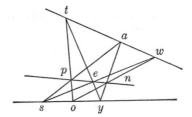

SECTION 12.1   *page 395*

1. $a = 3b + 10$: $(0, 10)$, $(-3, 1)$, $(1, 13)$

2.   (a)   Slope 3, zero 2
      (c)   Slope 2, zero 2
      (e)   Slope 3, zero 4/3

4. $f(x) = x + 4$

6. $C = 500 + 10u$

8. $\$10.71$

10.   (a) $86°$ (b) $32°$ (c) $212°$

12. $C = \frac{5}{9} (F - 32)$

SECTION 12.2   *page 400*

1. None. None.

3. None.

5. $x = \frac{5}{3}$

7. $4x - 6$

SECTION 12.4   *page 406*

1. (a) $x = 5/6; f(x) = 47/12$ (c) $x = 3/2; f(x) = -13/4$

2. With a and b fixed, a change in c shifts the graph of the function vertically by the amount of the change.

5. $-f(x) = -3x^2 + 4x - 2; f(-x) = 3x^2 + 4x + 2$

7. $f(x) = 3, 5, 5, 11, 11, 21, 21, 35, 35, 53, 53, 75, 75, 101, 101, 131$

9. Approximately .3 and 1.7; 2, $\frac{1}{2}$

11. $x = 1; f(x) = 3$

SECTION 12.7   *page 410*

1. $(x - 5)/3$. The set of real numbers ≥ 5.

3. $|x| \leq 3; 3 \geq f(x) \geq 0; f^{-1}(x) = f(x)$

5. They are symmetric to the line $y = x$.

7. $-3/2 \leq x; f^{-1}(x) = \dfrac{-3 + \sqrt{17 + 4x}}{2}$

SECTION 12.9   *page 416*

3. (a) $\dfrac{x - 5}{3}$ (b) $y = \sqrt{(x)^2 - 4}$, where $x \leq -2$

   (c) $\frac{1}{2}(3 + \log_e x)$ (d) $\frac{1}{5}(e^x + 1)$

5. $7\frac{1}{2}$ years; 6.7 years

7. $N_0; \frac{5}{8}$ hours; $10^8 N_0$

9. (a) 3.44   (b) 2.1931   (c) 558   (d) 3.9228

SECTION 12.11   *page 423*

2. $1 \leq |x| \leq \infty; -\infty \leq x \leq +\infty$

4. (a) .9211   (b) .1003   (c) .2675

6. (a) $.65; (\pi - .65); (2\pi + .65)$

   (b) $.10; (-.10); (2\pi + .10)$

   (c) $.87; (\pi + .87); (2\pi + .87)$

10. $.529 + .842i$

INDEX